The Evolution of
HUMAN NATURE

This book is published
with the assistance of the
DAN DANCIGER PUBLICATION FUND

The Evolution of

HUMAN NATURE

C. Judson Herrick

AUSTIN. UNIVERSITY OF TEXAS PRESS. 1956

80

© 1956 by the University of Texas Press
Library of Congress Card Catalog Number 56-7393
Printed and Bound in the United States of America

Acknowledgments

The technological marvels of our time are the natural products of a half-century of advancement of knowledge at an unprecedented rate. It is the business of science not only to accumulate this knowledge but also to make practical use of it for the good of mankind. The purport of this book is to show what some of the available knowledge about human nature means for the guidance of human conduct. The factual material and the principles derived from it have been selected from diverse domains of human experience and interpreted in the light of my own experience. I have made free use of the published work of others, but the interpretation of this evidence is my own responsibility. The source of every quotation from published work is cited in the text. Special permission to quote the longer extracts has been courteously given by several publishers, including the following:

Henry Holt & Co., L. L. Whyte, *The Unitary Principle*, 1949; short quotations from several other works; and two figures from Herrick's *Neurological Foundations of Animal Behavior*, 1924. John Wiley & Sons, Inc., D. O. Hebb, *The Organization of Behavior*, 1949. The Ronald Press Co., Heinrich Klüver (Editor), *Biological Symposia*, vol. 7, 1942. McGraw-Hill Book Co., Inc., H. Margenau, *The Nature of Physical Reality*, 1950. Princeton University Press, J. Hadamard, *The Psychology of Invention*, 1945; E. G. Conklin, *Heredity and Environment*, 1915. Cambridge University Press, G. E. Coghill, *Anatomy and the Problem of Behavior*, 1929; C. S.

Sherrington, *Man on His Nature*, 1952; E. Schrödinger, *What Is Life?* 1944. Yale University Press, R. M. Yerkes, *Chimpanzees*, 1943. University of Illinois Press, P. Bailey and G. von Bonin, *The Isocortex of Man*, 1951, figures 21 and 93. *Proceedings of the National Academy of Sciences*, G. E. Coghill, vol. 16, 1930; A. L. Kroeber, vol. 35, 1949; C. J. Herrick, vol. 16, 1930, and figures 1–4, vol. 19, 1933, p. 8. *The American Journal of Psychology*, G. E. Coghill, vol. 51, 1938; H. M. Johnson, vol. 58, 1945. *Natural History*, F. A. Beach, vol. 56, 1947. *Journal of Philosophy*, C. J. Herrick, vol. 12, 1915; W. H. Sheldon, vol. 38, 1941; A. F. Bentley, vol. 38, 1941; A. C. Garnett, vol. 39, 1942.

Human nature has so many facets that no one can claim proficiency in all of its aspects. The author has, accordingly, sought the advice and criticism of many colleagues in specialties other than his own. This indispensable help has been so generously given by these collaborators in many ways and there are so many of them that their names cannot even be listed here. To each of these good friends I express my cordial thanks. Among these collaborators the University of Texas Press must receive special mention and commendation for indulgent and efficient management of the details of publication. Both the Press and the author are indebted to the generosity of the late Mr. Dan Danciger of Fort Worth. I am honored that my book is the first publication to be issued by the Press with the assistance of the fund which he established shortly before his death.

C. Judson Herrick

Grand Rapids, Michigan
February, 1956

Contents

1. Introduction   1

> The purport of this book, 1; Some problems of human biology, 3; The biology of human conduct, 5.

PART I.   THE EVOLUTION OF BEHAVIOR
Biological Factors of Psychobiology

2. Factors of Behavior   13

> What is behavior? 13; Control of behavior, 16; Motivation, 18; Mental factors, 22; Values, 23; Psychobiology, 24; Summary, 25.

3. Methods of Study   26

> The science of behavior, 26; Empirical and normative sciences, 28; The method of natural science, 30; Facts: their meaning and value, 32; Summary, 37.

4. The World in Which We Live   39

> The nature of our world, 39; What is real? 40; Laws of nature, 42; Laws and universals, 44; Summary, 45.

5. Mechanisms of Living   46

> The vital process, 46; Mechanistic and vitalistic explanations, 47; The nature of mechanism, 54; Mechanical order and disorder, 61; Summary, 64.

6. Human Engineering   66

> The human machine, 66; The search for causes, 71; Summary, 74.

7. Patterns of Behavior   76
   Classification of factors, 76; Wholes and parts, 78; Total
   and partial patterns of behavior, 80; Summary, 85.

8. Analytic and Integrative Factors of Behavior   86
   Analysis and synthesis, 86; The analytic factors, 88; Integration, 89; Disintegration, 98; Summary, 101.

9. Levels of Organization   103
   Levels of analysis and integration, 103; Laws of structure
   and laws of change, 110; Summary, 110.

10. Trends in Evolution   112
   General principles of evolution, 112; Factors of organic
   evolution, 114; Classification and biological rank, 119;
   Progressive evolution, 123; Summary, 127.

11. Adaptation: Means and Ends   128
   Adaptation, 128; Means and ends, 131; Summary, 135.

12. Evolution of Value   136
   The natural history of value, 136; Human values, 141;
   The relational nature of value, 145; The goodness of
   value, 147; The evaluation of values, 150; The profit
   motive, 152; Is truth a value? 154; Summary, 156.

13. Evolution of Experience   158
   The natural history of experience, 158; The nature of
   experience, 160; The growth of experience, 165; Summary, 167.

14. Social Factors in Evolution   169
   Social organization, 169; Totalitarian and individualistic
   social patterns, 171; Innate and acquired factors, 177;
   Human social structure, 179; Democracy, 183; Summary, 187.

15. The Social Sciences   189
   Sociobiology, 189; Personal factors, 192; Cultural factors,
   195; Cultural values, 199; Summary, 204.

16. The Self   205
   The biological self, 205; The worth of the person, 208;
   The self as a free agent, 211; Summary, 217.

17. The Outlook   219
   The critical question, 219; The answer, 220; Education
   for democracy, 223; The key to progress, 226.

PART II. THE EVOLUTION OF BRAINS

Neurological Factors of Psychobiology

18. The Spiritual Life of a Mechanist   233

19. The Origin and General Properties of the Nervous System   239

Neurosensory and neuromotor relations, 239; Mechanisms of analysis and integration, 243; The analytic apparatus, 244; The integrative apparatus, 248; Reflexology, 254; Summary, 255.

20. The Nervous Functions   257

The expanding horizons of psychobiology, 257; Nervous conduction, 258; Peripheral and central relations, 261; The neuron and the synapse, 262; Polarized fields, 263; Summary, 269.

21. Psychophysics   270

Three revolutions in mechanics, 270; Space, time, and space-time, 272; The dimensions of integration, 275; Mental work, 279; Summary, 282.

22. Mental Functions   284

The mythological mind, 284; Animism, 285; Mind is minding, 288; Summary, 296.

23. A Biological Analysis of Mental Processes   297

A neurologist looks at his own mind, 297; The patterns of mentation, 299; The scope of psychobiology, 302; Summary, 304.

24. The Beginnings and Growth of Mind   306

Panpsychism, 306; Psychogenesis, 308; Motility is the cradle of mind, 312; Summary, 318.

25. Evolution of Mind   320

The limitations of method, 320; Mental integration, 322; The primate mind, 323; Summary, 328.

26. Sensation   330

The senses, 330; Factors of sensation, 331; Temporal and spatial factors, 334; Summary, 338.

27. Perception   339

Criteria of perception, 339; Temporal and spatial factors, 340; Motor factors, 345; Integrative factors, 349; The "purposive" quality of perception, 351; Summary, 352.

28. Learning and Intelligence 354

Intelligence and learning contrasted, 354; Learning, 355; Intelligence, 359; Mechanisms of learning and intelligence, 360; Measurement of intelligence, 362; Summary, 367.

29. The Origin and Evolution of the Cerebral Cortex 368

Brain and mind, 368; Cerebral and cerebellar cortex, 369; Origin of the cerebral cortex, 370; Factors of cortical evolution, 375; Summary, 383.

30. The Structure of the Cortex 384

Comparative anatomy and physiology, 384; The human cortex, 387; The web of cortical tissue, 390; Summary, 395.

31. Some General Functions of the Cortex 396

The cortex is a facilitating mechanism, 396; Signs, signals, codes, and symbols, 401; Summary, 405.

32. Localization of Cerebral Functions 406

The nature of the problem, 406; Two kinds of localization, 409; Evolution of localization, 410; Cortical localization, 412; Localization of cortical integrative functions, 414; The seat of consciousness, 427; Summary, 430.

33. The Mechanics of Mentation 431

The apparatus of cortical synthesis, 431; The field of mental processes, 438; Cortical use of signals and symbols, 441; Summary, 448.

34. The Dimensions of Mind 450

Facts and theories, 450; Pioneers of psychobiology, 451; Theory of dimensions, 453; The open door, 458.

Epilogue: The Unknown God 461

Bibliography 467

Index 489

The Evolution of
HUMAN NATURE

CHAPTER ONE

Introduction

The purport of this book

Human nature interests me because it is my nature. My interest in the rest of nature is always tinged with this personal reference, whether I recognize it or not, for we can see the surrounding world only through human eyes, and our apparatus of perception is at best an imperfect instrument. We look at human nature, too, as spectators, but we also have the unique ability to look at it from inside the works. The extraspective and the introspective methods of observation have equal scientific validity, and both methods are subject to the hazard of erroneous interpretation. To understand human nature and so learn to control behavior for our own good, each of these components of experience—the objective and the subjective—must be examined separately and in their reciprocal relationships. Such an examination is the theme of this book.

The human body is the most complicated mechanism of comparable dimensions in our known universe. Obviously even a sketchy outline of its complete structure and operations could not be included between the covers of one book. I have selected for consideration only those topics which seem to me significant for the management of human affairs, both personal and public, and which lie within the range of my own competence as a biologist. The factors of human experience and the resulting behavior will be examined in a search for their biological origins and relationships. But since an understanding of these relationships requires excursions beyond the conventional limits of biology, psychology, and all the sciences of man, we shall not hesitate to overstep these limits whenever such an excursion promises to be helpful.

It took a long time to make a man. Records preserved as fossils indicate that more than five hundred million years elapsed between the appearance of the first recognizable organisms and that of the animal the anthropologists are willing to call a man, that is, a member of the genus Homo. Our species, Homo sapiens, the wise man, has been around for several hundred thousand years. He was not very wise at the beginning, but in due time he did learn to talk, to use fire, and to invent useful tools. The learning process has been going on continuously and at an accelerated rate until now, but Homo sapiens is not as wise as he thinks he is. Recently it has become apparent that he failed to learn how some of the fundamental biological principles must be adapted for successful living at his present stage of cultural evolution. His vast accumulation of knowledge has not yet given him the wisdom to keep the peace with himself and with his fellow men. Unless this defect can be remedied, and that right soon, his name may have to be changed to Homo stultus.

The law of the survival of the fit has not been abrogated in the human domain, but the times have changed since primitive man fought his way up from barbarism. If our human nature does not change with the times, Homo sapiens will perish just as the dinosaur did and for the same reason. We have, however, a significant advantage over the dinosaur, for we have wit enough to discover some of the laws of evolutionary change, to recognize this shift in the quality of fitness of human behavior, and to adjust our conduct accordingly— assuming that we also have the will. The efficient causes of the disorder that now threatens our security will be found not in our natural surroundings but inside ourselves. Under our present conditions of social organization, fitness for survival depends neither on brute strength nor on the mere accumulation of information, scientific or any other kind. The critical issue now is: are we willing to learn how to apply the strength and knowledge we now have to the further search for a wisdom that will permit us to keep the peace and to co-operate in mutually helpful ways, or shall we continue to carry suicidal policies of personal and national aggression to the inevitable result of self-destruction?

These problems have been approached from various standpoints, including, among others, political expediency, economic welfare, public health (physiological and mental), ethical justice, and human biology. Our primary concern here is with the last-named of these—a search for the biological principles with which all human conduct must conform if civilization is to survive and prosper. This is the most fundamental approach, because all human activities are natural vital processes, and the appropriateness of the natural process in every particular activity is to be evaluated in terms of the way it affects the lives of people.

The knowledge of the steps which must be taken to remove the primary causes of our most serious personal and social disorders is available—as it never was to the dinosaur. The purport of the inquiry made in this book is a search for the available information about the natural history of human nature and its biological origins in the expectation that the necessary steps to be taken will be revealed. But the critical problems are educational. There remains the vital issue: how can all the peoples of the world be induced to apply this knowledge with the wisdom of men rather than with the cunning of brutes?

Some problems of human biology

Among our human activities are a number of things we don't like to do, but we do them because we must. Most of us have to work for a living, and few of us find all of the consequent duties agreeable. We don't like to get up regularly every morning to punch a time clock or meet early appointments. We don't like to pay taxes, and we dislike the obligation to obey certain civic laws. We would prefer to do as we like about the management of our own affairs. But Thomas Huxley admonished us many years ago that a man's worst difficulties begin when he is able to do as he likes. If we like what is not good for us and yield to the cravings, disaster is sure to follow.

In view of the catastrophes which now threaten our security and of the partisan controversies which thwart effective remedial measures, it looks as if our likes and dislikes should be more realistically evaluated. Men have a wider freedom of choice about what they may do than any other animals have, but we pay a high price for it: the freedom to select what is good for us necessarily carries with it the freedom to go to perdition if we choose unwisely. This freedom is the badge of our humanity, but we can only prove our right to the badge by using it like men, not beasts.

Some behavior is good and some is bad—if good and evil are defined biologically in terms of what is advantageous to the behaving animal. In the lower ranks of animals the choice between good and bad behavior is made automatically and inexorably. The unfit are eliminated; the fit survive and their fitness is progressively enhanced in accordance with the well-known laws of natural selection and other biological principles. But in the human domain the criteria of fitness are different. A change in what constitutes good human behavior has been going on gradually for a million years or more, and it has now reached a critical stage.

Our civilization and all its accumulated wealth and values are in dire peril just because people have not recognized that the criteria of fitness (the biologist's "survival value") have shifted from the physiological level of bodily security and comfort to the psychological and moral levels. What is "right" ("adaptive," the biologist would say) for army ants and ravening wolves to do is utterly and fatally wrong behavior in human society today. And by wrong I mean biologically wrong, quite apart from any political or moral issues.

These are controversial questions, and the confusion which now prevails among philosophers, statesmen, religious leaders, and men of affairs about how to act in the present emergency too often results in stalemate or in decisions made on the basis of wishful thinking, hunch, or concession to pressure of special interests. In circumstances where it is necessary to make a choice of one of several possible courses of action, it is wise to search the record for evidence of the consequences which have followed action in previous similar instances: this is the scientific method. This way of reaching decisions in the light of all relevant past experience has given us, for instance, the triumphs of modern engineering; it is equally applicable and fruitful in the domain of social adjustments. Controversial issues may be further clarified if the inquiry is widened to include a biological examination of the origins and evolutionary history of various patterns of behavior and the factors of their operations.

It is thoroughly unscientific to assume, as is too often done, that biological evolution reaches its climax in subhuman animals and that human evolution has advanced beyond the biological into a transcendental domain of different order. On the contrary, the fact is that all human capacities, activities, and experiences are biological functions, whatever else they may be too. Human intelligence and human social organization have indeed advanced far beyond those of any other animals, but they are nevertheless functions of animal bodies and the laws of biology are not rescinded in human societies. Human biology is unquestionably different from anthropoid biology, yet every human action and every human experience is a biological event.

The biology of human conduct

Human conduct, no less than the behavior of all other animals, must conform with the natural laws of the world in which we live. Failure to make these adjustments results inevitably in misfortune. It is our purpose here to outline the evolutionary history of some of the factors of human behavior from a strictly biological point of view and to see how this knowledge may be applied in the solution of problems of adjustment to present conditions.

All of the sciences of man and all of his arts and other accomplishments contribute to our knowledge of human patterns of behavior, but the complete story cannot be written from these sources alone. To understand the apparatus of human behavior and how it works we must know not only the details of its construction but also how it came to be. The evolution of human culture did not begin with an Adam and Eve. Its roots strike deep into prehuman cultures and practices, and the entire history of organic evolution must be surveyed. Such a survey may not only reveal the biological origins of all human capacities but also trace the successive stages of the gradual elaboration of their mechanisms.

We need to know which factors of behavior are biologically determined by the past history of the human race and of its several genetically and culturally different subdivisions—and therefore inborn and common to all members of a community—and which factors are individually acquired by personal experience. This knowledge is hard to get, but it is important because the practice of education, of medicine, and of all social enterprises must be adjusted both to the innate capacities and limitations of the people and also to the environing conditions in which they grow up and live their lives. Our heredity is given; we must accept it as it is; but this does not mean that there is nothing we can do about it. Our success in life depends very largely upon our ability to recognize and evaluate native capacities and limitations, to make the most of the former and to compensate in every practicable way for the latter. This cannot be done intelligently unless we know what these capacities are and how to make the best use of them with the resources available.

A comprehensive study of animal behavior must include description and explanation of everything that animals do. The activities of the human animal are so diversified and so different from those of other living creatures that the whole history of human development and prehuman evolution must be taken into account and all current human enterprises must be surveyed. In short, the study of behavior has ramifications extending throughout the whole range of the natural sciences and beyond that sphere into all humanistic interests. To understand what an animal is doing now and how he does it we must know not only the immediate antecedents of the act and the bodily apparatus employed but also the remote antecedents in personal history and the history of the species. Embryology and phylogeny are as important to behavior as to anatomy and physiology.

All thinking is tied, directly or indirectly, to action. Exact knowledge of the processes and mechanisms of behavior is therefore indispensable for full understanding of our mental processes, and these in turn have no practical significance except as they come to expression in appropriate behavior. Scientific study of behavior, then, must go deeper than description of overt action and include its motivation, an evaluation of the ensuing results, and detailed description of all the intervening bodily processes involved. This is a large order.

Even a cursory survey of the diverse topics mentioned would require an encyclopedia of many volumes. What we plan to do here

is to extract from currently available knowledge some general principles that may have heuristic value in pointing the way toward more
successful solution of problems of conduct as they arise. No attempt
is made in this work to assemble the factual data about animal behavior of various grades of complexity, but the conclusions reached are
documented by references to representative samples of the literature.

The field to be surveyed must not be fenced in by arbitrary bounds;
we shall feel at liberty to make excursions into any territory we like
without regard to the limits of the conventional domain of behaviorism. If this makes an inconveniently big and heterogeneous book,
there is an easy way out—let the reader skip the parts that are not
relevant to his interests. In a recent book that is heavier than this one
the author (Margenau, '50, p. 219) remarks, "A book, like a public
building, should have emergency exits." To mark these exits more
clearly, some of my obiter dicta are set apart in smaller print and may
be passed by without loss of continuity of the rest of the text. The
summaries at the ends of the chapters may suffice to keep the continuity intact if large sections are omitted. The author's selections of
topics for discussion have been guided by a few principles which clarify
many aspects of behavior—so many, in fact, that the reader will find
the principles frequently mentioned in different contexts. This repetition is intentional, because behaviors result from diverse causal situations in each of which the causal factors have different relationships.
The Index will enable the reader to assemble these scattered references.

It should be stated at the outset that many relevant facts and
principles are intentionally omitted, either in the interest of holding
the work down to moderate length or because they lie outside the
range of the writer's competence. A discussion of the general principles of behavior can most profitably be written from the standpoint of
the author's interest and experience. My experience as a biologist
provides the foundation upon which I must build, but a useful structure cannot be made out of foundation stones alone. Many other
different kinds of material must be found and adapted for their appropriate uses, and these must be searched for in all likely places.

I did not devote sixty years to intensive study of the comparative
anatomy of the nervous system merely to collect dead facts or to add

to the store of "accumulative knowledge." I wanted to find out what these animals do with the organs they have and what they do it for, with the expectation that this knowledge would help us to unravel the intricate texture of the human nervous system and show us how to use it more efficiently. The unflagging toil of hundreds of qualified experts in diverse fields of science has abundantly fulfilled this expectation, but we have disastrously failed to apply the knowledge to anything even resembling successful treatment of the disordered behavior that now prevails in our troubled world. We can do better if we really want to and are willing to pay the price.

The price that must be paid is high but not exorbitant nor out of reach. Human patterns of socialized behavior are unworkable without some sacrifice on the part of every one of us of highly prized personal prerogatives. The ends that we work for must be judiciously chosen so as to ensure a proper balance between personal profit and the welfare of the community of which we are members and whose prosperity is essential for our own survival and comfort.

Behaviorism is not a cult. It is one of the cardinal ingredients of the broader science of psychobiology, and the interplay between biological and psychological factors must be recognized and consistently scrutinized at every turn of the inquiry. In other publications of mine I have discussed the general principles of psychobiology that are relevant to our present inquiry; these works are cited in the appended Bibliography. The unseemly number of references to my own publications may be explained, if not justified, by the fact that the evidence for the conclusions here expressed is more fully presented in those earlier, more specific works than can be done in this text.

In Part I of this book certain biological factors of behavior are selected for critical analysis and evaluation, but without detailed description of the mechanisms employed. However, in all except the most primitive animals, the nervous system is the dominant apparatus of regulation of behavior, and the most puzzling and critical problems of theoretic psychobiology and the practical regulation of conduct are concerned with the functions of the nervous system. Part II, therefore, summarizes these functions. The summary includes an outline of the evolution of the nervous system, the characteristic features of the nervous functions, and the biomechanics of the relation between mind as subjectively experienced and the bodily organs concerned. It is shown that there is a natural mechanics of mentation and that the mechanical principles involved are of different order from those of all other vital processes. The origin and evolutionary history of pre-mental and mental experience are sketched in outline.

Principles of psychobiology are discussed in both Parts I and II, and the discussions are intimately related, since the evidence from which the principles are derived is stated variously now in one part, now in the other. The conclusions reached are drawn both from the field of general biology (Part I) and from the more specialized domain of neurology (Part II).

PART I

The Evolution of Behavior

Biological Factors of Psychobiology

CHAPTER TWO
Factors of Behavior

What is behavior?

We must get a clear idea of what we are looking for before we can decide what kinds of facts are relevant to our inquiry. Behavior is usually defined as the visible expression of bodily activity, but it is evident that we cannot understand these overt acts by simple inspection, which tells us very little about what causes them, how they are done, and why. The answers to these questions may be found in unexpected places.

Any particular behavioral act results from a series of more or less complicated external and internal events which are related with one another in the process of adjustment of the living body to its surroundings. This series includes the events which motivate the act; the nervous and other internal processes that analyze the relevant experiences and canalize the flow of nervous impulses into appropriate organs of response; the action of the muscles, glands, and related organs that execute the behavior; and the objective toward which the behavior is directed. If we want to get the full significance of the easily observed act, all the other components of the situation must be taken into account, for the behavior is meaningless apart from the motives which instigate it and the consequences which follow it. In some inquiries the hidden internal processes that intervene between stimulus and response may be neglected; but all of these are essential components of all animal behavior. Some valuable general princi-

[13]

ples of methodology may be derived from inquiry into the properties of "behavior as such," abstracted from consideration of mechanisms employed or antecedents and consequences of it. But the field of application of such principles is restricted, and our interests here have far wider range.

A survey of the vast collection of recorded facts about animal behavior gives the impression that the factors of behavior are innumerable. Every act has some unique qualities. To make sense out of this heterogeneous mass of data it is convenient to arrange the various kinds of behavior in a graded series of successively more complicated patterns. These patterns on the whole are biologically successful or the animals would not survive, but some of them yield more diversified and richer satisfactions than others and some are injurious. We term "higher" those which increase and refine the satisfactions won; and, as will appear, the usual ranking of animals from lower to higher is based upon two classes of criteria. One class includes those factors of structure and behavior that satisfy the needs and appetencies of the animals themselves and that are evaluated according to the range and efficiency of the internal controls of the bodily processes. Criteria of the other class are evaluated in terms of the measure of control of environment that the animals exhibit. Man is commonly ranked at the top of the scale because of his pre-eminence in both of these respects.

The contrast between the internal or intrinsic factors of behavior and those which involve adjustment to surrounding conditions may be viewed more broadly and with different emphasis by classifying the former as integrative and the latter as analytic. This is essentially the same as Coghill's fundamental distinction between total patterns and partial patterns of behavior (to which the reader's attention is directed in Chapters 7 and 8).

These and all other classifications of behavior are useful devices for systematizing research and clarifying description; but it must not for a moment be overlooked that all of them are artifacts of method. The factors of behavior are so intricately interrelated and so differently related in every act that these man-made devices may give an unbalanced picture of the actual situation. It is very difficult to see any behavioral act as a whole and to grasp its significance in the total complex of the vital economy.

Successful living for a man, a family, or a nation depends on keeping the internal affairs of the behaving body in harmonious working order and in appropriate adjustment to the external conditions upon which the body depends for the satisfaction of needs and desires. This requires some control of the process to set its direction in ways that are satisfying. A common characteristic of "normal" behavior is that it is directed toward some profitable end. The animal or the social body may or may not have any clear-cut awareness that this is so, but the fact remains that utterly random behavior is biologically meaningless and practically useless.

Every act of every man, every other animal, and every social organization is a *transaction* (Dewey and Bentley, '49); that is, it is an interplay between, on the one hand, a living body (an individual or an organized group of individuals) having some characteristics common to its kind and some that are unique to itself, and, on the other hand, the physical and social environment upon which that body depends for survival, comfort, and prosperity.

Any particular example of behavior is patterned in large measure by the biological and social situation within which it is set, but there are also internal factors of even more importance. The motivation of the act and the manner of its performance are influenced primarily by the need of the moment and the bodily organization available for satisfaction of the need. Some behavior is motivated internally (by hunger, for instance) and some by external events. In every instance what is done about it is limited by the structural organization of the body, that is, by the organs available for appropriate action; and what form the appropriate action may take depends on the end toward which it is directed and the internal and external resources that can be utilized to reach that end. An animal can act only with the bodily equipment it possesses, and thus possible patterns of performance are confined within a restricted range. These limits have been established during the past evolutionary history of the species. Within these limits the individual's personal experience may establish habitual ways of behaving that influence the present act. The act itself may result in transient or enduring changes in the internal organization of the body (fatigue, increase of muscular power by exercise, etc.) or in readjustment of surrounding things.

Human behavior is set in a social frame. All conduct and its motivating thoughts and feelings are continually influenced by the attitudes and behavior of other people and by the situations in which the actor finds himself; but the response of each person to these attitudes and situations depends on his own individual qualities. Even in the exigencies of war-combat, whether the soldier comes out of the battle strengthened and stabilized or irreparably shattered by a war neurosis depends in large part upon personal qualities that were his own before he entered the army.

We are led to the general conclusion that every behavioral act is the resultant of the interplay between presently operating agencies and a structural organization with a pattern of action that has been elaborated during the previous experience of the individual and of his species in the long course of evolutionary change. It is also clear that during the progress of these changes "behavior evolves from within outward" (Yakovlev, '48); that is, the *primary* determiners of the patterns of behavior reside within the organism, not in the environment. In all studies of behavior the focal point of interest is the behaving individual, for behavior is primarily personal and its effect upon the person is the crucial issue.

This statement does not carry the implication that any behavior is exclusively motivated by the internal factors, for environmental influences (immediate or previously experienced) are always present, and in some situations, particularly in the social relations, the external factors are clearly predominant. Yet an over-all survey of the evolutionary and personal development shows that the intrinsic factors play the larger part in shaping the course of this development. How the organism adjusts to the environment depends primarily on the qualities of the organism itself.

Control of behavior

When primitive man learned to domesticate wild animals for his own pleasure and profit, a long step was taken in the progressive expansion of human industry. The beasts became the servants of men through man's intelligent control of animal behavior.

When the family circle was enlarged to include the clan, the tribe, the nation, another type of control was instituted: man's own behavior was controlled by social forces. The workings of custom, tradition, taboo, and formal legislation transformed feral man into a domesticated animal. The individual's conduct was more or less rigorously subject to social sanctions; and to the extent that this control was effective he became a servant of his community—that is, his behavior was controlled by the "culture" of which he was a member.

A third type of control emerged within the culture when it was recognized that an individual could best derive advantages from community life through voluntary renunciation of some personal preferences and advantages. The unconstrained acceptance of an obligation to sacrifice a number of personal interests for the general welfare—which we call altruism—is the foundation of all moral practice. These moral sanctions are not imposed from without. They are established by each person for himself, and they can be enforced only by his own choice. Morality cannot be impersonal or involuntary. Moral control of conduct is self-control, and the agency employed is a mental process that is usually named the conscience.

Behavior is studied scientifically because we want to find out how to control it more efficiently—our own behavior, the conduct of other people in their personal, social, commercial, and political relations, and the behavior of the wild and domestic animals with whose ways we must be familiar for our own protection and profit.

Successful control of behavior involves a selection of those ends toward which the behavior is directed that will yield the maximum profit to the organism and to the species or group of which he is a member. In all animals a large part of this selection of biological values is made physiologically and unconsciously by what Cannon ('39) called "the wisdom of the body"; but successful control of human behavior requires also a wisdom of higher order that goes beyond the primitive values that are selected physiologically. There must be intelligent appraisal of all biological values, including hopes, aspirations, and moral sanctions, and a choice of those values that yield satisfactions of higher order than mere survival and comfort.

Motivation

A motive is defined in general terms as "that which incites to motion or action." In the mental sciences the word is usually given a more restricted meaning, as expressed in Baldwin's *Dictionary of Philosophy and Psychology:* "Any conscious element considered as entering into the determination of a volition." Since the conscious elements cannot be recognized with precision in most animal behavior, we must here accept the more general definition.

There is a reason for everything that an animal does, though the creature may not know what it is. This is what we want to find out. The most direct approach to this question is an examination of every kind of behavior in a search for the actual results achieved. Such a survey by the competent psychologist Harvey A. Carr ('25, pp. 73, 391) led him to a simple formula which we shall take as our point of departure in the present inquiry. Professor Carr concluded that the end toward which most animal behavior (including that of mankind) is directed is the "satisfaction of the motivating conditions." The implications of this generalization are very broad, as will appear when we come to examine them in various contexts.

The motivating agencies may be outside or inside the behaving body. Many of the external factors of motivation are beyond the control of the animal. The only thing he can do about the change of seasons is to adjust his behavior as best he may to the cold of winter and the heat of summer. Although he cannot manage his climate, he may be able to alter his surroundings in adaptation to it. Muskrats, for instance, select home sites in suitable places as they find them, and build ingenious houses for their winter quarters in stagnant water. Beavers in northern climates build similar and better houses, and where there is no stagnant water they themselves provide it by building dams on small streams. In places where most of the surface drainage is in dry washes that flow only during occasional rains, as in the mesa country of New Mexico, they adjust to the situation by excavating deep burrows in the banks of the larger rivers.

The motivating agencies for these transactions are very complicated mixtures of internal and external factors. They include the external surrounding conditions, the intrinsic ingenuity of the animals themselves, and a simple social organization that facilitates teamwork. We see also that various kinds of animals adapt themselves to identically the same external conditions in a surprising variety of ways. The diversity of patterns of these modifications of behavior is determined primarily by the structure and ways of life of the animals themselves. It is not imposed upon them by the environment. Obviously, then, the critical factors which determine many patterns of behavior are internal to the animals and (in the instances mentioned) also to the organization of their social groups. No one of these factors and no class of factors can be accredited as the exclusive motivating agency.

A behavioristic school of sociologists, ably led by George A. Lundberg, insists that the search for motives should be rigorously excluded from social science. It is a futility because it is an "animistic" pursuit. To this I reply that the "anima" of current psychobiology is not a metaphysical demon to be exorcised but a vital process to be examined scientifically in all of its biological, psychological, and sociological relationships. Every act of a living body is motivated by something. Though it is as true of a man as of his motor car that motive power is derived from the fuel consumed, the pattern of its manifestation in man's behavior is determined by a complex of factors, some of which are observable only introspectively as emotions, ideas, and aspirations. If the recognition of these factors and their critical scientific study is "animism," let us have more of it (page 285).

Some human conduct is motivated by a clear-cut idea of what is wanted. The thing needed or desired is purposefully sought, and the outcome is registered in the mind as an experienced fact which usually has an emotional coloring. We like it or we don't. Another large part of our behavior is carried on quite unconsciously. We do not attend to it and may not be aware that we have "behaved." In even the most carefully executed intentional behavior there are many components which escape our notice. In so simple an act as reaching for a piece of candy and swallowing it, we are not conscious of the movements of the several muscles individually; it is the movement as a whole to which we attend. Secretion of saliva is involuntary. One may not realize that it has taken place, yet it is an essential part of swallowing. If one had to control intentionally the degree and timing of contraction of each separate muscle used in every act, he could not walk or talk. Our minds are not geared for that sort of performance. Indeed, in the acquisition of a skill like typewriting or driving a motor car, the first step is to learn to reduce the routine movements to the level of automatisms so as to release the mind from attention to them.

It is clear that in organisms other than man conscious participation in the process of behavior plays a relatively smaller part as we pass from higher to lower members of the animal series, until in the simplest animals and in all plants we cannot be sure that it is present at all. Our attention, accordingly, may well be directed at first to behavior as objectively manifest, beginning with the simpler forms which are not complicated by any recognizable conscious components.

This, in fact, is the common practice, and a vast amount of research has been recorded in this field. But the "objective psychologist" cannot so simply dispose of consciousness and get along without it, because the observed behavior must be consciously perceived by somebody, who then translates his own subjective experience of it into an objective record. The observer knows what is going on in his own mind, and, when he has accumulated sufficient perceptual knowledge, this enables him to form a more or less reliable judgment about what is going on in the objective world.

The internal factors of motivation and the mechanisms employed are described in detail by Hebb ('49, chaps. 8 and 9). The external factors of personal motivation influence all behavior directly or indirectly, but it will not do to give them the dominant role even in the simplest types of action systems. Human behavior particularly cannot be satisfactorily accounted for by environmental and cultural agencies alone, as claimed by one school of cultural anthropologists (Chapter 15).

That the intrinsic factors of biological motivation are of larger significance for behavior than the extrinsic factors at all levels of organization was corroborated by Coghill and supported by convincing evidence. His writings on this subject I have assembled ('49, chap. 15), together with some comments of my own, and the argument need not be repeated here.

Most behavior is obviously directed toward some end. The objective may be something advantageous or satisfying to the individual, or it may be something favorable to the species or group to which he belongs. These two motivating agencies act differently and sometimes they are in conflict. The social factors of behavior will be examined in due course, but attention is first directed to some of the simpler personal aspects.

An animal or a man ordinarily behaves in order to accomplish something that promotes his own welfare, that satisfies a need or desire. If the need is urgent and satisfaction is not achieved, then he tries something else. Behavior that may seem to an observer to be random is not random from the standpoint of the behaving animal. His every action is the result of causes that can be discovered, and these activities are more or less systematically organized.

People and all other animals sometimes do things that are not good for them, but what they do must in the aggregate be beneficial or they perish. Although behavior is normally goal-directed, situations sometimes arise which frustrate the satisfaction sought. If the frustration is not overcome by trial and error or otherwise, the normal course of behavior is disrupted, with results that may lead to catastrophic disorder and eventually to a pathological neurosis. Such abnormalities of conduct can be avoided or remedied only if the causes of the frustration are recognized and corrected.

The goal of normal behavior, we repeat, is satisfaction, which may or may not be consciously recognized as such. This directive behavior is here called "goal-directive," whether or not the goal is consciously recognized. Schneirla ('49, p. 270) would restrict the term to patterns of behavior which "are anticipated in terms of their expected outcomes." I prefer the more inclusive definition, both because we have no reliable criteria for determining whether the animal is aware of the end for which his behavior is adapted, and because consciously purposeful behavior has undoubtedly emerged from biologically adaptive behavior in which no conscious purpose can be recognized.

Whatever name we choose to apply to it, the directive quality of normal behavior is fundamental. This quality gives us the only basis we have for predicting the behavior of other creatures, and especially of other people, and so gives some promise of control of behavior, which is what we are after in the upshot.

Mental factors

So much of the behavior of the higher animals and especially of men is obviously incited by consciously recognized motives and carried on with intelligent control that mental processes must somehow be fitted into our factorial analysis of behavior. And here we meet our most difficult and controversial problems. Mentation as an integrative vital process is, of course, one of the strictly internal factors of behavior—and yet it is so dependent upon what is going on outside of the sphere of awareness that its status seems to be ambiguous.

Our most reliable information about the conscious components of behavior has been derived from scientifically controlled introspection, and our knowledge of the unconscious components has come through perception of things and events in our objective world, including, of course, our own bodies. We know that a particular action, such as stopping a motor car in front of a red traffic light, may be examined by both of these methods and that the two sets of data fit together harmoniously in what we call a voluntary act. The fit is snug and smooth so that the driver of the car does what he intends to do with precision. The two sets of data—the subjective and the objective— when examined separately seem to be disparate and incommensurable, yet actually we know that they are not because, if they were, a purposive action would be impossible. The exact nature of the relation between the bodily mechanism that executes the behavior and the emotive and intelligent processes that control it is a basic problem which cannot be evaded in any comprehensive study of human behavior.

In most physiological experiments any conscious experiences that may be had by the animal under observation are neglected. In order to be sure that they are excluded where painful operations are involved, the animal is anesthetized, for these feelings are not subject to control by the procedures of conventional physiology. A very wide range of observations and experiments on normal animal and human populations can profitably be made by students of animal psychology, child psychology, mob psychology, ethnology, economics, and so on, quite objectively. This is good science, but it is not all of our science, for in some of these fields conscious motivation and control are critical factors and no amount of knowledge of the objective world can be substituted for these factors. It is essential, therefore, to state explicitly that in this inquiry we accept the statement of G. V. Hamilton ('48), an experienced psychiatrist: "Subjective phenomena, *as these are experienced by the persons who report their occurrence*, do not need to be translated into anything else in order to be dealt with as objectively as we deal with all other biological phenomena." (The emphasis is his.)

That school of behaviorism which rigorously excludes consciousness from the field of study has contributed much of value for an understanding of the physiological aspects of behavior, human and other, but it can never take us all the way through to a satisfactory solution of the problems involved in human conduct. Human mentation is dependent upon these physiological processes that can be studied objectively and has emerged from them in the course of the evolution of mind. It is essential that we know as much about them as possible, but human behavior cannot be fully explained by them. Modern behaviorism arose within the domain of psychology and here it must remain. This domain is wide enough to embrace all components of the vital processes that eventuate in conduct. How this domain is to be defined, from the behaviorist's standpoint, will receive further consideration.

Values

Two classes of values are distinguished: biological values that are patterned physiologically; and rational and emotive values that are patterned psychologically. Both types of evaluation are vital processes, and the two classes are biologically interrelated. The evolution of value is discussed in Chapter 12.

Values are not motivating agents in the sense that they furnish motivating power. However, they may be important factors in the motivation of behavior because of their influence in the determination of the *patterns* of behavior. The same remark applies to most of the other factors of behavior with which we are here concerned.

Psychobiology

Both conscious and unconscious factors of human behavior are vital processes, but they differ radically in quality, in the biomechanics of operation, and in the results achieved. Scientifically acceptable principles of psychophysics have not yet been discovered; but enough is known to make it clear that those vital processes which eventuate in conscious experience are derived in the development of the individual and in the evolutionary development of the race from premental patterns of action, the properties of which are open to inspection by the conventional methods of objective science. This opens up a field of inquiry which is now under active investigation.

Our fragments of knowledge must be united into a coherent and consistent unitary system in which all factors take their appropriate places in the cosmic order. This is strictly a scientific problem to be solved by appeal to verifiable factual evidence with broad scientific vision. Science must not pass the buck to metaphysics. What we are trying to do here is to take at least a short step in this direction, and it immediately becomes apparent that we cannot go far in this quest without careful scrutiny and perhaps revision of some widely accepted scientific dogmas. For this reason we shall in the next chapter examine some features of scientific method that are relevant to the present inquiry.

The most comprehensive summary available in English of the recorded facts about animal behavior is in three volumes, *Comparative Psychology* by Warden, Jenkins, and Warner ('34 to '40). Warden's *Animal Motivation* ('31) deals specifically with the albino rat. Maier and Schneirla ('35) have published a systematic work on animal psychology, with extensive bibliography. Washburn's *The Animal Mind* ('36) also has a good bibliography of 1,683 titles. On protozoan behavior reference is made to Jennings ('06). The work of Zuckerman ('32) and that of Robert M. and Ada W. Yerkes ('29 and '35) give a wealth of observations on the behavior of the higher subhuman primates, with references to other sources. A small book by David Katz ('37) gives an interesting introduction to comparative psychology. Concise summaries are available in the articles "Animal Behaviour" (Allee, '47) and "Psychology, Comparative" (Schneirla, '48), in the current issue of *Encyclopaedia Britannica*, and also in Schneirla's critical essay ('49) "Levels in the Psychological Capacities of Animals." A general neuropsychological theory of behavior by Hebb ('49) merits special mention.

The works of Edmund Montgomery, issued from 1861 to 1910, were based on much biological research and thorough familiarity with ancient and modern philosophy. These publications show remarkably keen analysis of the essential properties of vital organization and a philosophical interpretation that was far in advance of his time. Keeton ('50) gives a critical survey of his life and work. During the first forty years of the present century G. E. Coghill laid a secure foundation for the study of the embryology of behavior, with formulation of principles that are broadly similar to Montgomery's. The present study is based largely on Coghillian principles (see Chapter 7). Both Coghill and I received our original inspiration and subsequent guidance from my older brother, the late C. L. Herrick, whose prescient program of psychobiological research is now after a lapse of sixty years approaching fulfillment, as explained in my surveys of his life and work ('54, '55).

Summary

The motivating agencies of behavior are separated into two general classes—the external factors and those which are intrinsic to the body itself. The former are here termed analytic processes, the latter, integrating processes. Most of these agencies do not furnish motivating power. Their significance for behavior lies in their influence upon the patterns of its manifestation.

From the standpoint of our examination of the evolution of behavior and its mechanisms, the internal factors are of far more critical significance than the environing factors. In this work attention is directed mainly to these internal factors, and especially to mentation as a vital process. But it must be kept in mind that all behavior is a transaction between the organism and the field within which it lives.

What we want is better control of behavior, and so our search is for controlling factors. Human behavior is in large measure controlled by conscious intent. The mental factors as vital functions, accordingly, must be given due consideration. Most behavior is directive, the end toward which it is directed being the satisfaction of the motivating conditions. The study of motivation must include both the conscious factors and the unconscious processes which precede and accompany them.

CHAPTER THREE
Methods of Study

The science of behavior

The systematized science of behavior is not much more than fifty years old. It has been my privilege to see the whole of this movement, which has shown changes in objectives and methods that were sometimes as bizarre as the accompanying styles of ladies' hats. At present the fashion tends to the conservative and eclectic, enjoining a selection of the best from previous contributions to be combined with new material to get a well-balanced structure of original design.

Because the problems now under investigation have so wide ramifications, it is necessary at the beginning of our survey to clarify our position regarding some features of methods and objectives of scientific work about which there are diverse opinions and practices. A systematic survey of the methodology of science would be out of place here. The only reference that need be made to the extensive literature of methodology is to say that our position is in general agreement with the survey of principles formulated by Cantril, Ames, Hastorf, and Ittelson ('49).

In a recent discussion (Rosenblueth, Wiener, and Bigelow, '43) a distinction is drawn between "behavioristic" and "functional" methods of study. "By behavior is meant any change of an entity with respect to its surroundings," without reference to the intrinsic structure and organization of the object in question. The latter are studied "functionally" apart from the "behavioristic" relations between the object and its surroundings.

The distinction drawn here is logically significant, particularly in mathematical analysis of inorganic and living automata (von Neumann, '51,

p. 2), but the terminology is unfortunate. In physiology it is practicable and customary to limit a study to a particular part of an organism, but these functions cannot be understood independently of their "behavioristic" relations. In living bodies no parts of the organism can be treated as "independent, elementary units" or "black boxes," the inner nature of which may be neglected. As Paul Weiss ('47) remarks, we can study the operation of a machine without knowing its structure or function, but its parts do not make sense in themselves but only as related to the whole in its transactional relations with the surroundings. All behavior is function in the ordinary meaning of these words, but this function must be defined more broadly than is customary in physiology. Coghill insisted that mentation is not a function in the ordinary physiological sense. This I grant, but I go further and have pointed out ('49, pp. 199–202) that if mentation as a vital process is a genuine factor of behavior its status as a bodily function must be admitted. In psychobiology we cannot treat the brain as a "black box" in the sense defined above, for the behavioristic significance of the inner nature of that organ is just what we want to find out.

The intent here is to keep this inquiry strictly within the boundaries of natural science, and what the limits of this domain are must be defined. Yet these boundaries cannot be drawn in sharp lines, because some of the data which must be taken into account are generally regarded as germane to the humanistic disciplines only and some of the theory invades the domain of naturalistic philosophy. What we are really after is a natural philosophy of animal behavior.

The reader must bear this objective in mind if the book as a whole should seem to be overloaded with theory—as the Dutch proverb has it, the sail too big for the ship. Perhaps our canvas is outsize, but correct theory we must have or the facts have no meaning for us. And it should also be recognized that our ship carries more ballast of well-validated factual evidence than is here invoiced. To find the meaning of facts we need well-conceived working hypotheses. If the facts are right they will stand. If the theory is wrong it will fall. But even an incorrect hypothesis may serve a useful purpose if it points the way toward a fruitful search for new facts and interpretations. Such pointing, at least, we hope to succeed in doing. The major problems of psychogenesis, for instance, have not yet been solved by anyone; we do not claim to have found the solutions, but we believe that the principles herein stated are fundamental and that they point the way toward fruitful lines of research in fields that have not as yet been fully explored.

Any methods used must be adapted to the nature of the problems studied and the materials available. However, there are a few general principles, to be discussed immediately, which should be observed; and the application of these principles must not be restrained by inflexible arbitrary codes of methodology or confined within arbitrary boundaries.

Empirical and normative sciences

The importance of adjusting the method to the subject under investigation comes out most clearly in the contrast between the empirical sciences (the so-called natural sciences) and the normative, or analytic, sciences. The aim and methods of these two domains of science are radically different, and much confusion has arisen from failure to observe this distinction and from the resulting mixture of categories. The empirical sciences are inseparably bound to human experience (actual or potential), and they deal only with existing things (again actually or potentially existing) in the integrated system of nature. The normative disciplines, typified by logic and mathematics, are developed wholly within the conceptual sphere; their cardinal methods cannot be successfully employed in empirical science except in a secondary way as useful tools of rational analysis.

In the normative sciences the postulated norms and standards of procedure are laid down in advance and the postulates may be anything you like, real or imaginary. For the purpose of the specific inquiry the postulate is accepted as a universal; it cannot be questioned. The conclusions follow of necessity if the logical argument is faultless. Whether or not a valid conclusion is factually true, that is, congruous with real experience, is irrelevant. This is illustrated by Bertrand Russell's oft-quoted description of mathematics as "the subject in which we never know what we are talking about, nor whether what we are saying is true," and by Whitehead's ('26, p. 32) definition of mathematics as "thought moving in the sphere of complete abstraction from any particular instance of what it is talking about." As Dewey ('38, p. 477) says, "It is, accordingly, impossible to give de-

scriptive value to the mathematical conceptions and propositions. They have instrumental and functional status."

In empirical science, on the contrary, the inquiry usually begins with a supposition or working hypothesis tentatively assumed to be true. The hypothesis is then tested and, if found to accord with properly controlled experience, is accepted as true, whereupon it becomes a "fact" or a "law of nature" that may be postulated in working hypotheses for further inquiries. The scientific norms come, not at the beginning, but at the end of the inquiry, and even so they are not universals, absolutely true, for they are based on fluid experience which is limited and imperfect.

Other definitions of the normative disciplines are current. For instance, Romanell writes, "A normative inquiry is concerned mainly with studying objects as they *ought to be* or with evaluating objects" (Leake and Romanell, '50, p. 35; see further comment on our page 215). The distinctions drawn in the preceding paragraphs are more general. They are supported by competent authority (very clearly by G. H. Mead, '36, chap. 13), and they accord with scientific practice. Jenkins ('48) denies the real significance of the distinction between normative and empirical science on general philosophical grounds. Without debating that question, I maintain that in science the distinction is important operationally. Empirical science has its norms, but, as explained below, they are not universals in the sense of the transcendentalists nor in the more restricted sense of the logicians.

The normative sciences are indispensable tools for the study of nature and as such must be employed with the utmost rigor. They are safeguards protecting us from logical fallacies and lax generalizations. In actual practice normative methods, particularly as these have been developed in logic and mathematics, work hand in hand with empirical methods, and many of our most fundamental discoveries in the physical sciences have been suggested and empirically confirmed under the guidance of mathematical geniuses.

Several recent books summarize the results of mathematical analysis of biological problems, e.g., Rashevsky ('48, '51), Thurstone ('47), Halstead ('47), Wiener ('48). It must be emphasized again that in such studies the mathematical analysis has only instrumental value. The conclusions reached must be checked empirically before they can be accepted as factually true. Thus Halstead ('47, p. 55) writes: "Factor analysis is primarily an exploratory tool. It is economizing in certain types and in some stages of behavioral investigations in that it provides rational bounds both for our search for related events and for our discourse. It does not define the factors isolated, although it may help to do so."

There is increasing demand for revision of the dogma now widely accepted that only quantitative data that can be numerically expressed have legitimate scientific standing P. W. Bridgman has remarked (Frank et al., '48, p. 190) that, if nature appears to be mathematical, it may be due to our insistence upon asking questions that we can and will answer only in mathematical terms. To Sir James Jeans's contention that the physical universe is constructed on mathematical lines an equally competent mathematical physicist, Sir Arthur Eddington, replies, "The mathematics is not there till we put it there." In this connection we may quote Herbert J. Muller's reference to such unmathematical truths as that one dollar plus a thousand dollars is a lot more money than a thousand dollars plus one dollar. The fact is that there is a vast range of natural processes in which the determining factors cannot be numerically expressed (page 150) and the significance of quantitative measurements is restricted. The recognition of this fact is especially important in the domain of human personal and social adjustment.

The method of natural science

A very large proportion of the actual work of scientific investigation is the drudgery of fact-finding, that is, the acquisition of what has been called "accumulative knowledge"; but what we are really after is the meaning of the facts, and this has been called "conceptual knowledge." This twofold nature of investigation suggests that a program of research may be divided into two stages, differing radically from each other in methods and objectives, the first factual, the second interpretative. Let us see how this works out in practice.

The accumulation of verifiable factual knowledge demands not only the utmost precision of observation and experiment with, so far as possible, measurement and quantitative expression of relations of things in space and time, but also unprejudiced judgment in the separation of the true from the false. The test of truth is congruence with the whole body of knowledge.

The next step is the systematization of the accumulated data. The recorded facts are classified in accordance with their relationships, and only when these relations are adequately known can the facts be classified or even described. An acceptable scientific description of any thing or any event is nothing other than an exposition of its relations to other things and events, as complete as is possible with the data at hand.

These relationships, in turn, are classified and generalized in accordance with observed uniformities and differences. The uniformities so discovered are formulated and codified as "laws of nature."
These laws are formulated, not as personal opinions, but as generalizations based on verifiable factual evidence. This means that private
subjective experiences are transferred to the public domain in the
form of a record which gives as true, that is, as realistic a picture of
nature as present knowledge permits. Our laws of nature are, in general, expressions of directive movement. This is what gives them their
predictive value.

During this stage of inquiry the most treacherous obstacles in the
way of sound scientific advancement are individual differences among
the observers and bias arising from unrecognized personal attitudes,
interests, and preconceptions. There is always a "personal equation"
which cannot be completely eliminated. The best we can do is to recognize it and make due allowance for it with all available checks and
counterchecks. These individual idiosyncrasies have been critically
and quantitatively studied, as in the astronomers' measurements of
reaction times and the psychologists' tests for recognition and statistical treatment of personality traits and attitude scales.

The steps just described comprise the first of the two stages of inquiry to which reference was made above. There is general agreement
that this is sound scientific procedure as far as it goes, and according
to the traditional code, which is quite generally accepted by both scientists and philosophers, the scope of natural science is limited to this
field alone. The traditional objective of so-called pure science is an
organized system of knowledge and principles free from any influence, so far as possible, of human imperfections, attitudes, and interests. This, I agree, is the ideal which we try to reach in the factual
stage of inquiry; but I insist that it is an inadequate conception of
both the scope and the method of natural science and therefore a mischievous perversion of the true function of science in human economy.
My contention is that this first stage of inquiry merely lays a foundation, as broad and firm as possible, upon which the really significant
structure of science can be fashioned. It should be noted that the steps
and stages mentioned do not in actual inquiry necessarily follow seri-
ally in the order given. The stages are logically related as indicated,

but in practice the temporal sequence is adjusted to the conditions met. Some interpretation is involved in every observation, and when obstacles are encountered a provisional theory or hunch may direct the next step.

The second stage of an investigation is concerned primarily with the meaning of the facts. Meanings are permeated with values. In a scientific investigation the initial choice of the problem to be studied is made in terms of the worker's interest, competence, and opportunity. The data accumulated are evaluated with reference to their relevance to the inquiry. Their classification and organization again involve evaluation in terms of the criteria selected. The possible conclusions are similarly evaluated and the one that best fits the data is chosen. Every step in the garnering, classification, and interpretation of facts is a valuation, and the truth discovered is valuable because it satisfies the discoverer and, in the long view, the interests of the public. There is abundant justification for Cantril's statement ('49): "I believe the history of science would indicate that when value-judgments are excluded from science, any datum becomes inert and useless, any abstraction becomes futile and without functional significance." In this connection see also Rapoport ('50) and Bronowski ('53). The values which are inherent in the organic structure of science are examined more in detail in Chapter 12.

Facts: their meaning and value

We want to get as much knowledge as possible about the world in which we live and about ourselves as living members of it. Having acquired this knowledge, what shall we do with it?

Facts and principles are of no account unless we can do something with them, and it may legitimately be demanded of science that it show what they are good for. We want to know what these facts mean, not to some detached omniscience, but in terms of human interests and problems of adjustment (Rapoport, '53). It is the significance of the facts for behavior that we want to discover, and that is why I deem it necessary to examine the general method of science in preparation for a survey of the evolution of behavior. In an examination of the relations between common sense and science Professor Dewey ('48) remarked that in a scientific inquiry "unless the materials involved can be traced back to the material of common sense concern there is nothing whatever for scientific concern to be concerned with."

Facts are the building stones of science, but science does not begin with facts. It begins with observations, which is a quite different thing (Whyte, '54, p. 60). If while walking past a quiet pool I poke my cane into the water, the stick seems to be bent. It is a fact that I did see the stick as bent, but it is not a fact that it was bent. The facts accepted in both common sense and science are interpretations, and how the observations are interpreted depends on the knowledge already available and the preconceptions derived from that knowledge. There is always a factor of uncertainty about any fact, and the principles, or "laws," derived from our factual knowledge are never absolute or final.

When I taught physics in a secondary school in 1891, the indivisible and indestructible atom was the foundation upon which the scientific structure was built. Some of my naïve pupils were skeptical and asked if I were not telling a fairy story. We know now that I was, though not in the sense they meant, and perhaps fifty years from now our present atomic theories may be regarded as quite as far from the true facts. But, after all, the facts and principles of a given stage of knowledge are all we have to work with, and we must do our best to make sense out of them.

The imposing structure of science is not built by sorting over the heterogeneous factual materials according to preconceived canons of logical categories or by trying to redress them to fit preconceived notions. Rather, the structure grows like an organism, each member of which selects from the available materials those which naturally take the places appropriate for the stage of growth reached in the process of development of an integrated body. The directions of this growth cannot be predicted, and any attempt to regiment it results only in obstruction and futility.

Large numbers of published scientific contributions are devoted exclusively to fact-finding—dry catalogues of animals, plants, minerals, etc., and descriptions of them. This is not useless knowledge, even though it is not used by many people. Its use may turn up in unexpected places. The intrinsic value of a fact as such may be nothing at all, but the meaning of the fact may be priceless. A spot of mold on

a bacteriologist's culture dish was regarded as an objectionable contamination until it was discovered that this mold produced a specific
chemical, penicillin, which proved to be one of the most efficient curative agents then known. The significant meaning of a fact had
emerged from a newly established relationship.

It is these meanings that we want, but we cannot find the meanings until we know the facts. I have illustrated ('44) the significance
of facts by an analogy. Until the meanings are revealed, either by the
discoverer of the facts or by some successor, accumulated knowledge
is only a token of potential value, like gold dollars stored in a government vault. So long as the gold remains in the vault it has no
value except as reserve. To be productive it must be put into circulation. Similarly, knowledge which does not meaningfully touch human
life would not be worth anything. The saving feature of this situation is that all knowledge does touch life; sooner or later it will be
fitted into place as part of the armamentarium of successful human
adjustment, so that our stores of even apparently useless facts comprise a valuable reserve upon which drafts are constantly being drawn
in the promotion of new enterprises. All advance in pure science and
most of the inventive marvels of applied science are directly dependent upon these stores of accumulated knowledge, much of which was
acquired with no expectation of immediate practical application. The
investment is sound because the token represents a real value that will
be apparent as soon as it is put into circulation. "Knowledge is not
merely an end in itself, but the only satisfactory means for controlling
our further evolution" (Huxley and Huxley, '47, p. 133). In short,
the prime function of science is to guide human behavior.

It is not necessary here to inquire into the meaning of meaning
further than to ask what is meant by scientific explanation. The question is dismissed by a British philosopher (Tute, '46), who assures us
that "the modern scientist no longer considers that he can explain
anything," and by an American philosopher's declaration that scientists may explain the world in a descriptive sense but they cannot understand it. I insist that an explanation that does not give us understanding is no explanation at all. A scientist cannot describe a thing
that he does not understand, for description is nothing other than an

exposition of relationships, and it is these relations that give us understanding.

A meaning is meaningless unless it means something to somebody, and (as we shall see in Chapter 12) a value has no existence apart from the person who cherishes it. Both of these concepts are generalizations of relationships; and because the subjective member of this relationship is personal and private the claim has been made and widely accepted that understanding and values as personally experienced are beyond the reach of science.

One philosopher has said to me that no meaning is private, for a meaning is propositional, and that values lie outside the domain of science because they are private passions. I challenge both of these statements, though I agree that meaning and value imply relationships and that it is the province of science to discover these relationships. But I go further and say that when these relationships are expressed as propositions and so publicized, the propositions are objects of regard that have scientific standing. The propositions are not the meanings or the values, but symbols of them, and as such are legitimate scientific data. The reality expressed by the symbol is an experiencing person and the things of which he has experience—and these two components of the relational complex must not be divorced by logical dialectic. Meaning as personally understood and true values as personally experienced belong in science by their own right, because they are essential members of the relational systems with which science is concerned.

The frequently expressed demand that natural science must be completely objective is manifestly absurd, for every factual datum is first experienced subjectively and its relations with the other data of experience are revealed only subjectively. The record of every observation is influenced by the observer's position, attitude, interest, and accumulated knowledge, by what he attends to and what he ignores as irrelevant. The observer adds something of himself to the observed data (page 61). The "fact" as recorded (in the mind and it may be on paper) is a selection of relevant data from among countless others. In other words, the data are evaluated, consciously or automatically, with reference to their relevance. The perception of an object involves an interpretation of the sensory data. Our ideas about the objective world are mental constructions, and the purpose of scientific inquiry is to build a structure of knowledge that stands in true and workable relation to the realities of the objective world in which our lives are set. The mentalistic factors cannot be excluded from any scientific inquiry, and in the study of human behavior they are the crucial factors of our most urgent problems.

The science of every community has a cultural background by which it is colored and by which the directions taken in its development are largely determined. But science is not passively molded by these cultural influences. Because science is the product of creative minds, it can and does succeed in standardizing our interpretations of the facts observed and in pointing the way to appropriate action with reference to them.

The humanistic attributes of science come to the fore in every inquiry about human conduct. The sciences of man and particularly the social sciences occupy a strategic position in the study of behavior, but they, even more than the others, have been handicapped and retarded by the outworn tradition of the limitations of science. It is foolish to try to find out what makes people behave as they do and to devise ways of controlling behavior for our own good, and at the same time to insist upon rejection of the factors without which the basic problems cannot even be formulated. For the interests and attitudes that motivate and regulate conduct, the values that people want and work for, are the key factors. A science which renounces its own intrinsic values is blind and dumb in that domain where keen discrimination and courageous speech are most needed.

One of the most urgent demands of our present perilous time is a radical change in the attitudes of both the scientific and the lay public toward science, its methods, and its significance in human behavior. The humanizing of science in theory and practice must go hand in hand with a better appreciation of the true objectives of science by the humanists.

The hopeful feature of our situation is that an increasing number of our most competent leaders in philosophy, science, and industry are throwing into the discard the outworn dogma that science must ignore human interests and values. The fundamental canons of both science and humanism are in flux. Science involves not merely knowledge but also wisdom, and wisdom comes not by observation (Bronowski, '53).

The preceding analysis of the nature and method of science was written before I discovered to my delight that essentially the same argument had already been elaborated more felicitously by a literary critic (Muller, '43). Rapoport ('50, '53) also has clarified the function of science in human affairs. I can support their principles of scientific humanism with evidence drawn from biological experience quite different from theirs. Our common objective is an intimate and understanding partnership of science and humanism so as to safeguard and enrich the lives of all of us.

Summary

The study of behavior has been complicated and confused by failure to distinguish two domains of science which are different in objectives and methods—the normative, or analytic, and the empirical, which is both analytic and synthetic. The test of the truth of a "fact" of natural science is consistency with the whole body of knowledge acquired by experience, not internal consistency of the reasoning process itself, as in the normative procedures of logic and mathematics. The latter procedures are essentialy tools in the search for truth, but by themselves cannot take us to the goal of understanding nature.

The actual procedure of investigation in the natural sciences is usually in two stages. The first is fact-finding, classification, and discovery of the relations of the facts among themselves. The aim here is to give an objective, impersonal description of the whole of nature, including human nature, with a minimum of distortion arising from the limitations, preconceptions, and personal interests of the observers themselves. This has been called "accumulative knowledge."

The second stage of the inquiry is the interpretation of the facts and laws to find their meaning. The meanings that we want to find in all science are those which are significant for us in shaping the course of our own behavior. Since human conduct is more or less subject to social control, the meanings sought must be those which have general significance for the community as a whole.

A strictly objective science does not exist and cannot exist. Mental-

istic factors permeate every inquiry, and in the study of human behavior they are crucial. Interest and attitude are intrinsic components
of scientific method, and all science is motivated and infiltrated with
human values. Since behavior is adjustment to the actualities of the
objective world, some attention must now be given to the characteristics of this world.

CHAPTER FOUR
The World in Which We Live

The nature of our world

Successful behavior is adjustment of the living body to the actualities of the world in which that body lives. We can talk in science only about the world as we know it. The world as known to the inhabitants of Mars (if there are any) might be quite different from ours. Since our treatment is naturalistic, it is appropriate to inquire what the naturalist means by nature, the naturalist being here defined as a student of nature in the broadest meaning of this term—it may be of all of it or of some part of it, such as human nature.

Nature, as science views it, has been described by Santayana ('05) as "the sum total of things potentially observable, some observed actually, others interpolated hypothetically." From this it follows that we are justified in "regarding nature as the condition of mind and not mind as the condition of nature." Natural science as of today, accordingly, may be said to embrace the sum total of human experience. It is an integrated body of knowledge about things that have come within the range of human experience and about ourselves as experiencing subjects.

This does not imply that science can claim a monopoly of everything that men experience, but it does mean that it has a legitimate interest in everything that comes within human ken. It is not the province of science to enter the domains of esthetics, religion, and transcendentalism, for instance, but it is concerned with these disciplines as human experiences which influence behavior, how they came to be, and the results of their exercise. The imaginative fantasies of both normal and mentally deranged people are real experiences, and we can look to science to tell us whether they correspond to anything in the veritable world of experience. The idea of the mythological unicorn is a real idea, and science can tell us whether such an animal exists and, if not, perhaps explain how the idea came into existence.

What is real?

The naturalist, then, must be some kind of a realist, that is, he must take a realistic attitude toward his own experience and also toward the things of which he has experience. He must believe in himself as a believing subject, for if his conscious experience is not real to him (real experience, I mean), then nothing else can be—not for him. Descartes was right about this when he said, "Cogito, ergo sum."

The reality of surrounding things, the things of our objective world, we cannot be so sure of; but we must believe that there is something real there, because if we don't adjust our behavior successfully to these verities we suffer for it. Our own experiences and the things that come within the range of our experience seem to be equally real to us. One's success as a behaving organism depends very largely upon skill in keeping these two realms of experience (the "subjective" and the "objective") in harmonious and efficient working relationship. Without the first a man can know nothing about the second, and the congruities observed in his objective world as perceptually known justify belief in the reality of these things, or at least of some of them. If it were not so, life could not go on, for the organism cannot adjust to chaos or to figments of its own construction.

What we do practically is to check every "objective" experience against the others and so learn to separate reality from illusion and fantasy. Natural science is a refinement of this practical common-sense method of validating reality, of finding the truth about things. And the things to be validated include not only external objects and events but also all the mental processes involved in the process of evaluation.

Since human experience is fluid, finite, and fallible, evidently natural science can never lead us to ultimate reality, the thing-in-itself for which philosophers have been searching for centuries. Experience gives only things-in-relation, and things can be defined and explained only in terms of these relations. All knowledge about things and all principles derived from this knowledge are relative. They are never absolutely true.

We need not concern ourselves here with the traditional philosophical problems of ontology—the ultimate nature of reality as such—but we do need a practical epistemology—an understanding of the theory and practice of knowing. To this some attention will be paid in subsequent chapters.

An eminent physicist, W. F. G. Swann ('39), in the course of his whimsical account of the physicist's difficulty in deciding what is real cites this definition, "The aether is a medium invented by man for the purpose of propagating his misconceptions from one place to another." Back of his whimsey is this statement of what the physicist means when he talks about real things: "The things which I shall call real are the principles which, in the ultimate analysis of things, are found to have the properties of harmonizing the phenomena of the universe as our senses reveal those phenomena to us." And he adds a suggested "definition of the word 'real' to the effect that it is a special form of the word 'realistic' applicable when there is only one candidate for the designation." This statement is perhaps good enough for the biologist and the psychologist too. What the physicist means by "the ultimate analysis of things" in this connection is explained and its philosophical implications are clarified in the last two chapters of Arthur E. Murphy's book, *The Uses of Reason* ('43). His conclusion (p. 309) is, "The only 'reality' that is fit to serve as the measure of philosophical truth is that which we apprehend by the disciplined use of all our powers." The only criteria of reality that have any practical significance are operational (Rapoport, '53).

Less inclusive is the statement by Henry Margenau ('50, p. 465): "Physical reality is the quintessence of cognitive experience." Margenau, who is a theoretical physicist and a profound philosopher, distinguishes "three rather obvious components of the real: The *enduring,* the *thing-like,* and the *efficacious,*" and his book is devoted mainly to the explication of these properties of the physical real. In the domains of biology, psychology, and sociology these three components of the real must be defined somewhat more broadly than Margenau defines them, because account must be taken not only of cognitive experience but also of emotional, purposive, and volitional experience and the resulting satisfactions. These are real factors of real behavior which cannot be neglected in a comprehensive scientific study of human behavior.

The alleged "enduring" property of the real also is open to criticism. As emphasized with vigor and ample evidence by Lancelot L. Whyte ('48), the Platonic idea that only the permanent is real is now giving way to the contrary view that the reality of change, of formative process, is far more significant for both natural philosophy and the practical management of our affairs. "There is," he says, "no sharp division between structure and process, because structure is a limiting case of process." And again, "Process has a self-developing tendency; it facilitates its own development."

We are concerned here with the process of evolution, the mechanical principles in accordance with which new patterns of behavior emerge, the present trends of the evolutionary movements, and the steps that may be taken to control these movements for the advancement of human welfare and the enrichment and refinement of the satisfactions to be won by our own creative efforts.

My brother developed a philosophy of "dynamic realism" which he did not live to formulate systematically. Such published and unpublished fragments of it as were available were assembled and issued posthumously (C. L. Herrick, '10). In one of his papers published in 1904 he wrote that his dynamic realism assumes "a unitary nature underlying all things. They have in common an energic character which implies, on the face of it, nothing more than efficiency or power to act, and this, of course, a fundamental philosophical necessity of all being." Lancelot Whyte's "unitary principle," to which further reference is made in the next chapter, is based on similar postulates.

In another context (Chapter 20) I have ventured to suggest that our practical realistic knowledge of the world must take account not only of the elementary particles of subatomic physics but also of the radiation fields associated with them. There is no "empty space" in nature and the theoretic perfect vacuum does not actually exist. Space in the presence of matter and its field has intrinsic dynamic properties in its own right. The "real things" that we experience are events in a polarized field with the experiencing subject at one pole of a complicated energic system. The diverse components of this system can be examined by experimental and logical analysis, but the "real thing" as we know it is the integrated system of the total field of the experience. A workable program of psychobiology must take this fact into account.

Laws of nature

The most fundamental law of nature revealed by modern science is that our cosmos is an integrated, orderly system of natural processes that are self-sustaining and self-regulating. There is no evidence that these lawfully ordered processes are in any way influenced by extraneous unnatural agencies. The patterning of these processes is determined by the intrinsic properties of the cosmic system as a whole and of its subordinate parts.

The natural world is pluralistic in the sense that it is composed of innumerable subordinate units, each of which has distinctive properties and some degree of autonomy. The behaving individual is such a unit, the properties of which are here under investigation. The living body is an integer which, again, has many subordinate parts. It is essential that the integrity of this body with all that it does be recognized and accounted for. This proves to be a difficult thing to do, and especially so in the human individual whose behavior is evidently motivated by both unconscious and conscious factors. The body-mind relationship presents a puzzling problem; the first step to be taken in a program of studying the problem is the rigorous exclusion of those traditional dualistic and pluralistic philosophies that treat body and mind as disparate entities in fundamentally different realms of being.

Because the observed patterns of natural events are continually changing, the laws of change are of primary importance. Most scientific research has been directed to the discovery of the uniformities of nature and the codification of these in a system of generalizations. This must be done before the changes can be interpreted. The time has come to devote more attention to the processes and mechanisms of these changes in the patterns of performance seen in development, in cosmic and organic evolution, and in the orderly flow of all natural events from atomic transformation to the marvelous creations of the human mind in art, science, industry, and philosophy.

This search for the laws of change is the most active program of current scientific research. It is now clear that in all natural processes there is a formative or creative factor, but it is much more difficult to find and describe the mechanisms of this apparently miraculous creative production of novelties than it is to discover the mechanical principles of those repetitive processes that yield uniform products. The constancies of nature are now far better understood than are the variables. If we wish to gain more efficient control of our own conduct and of the things and people that we have to get along with, we must know these two systems of laws—the laws of the standardized uniform ways of doing things and the laws which indicate the trends of the incessant flow of change. Both systems are essential for successful adjustment to things as they are and prediction of the probable future course of events.

Nature is process. There is nothing static in it anywhere. A range of mountains is a transient phase of the topography when viewed in geological time, and every atom of its structure is vibrant with activity. The repetitive processes, such as the tides and the recurrent seasons, are also subject to change. When the pattern of organization of any natural mechanism is changed so that a different kind of product is delivered, this is regarded as a creative act (pages 57, 58, and 60), but this creation of novelties does not imply that something is made out of nothing. It is the task of science to discover the laws in accordance with which these changes take place.

Laws and universals

The laws of nature are often called universals on the supposition that they express immutable natural principles that are always and everywhere the same. But the quest for such absolute universals in the domain of empirical science is a futile endeavor. The laws for which we are searching are general principles which have been shown by adequate tests to have the highest degree of probability. They are always existential in reference, that is, they are expressions of actually or potentially observable uniformities of natural things and events. The uniformities may be those of stable constancies of form, those of repetitive action, or those of the laws of change. These scientific generalizations are valid only within the range of the experience available.

The principles of Euclidean geometry and Newtonian mechanics were regarded as universals until it was shown that some phenomena of subatomic physics and astronomy cannot be fitted into these frames of reference. The older principles are still valid within a restricted field, but they must be supplemented by principles of wider scope.

The word "universal" is ambiguous and should not be used in empirical science without qualification. It has three meanings in current use: (1) metaphysical universals that are regarded as absolutes in a realm that transcends human experience; (2) logical and mathematical universals that are valid as such only within the frame of discourse defined by the postulates adopted; (3) verified generalizations of experience, the so-called laws of nature. The first two belong in the normative disciplines. The third is all that we ever get in empirical science, and these generalizations are never absolute, being subject to change as experience is enlarged.

The laws of thought as formulated in psychology, logic, and philosophy are expressions of the intrinsic quality of man's mental equipment. These laws, including the rules of formal logic and of mathematical computation, are regarded by the naturalist not as universals of some inscrutable realm which transcends nature but as propositions which describe the lawfully ordered operation of the human mind, a mind that has attained its present competence during development of the race and of the individual in the light of and through the agency of the experiences had. Neither the canons of logic nor the axioms of mathematics are finished and stable; they change as experience is enlarged, with accompanying increment of mental capacity.

Summary

Our success in life depends very largely upon our skill in keeping our mental operations in harmonious and efficient working relationship with what is going on in the world in which we live. We depend on science to give us true knowledge about this world and about ourselves as knowing subjects. Generalizations of the observed uniformities must be tested for validity in every practicable way and if they stand this test they are codified as laws of nature, which may express uniformities of structure, of repetitive processes, or of changes that result in the creation of novelties. Laws concerning changes are especially important to the science of behaviorism, for evolution, growth, and reasoning are creative processes.

The laws of nature are not universals in the sense of this word as used in metaphysics, logic, and mathematics. They are general principles which have been shown by adequate tests to have the highest degree of probability, and they are always existential in reference.

CHAPTER FIVE

Mechanisms of Living

The vital process

The process of living, as Herbert Spencer long ago explained, is the correspondence or interaction of the living body as mechanism with the other natural mechanisms of the world about; or, as Dewey says more concisely, it is a *transaction*.

The living mechanism makes a varied assortment of products. Some are structures that are incorporated within its own organization. Some are outside fabrications—such as birds' nests and airplanes. Others are transformations of energy patterns within and without the body, and these transformations, of course, are inseparably bound to the colligated changes in structure. Behavior is a product of this third class.

Among the distinctive vital properties of the living mechanism the following are commonly mentioned:

1. The organism is self-sustaining and self-regulating. It takes up its own wear and spontaneously repairs damage. It maintains a relatively steady state of internal operation (homeostasis), with a tendency toward dynamic equilibrium and periodicity of action.

2. It is an "open system" (Bertalanffy, '50), with constant interchange of materials and energy with environment. In the living body there is local arrest or reversal of entropy, with increase of heterogeneity and complexity rather than a trend toward degradation to homogeneous low-level organization.

3. It reproduces itself, transmitting its own distinctive character-

istics to immediate offspring repetitively generation after generation, by means of self-duplicating genes which are autocatalytic enzymes.

4. Its activities are to a large extent self-directed, although these intrinsic functions may be under more or less control by external agencies. There is functional specialization of the parts (division of labor), and dominating this process there is integration which maintains the unity and efficiency of the whole body. The behavior of living bodies is generally goal-directed, not random.

5. It is creative, in the sense that new patterns of structure and behavior are constantly fabricated.

6. Pre-eminent among the creative activities, in higher animals, are those that we call mental, involving more or less awareness of what is going on and conscious control of behavior.

It must be granted at once that all these distinctive properties, except perhaps the last, are relative. It is possible to find in both natural and artificial machines some factors comparable to one or more of them, although at a lower level of organization. A river system is self-regulating; a catalytic process propagates itself; most inorganic processes (as we shall see) are directive, not random; and every mechanism is a creative agent—it makes something. Nonetheless, organisms do differ from inorganic processes and objects in the ways mentioned. The patterns of their performance are distinctive, and nothing like them is found in the inorganic realm. This is even more conspicuously true of mentation. Are these distinctive patterns non-mechanistic and incommensurable with the rest of nature? The answer to this question depends upon what we mean by mechanism.

Mechanistic and vitalistic explanations

We are here treating behavior as the operation of a natural mechanism. Many vital processes that eventuate in behavior go on in accordance with well-known mechanical principles. There are, for instance, adjustments for the distribution and appropriate application of mechanical strain; various ingenious devices for controlling the flow of fluids and regulating internal temperature; utilization of the physical properties of surfaces and the permeability of membranes; chemical reactions in unlimited variety and the associated changes in electrical potential. These and many other functions are mechanical in the ordinary sense—that is, they are common properties of living and lifeless bodies.

Physiologists have succeeded in explaining so many vital processes in terms of the laws of inorganic mechanisms that some of them are convinced that all functions can be so explained when our knowledge is complete. Some biologists believe that this can never be realized. The vitalists claim that life is nonmechanistic because organisms are unique and have some properties that are inexplicable in terms of conventional mechanics. That the vital processes are unique there can be no question, but if there is any break in the continuity of causal relations between the organic and the inorganic, then natural science is baffled and the field must be surrendered to the vitalists and the other metaphysicians. This issue must be clarified before the problems of behavior can be resolved.

The long controversy between the vitalists and the mechanists reached a climax in the early years of this century. Radical improvements in the methods of experimental embryology yielded spectacular advances in developmental mechanics. A new science of experimental genetics was born. The study of behavior was stimulated by schools of objective psychology in Europe, and in America by cults of radical behaviorism uncontaminated by any mentalistic paraphernalia. At the turn of the century the study of the embryology of behavior was in its infancy. Only fragmentary observations had been recorded, interpretations were speculative and too often, as we now know, based on inadequate evidence. In the next following decades the intensive experimental study of developmental mechanics was so successful and enlightening that the field came to be dominated by the conviction that all vital processes can be *reduced* to the physicochemical categories of the inorganic realm.

But this goal has not been reached. Moreover, it probably cannot be reached, because it proposes a reversal of the proper procedure in the study of biomechanics. Actually, vital processes face the other way about, forward not backward, and the key problems of biology are not analytic but synthetic. So when a professor of psychology in a great university wrote a book about human behavior (A. P. Weiss, '29) on the postulate that "all forms of social activity or achievement are ultimately reducible to electron-proton interactions," no great contributions to problems of human adjustment resulted. The same fallacy of method appears in Leslie A. White's interpretation of human culture. He writes ('49, p. 375): "Human behavior is determined, therefore, by culture. But culture is not determined by man, by his wishes, will, hopes, fears, etc. . . . Everything in the cosmos can be interpreted in terms of matter and energy, whether it be a star, atom, cell, or man" (cf. the quotations from White's other papers on page 195).

Yes, it can be so interpreted, but it is a fundamental error to assume that a satisfactory interpretation of higher levels of organization can be made in terms of lower levels only. This is because new properties emerge at each level of change. The properties of a molecule are not those of an atom, although the former are derived from the latter. Living matter is made of lifeless ingredients, but life is a property which is not found in these ingredients, and it cannot be explained in terms of their properties alone. What we want to find out is the meaning of these differences and the mechanisms involved in their production. Whether we are dealing with an atom, a galaxy, or a man, the distinctive properties of a whole are significantly different from those of its parts and cannot be completely explained by them.

Human nature has developed from animal nature, but a man is something more than a brute. The true measure of man is the pattern of performance; and this pattern is determined far more by wishes, hopes, and fears than by any external environmental influences. This is not a philosophical speculation. It is a fact of everyday observation confirmed by biological and psychological analysis of motivation.

It is granted that reductive explanation is preferable in so far as applicable. It is the simplest explanation and so takes precedence in accordance with the law of parsimony. But, to quote Beck ('49), "in the logic of science there is a principle as important as that of parsimony: it is that of sufficient reason." If reductive analysis proves to be inadequate to explain all the phenomena, we must be careful "not to simplify so far that the explanation is inadequate to the facts to be explained." It is true, as Jacques Loeb said, that as long as a life phenomenon has not yet found a physicochemical explanation it usu-

ally appears inexplicable. But it does not follow that the explanation
when found can be expressed in the physicochemical formulations of
today's science.

The "reduction theory," as defended by Hockett ('48), undoubtedly adequately describes the major part of scientific achievements
from the beginning of science until now. It is sound method and it
must be carried to the limit of its possibilities. But I maintain that it
cannot take us all the way to the goal.

It is essential, then, that in any inquiry into the mechanisms and
results of the evolutionary process we recognize clearly the scope and
limitations of reductive explanation. The analytic procedures which
bring to light the simple ingredients which are recombined in new
patterns at every transition from one level of organization to a higher
level give us knowledge needful for understanding the structure and
operation of the thing that emerges from the change. These researches
take us back to beginnings. But the chief value of knowledge of origins
and past history derives from generalizations that give guidance for
prediction of the future.

Higher levels of specialization have emerged from lower, and
having emerged they cannot be reduced to the germinal simplicity of
their origins. We must look at nature as a going and a growing concern, and our prime interest is in the processes of growth and differentiation which face forward toward the future. We can do nothing
about the past, but if we know the trend of past events and the laws
of past and current changes we can predict the probable future course
of events and perhaps do something about it. We are more vitally
concerned with new developments, with future changes, than with
past history.

Most natural processes are directive, not random, and an over-all
view of nature so far as now known points toward progressively
greater diversity and specialization rather than toward degradation to
lower levels of organization. The law of entropy is commonly regarded as a universal principle, but this universality has been questioned.

Attention is called by Bertalanffy ('50) to the difference between
closed and open physical systems. The latter are never in true equilibrium, but maintain themselves in steady states by continuous ex-

change of materials with environment. The second law of thermo-dynamics is a rather special case in that it applies only to closed systems. It does not define the steady state as this is exhibited in vital processes. Entropy may decrease in open systems. Therefore, such systems may spontaneously develop toward states of greater hetero-geneity and complexity.

In the organic realm all growth and all progressive evolution manifest an apparent reversal of entropy. In this domain entropy means degeneration, death, and decay. It may well be that the reversal of entropy is true for the cosmos as a whole and that the process of degradation that we call entropy is merely a local and transient episode in a vast domain of creative process that is continuously enlarging and progressively differentiating. In fact, this possibility may be regarded as a probability, because there are no strictly closed systems in nature. Nothing that exists is completely isolated from its surroundings. The second law of thermodynamics—"the entropy of a closed system never decreases"—is experimentally confirmed in certain selected types of situations where the system in question is closed, or isolated, in respect to the measurable quantities under investigation, but this does not mean that the law is a universal principle applicable to all existing things.

This topic has been discussed with due regard to current movements in mathematical physics by Brillouin ('49). He concludes that the universality of entropy has not been proved and in the nature of the case cannot be proved. Indeed, he goes so far as to say, "The entropy content of a living organism is a completely meaningless notion." To this he adds a pertinent and provocative suggestion: "We have been looking, up to now, for a physicochemical interpretation of life. It may well happen that the discovery of new laws and of some new principles in biology could result in a broad redefinition of our present laws of physics and chemistry, and produce a complete change in point of view."

Such a broad redefinition is attempted by the physicist Lancelot L. Whyte ('49). "The clue," he says, "to the order of nature may not be a principle of permanence, but a universal pattern of process displaying an invariant one-way tendency." His search is for "a fundamental principle of the development of pattern." The most significant feature of pattern is symmetry, broadly defined, and in his work three-dimensional spatial symmetry is the primary concern. The formal statement of this principle (p. 8) is very brief: "Asymmetry tends to disappear, and this tendency is realized in isolable processes."

His original text must be consulted for the interpretation of this cryptic sentence. The meaning of its terms and the applications of the principle to the heterogeneous mass of scientific knowledge are too technical and complicated for summary here, but the trend of the argument may be indicated by a few quotations and comments.

A completely isolated process is a stable closed system in which perfect symmetry prevails. "The unitary principle defines a finite phase of process leading toward a symmetrical and stable end-state" (p. 53). "All stability is due to symmetry, and asymmetry is the source of change" (p. 71); but "no stability is absolute" (p. 54). There are no enduring isolated systems in nature, for every system has some disturbing relations with other systems. An incompletely isolated system is an open system. "No system is ever completely isolable, nor isolable in any respect for ever. . . . Every isolable system tends toward its symmetrical state, but no system remains isolable indefinitely. Nature is a disturbed system of systems, and there is never anywhere a final end to process" (p. 13).

The second law of thermodynamics applies only to closed (isolated) systems; entropy is not a universal principle; indeed, it is never absolutely true because there are no completely isolated systems in nature. The so-called closed systems are closed or isolated only in respect to certain properties that can be quantitatively measured in numerical units, and it is only in this domain that entropy prevails.

The unitary principle "provides a nonquantitative *theory of tendency* applicable to a wide class of one-way processes. It leads, for example, to a theory of organism using terms which are equally relevant to 'physical' and 'mental' processes, and do not imply any fundamental dualism" (p. 45). "The physical science of structure has hitherto been mainly concerned with the measurable properties of thresholds and termini. The unitary method draws attention to the one-way character of temporal sequence of the processes which occur between these limiting states" (p. 57). It is claimed for the unitary principle that it "presents all the constituent processes of the organism as co-ordinated components of one comprehensive one-way process" (p. 102). "The unitary principle is an instrument for organizing existing knowledge and for guiding theoretical and practical research" (p. 158). It is not a revolutionary theory. Its advantages "all consist in the unification, extension, and improvement of existing scientific theory."

In this work Whyte does not deal explicitly with heredity, evolution, and mentation. The principle has this advantage, that it deals with *process* in a nonquantitative way and so avoids the rigidity of the current numerical systems of analysis. Lillie ('51) published a helpful summary and critique of the biological implications of the unitary principle, and Whyte in a later work ('54) develops these ideas further.

These basic issues must be clarified before the mechanics of vital processes can be understood. The interpretations which have just been cited are not acceptable to all competent authorities. Seidenberg, for example, in a trenchant book ('50) examines organic evolution and human social evolution, in particular, on the assumption that these processes must conform with the second law of thermodynamics. From this premise he reaches disquieting conclusions which are diametrically opposed to those which others derive from the same factual data. The present trend toward social organization, he says, has the inevitable result that "in the mechanization of society and dehumanization of the individual we cannot fail to see the eclipse of the spiritual structure of man." In a critical review of this work Bentley Glass ('51) shows that the basic assumptions are biologically inadmissible and that a highly organized collective society requires more, not less, capacity of *individual* intelligence, initiative, originality, and freedom. And to this list we may add basic morality.

A more technical discussion of the relation between vital processes, including mental acts, and the second law of thermodynamics is found in Grünbaum's essay "Time and Entropy" ('55). His explanation of the meaning of time involves two tasks: (1) the discovery of those properties of the inanimate world which confer an "arrow" upon physical time quite independently of human awareness of it, and (2) the assembly of evidence that man's subjective sense of the unidirectional quality of time is a function of his *participation* in the physical processes which exhibit the "arrow of time."

The first task deals with entropy; in the second it is shown that man's conscious participation in the events observed is a causal factor in the determination of what actually occurs. His intelligent use of memory permits a forecast of the probable consequences of any contemplated course of action. This gives to man a range and pattern of freedom of action which is unique and yet not indeterminate (cf. my comments on page 211). Here, as in his earlier paper ('52, p. 671), Grünbaum shows that this type of determinism must not be identified with fatalism, for, "unlike fatalism, determinism allows causal efficiency to human actions."

The intrinsic directiveness of many vital processes is as well established by factual evidence as anything in biology. To deny it simply because we do not understand it or do not like it is a futile device as old at least as the Greek Eleatics and as modern as Mary Baker Eddy.

Some of the literature on emergence which is of significance for behavior is cited by Lillie ('45, pp. 16, 157; see also his subsequent papers, '48, '48a, '48b), Wheeler ('28), Montgomery ('07), and Morgan ('26).

The biochemist Jerome Alexander has written ('48) a book on the nature and origin of life in which he emphasizes the role played by catalysis in the fabrication of what Lillie calls novel emergents. He devotes a chapter to "Catalysis as the Efficient Cause of Evolution." The mechanism and significance of autocatalysis are briefly discussed by Whyte ('49, p. 60). This is perhaps a first step toward an understanding of the mechanics of those intrinsic vital processes that are genuinely creative. Many complex mechanical systems exhibit the property of hysteresis, which means that the configuration of the system is dependent upon its history, that is, upon its past experience. Novelties emerge by virtue of changes in the intrinsic organization of the mechanism at work. Thus we have magnetic, colloidal, and elastic hysteresis. Conditioning of reflexes, learning, and many other kinds of behavior in living bodies involve hysteresis. The properties of these systems have been investigated mathematically by Rashevsky ('48). The role of enzymes in catalysis is graphically portrayed by Haldane ('49). And see our page 215 for an application of the principles of homeostasis to social phenomena. The continuity of patterns of structural organization and the related patterns of behavior of increasing complexity from atoms to the highest levels of vital processes are graphically portrayed by Baitsell ('55). At each successive level new properties emerge, and all these submolecular and supramolecular activities are shown to conform with some physicalistic principles common to all of them. The known principles and mechanisms of animal development and the problems awaiting solution are well summarized in a recent book by Willier and others ('55). For a clear description of the mechanisms of vital processes as revealed by current studies of genetics, read H. J. Muller's essay "Life" ('55).

The nature of mechanism

Casual inspection shows that a machine is a specific kind of structure that operates in accordance with natural laws and delivers some specific kind of product: shoelaces, perhaps, or a hurricane or a litter of pigs. In this setup three components are commonly recognized: (1) material structure, (2) energy expressed in action or function, (3) the pattern of structure and performance. This analysis, of course, is merely a convenient logical instrument devised as an aid to inquiry, for actually these are inseparable components of everything of which we have experience and of the act of experiencing itself. Let us examine them a little more closely

1. Matter used to be regarded as the stable inert framework of the universe, pushed about by forces acting upon it. But really we know nothing about matter except what it does, and it is now defined in terms of its own activity. A material thing, so far as we now know, can best be described as an equilibrated system of energy. If this dynamic system is in relatively stable equilibrium, we have an enduring structure, say an atom or a chicken, the properties of which are determined by the pattern of its own intrinsic activity. If there is a

radical change in the pattern of performance, we have a different structure, as occurs when a particle of radium is spontaneously transformed into lead or an egg becomes a bird. I have quoted ('55, p. 77) a comment expressed by my brother Clarence fifty years ago: "We must not forget that structure is behavior in instantaneous photograph." Lancelot Whyte ('54, p. 27) says that " 'structure' is a name for the effective pattern of relationships in any situation," and these relationships are never static.

According to Whyte's unifying principle, "formative process" is a fundamental property of everything in nature. Matter, he says, is the terminal and relatively stable limit of a directive process which may be, under some conditions, reversible, for matter can be transformed into energy according to Einstein's conversion formula $(E=Mc^2)$, and conversely.

Structure, then, is best described as organization and defined according to the pattern of organization manifested. What may be the ultimate reality (in the metaphysical sense) back of that organization we do not know and we do not need to know in order to make efficient use of the knowledge we already have.

2. Energy is not now regarded as something that acts upon matter. It is interchangeable with matter in measurable relationship, and matter and energy seem to be different phases of an underlying something as yet not satisfactorily defined. This is graphically illustrated by Harlow Shapley's remark ('45) that the energy of the sun's radiation is four million tons of light per second. Whatever may be the actual relation between matter and energy, they are not dissociated. We know many properties of energy through the behavior of the related matter, yet in current physical theory energy seems to be the more fundamental (or at least the more useful) datum. If structure is determined by the pattern assumed in the manifestation of energy, then pattern must be reckoned with and given significance equal to that of matter and energy, for pattern is the basic feature of structure (Whyte, '54, p. 27).

3. Pattern is not a mere abstraction, a figment of the mind. It is an observable property of everything there is. The telegrapher's key is patterned in terms of the shape—that is, the spatial relations of its parts—and the tensile strength, electrical conductivity, and other

properties of the material. The message sent is patterned in terms of the temporal relations of dots and dashes. These patterns have meanings for us if we can decipher the code. Patterns of structure and performance are crucial issues in every scientific inquiry, and conspicuously so in biology. No specific kind of energy is manifest in vital processes, and no chemical elements are peculiar to living bodies. It is the patterns of energy and of structural organization that are distinctive.

Theoretically all observed patterns can be described in units of measurement, but many of them cannot with any available technique be quantified and we get along as best we can with qualitative statements. It may well be that the nature of some of these qualities is such as to defy any measurement in numerical units.

It is important to note here that pattern and energy are not independent variables. All matter has an available intrinsic store of energy which has been called energy of arrangement or binding energy. Furthermore, the space between the elementary particles of matter is not empty. It is an integral part of a dynamic field which has pattern.

There seems to be general misunderstanding about how a machine makes its product, the mechanism being commonly regarded as inert structure passively operated by forces external to it. On the contrary, the machine, whether natural or artificial, is an active participant in the process, with a restricted range of freedom of action. Otherwise it could not make anything. This seems perfectly obvious from simple inspection of any mechanism in action, but it is so often unrecognized, even by scientific experts, that I wrote a book about it ('32; cf. '28, also '49, p. 199).

We say that a machine in operation is "working," and a factory full of machinery is often called "the works." These are correct expressions, for it is the business of a machine to do work. If we accept the current definition of work as motion against resistance involving expenditure of energy, two kinds of work are generally recognized. The resistance may be external to the working mechanism, as when a weight is lifted against gravity by a crowbar, or it may be internal to the mechanism itself, as in overcoming friction. In the latter case there may be a change in the pattern of subatomic, atomic, or molecular movement, as when heat is generated by friction or strain is resisted.

When a workman lifts a heavy stone with a crowbar both external and internal work is done. The laborer knows very well that he is working, but is the bar working? If the steel is not properly tempered, the bar bends. The worker throws it aside with the remark, "It won't work." He is right. Resistance against strain is work. The energy changes involved in this internal work have been subjected to complicated mathematical analysis (Margenau, '50, p. 195). Strains, or tensions, play an important part in most mechanical operations, and increasingly so as we pass from the inorganic to the organic, human, and social levels of organization.

We are inclined to define mechanism too narrowly, after the model of the movement of a watch enclosed in its housing, and to neglect the other indispensable factors. But we must recognize that the conception of mechanism does not make sense unless account is taken not only of the apparatus that determines the quality of the product but also of the materials and energies used and their sources and everything that results from the operation. Every natural system, for example, a volcano or a solar system, regarded as mechanism has intrinsic creative power, and none is a tightly closed system. Its field of operation may be as small as the volume of an atom or as wide as the solar system or the metagalaxies.

Many years ago I got a good definition of a volcano from an eminent authority—the president of the National Academy of Sciences—who quoted from a schoolboy's essay: "A volcano is a mountain what is busted and squirts out stuff." The geologist can accept that definition and go on from there to find out what busted the mountain, where the stuff came from, and what it does. He finds, what everybody already knew, that there is nothing passive about a volcano. When it makes an earthquake and a lava flow, it is working at it, and the work it is doing is its own business, not that of Jove or any other outside agent.

This implies that every mechanism is an automaton in the sense defined by von Neumann ('51). But no actual mechanism is an independent, self-contained automatic unit, for its intrinsic qualities as mechanism depend in part on the nature of its transactions with its

surroundings. Many people think that living bodies cannot be regarded as automata because they can create novelties, such, for instance, as those observed in organic evolution. This belief is not well
founded, for von Neumann gives an explanation in rigorously mechanistic terms of possible ways an autonomous organism can reproduce
itself and during this process create mutations.

The kind of work performed by a machine was clearly stated by
D'Arcy Thompson ('42) in his great work *On Growth and Form*:
"From the physical point of view, we understand by a 'mechanism'
whatever checks or controls, and guides into determinate paths, the
workings of energy." This control is an active process which involves
expenditure of energy and is directive. The thing made is different
from the stuff out of which it is made, and this ability to change the
pattern of organization is the source from which the creative processes
of nature are derived—as creation is defined on page 44. These are
distinctive properties of mechanism as such, and they are everywhere
apparent. They are illustrated perfectly by so simple a mechanical
process as the making of water by chemical combination of hydrogen
and oxygen, as was pointed out in 1865 by Claude Bernard and again
more recently by a philosophically minded engineer, A. Boyajian
('44), whose comments are so germane to our theme that they are
quoted at some length.

Boyajian reports an imaginary conversation between the philosopher
Kant and the physicist Michelson. With the author's Kantian metaphysics
we are not here concerned, but some reflections, which introduce the
dialogue, upon the growth of ideas about the chemical equation are pertinent here.

In the early days of chemistry, attention was directed mainly to the
matter involved in chemical reactions. The equation for the formation of
water from its elements was written as

$$2H_2 + O_2 = 2H_2O$$

in which no account is taken of the energy involved in the reaction. In the
familiar laboratory experiment an electric spark is introduced into the mixture of hydrogen and oxygen to start the reaction; in other words, there
is an energy factor on both sides of the equation. The correct equation as
now written is

$$2H_2 + O_2 = 2H_2O + 293,000 \text{ Joules.}$$

"This equation," Boyajian says, "satisfies the law of conservation of mass
plus energy, whereas the old one would not, because $2H_2O$ is a little lighter

than $(2H_2 + O_2)$ at the same temperature." Now he asks, "But is the new equation really complete?" It is suggested that it is not, "and that some day we shall add to the right-hand member of the equation a third term representing a mental factor:

$$2H_2 + O_2 \longrightarrow 2H_2O + 293,000 \text{ J} + X$$

the X in this equation being the mind-stuff that is necessary to balance the equation." I noticed that in the last formula the equality sign was replaced by another symbol and in response to my inquiry for the reason Mr. Boyajian wrote:

"You allude to the fact that in my third equation the equality sign has been changed to an arrow. That had a double significance. First, as the equation became more up to date, its typographical form also was made to conform. Chemistry books nowadays use mostly arrows instead of equality signs. Second, the reason for the change in the convention is that chemical equations represent a reaction moving in a certain *direction*. . . . And I would call particular attention to the fact that later in my article I have pointed out that X is another aspect of the physicochemical system and not an additional factor. To use Coghill's language, in my opinion, 'mentation' would be a simple shorthand psychological statement of a complex biochemical process, rather than an addition to it."

What is important for us here is that no chemical "equation" represents a static balance. It symbolizes a process, and this process is directive. The process is set in motion by a disturbance of an equilibrated system of energy, and it continues until a new and different equilibrated system is established. The essential feature of this reaction, and of every other mechanical action, is a change in pattern of organization and performance; or, otherwise expressed, there emerges a new product with different properties. In Boyajian's formula the "X" admittedly stands for an unknown. It may simplify the problem if at this level of organization we call this unknown "pattern" instead of "mind-stuff." At the higher levels of the organic realm this pattern takes the form that Schrödinger ('44) calls "code script" and Coghill ('38) calls "mentation." The concept of pattern carries no implication of panpsychism here, though it does not exclude that hypothesis if one wishes to adopt it.

The chemical reaction as directive action is not indeterminate. Whether or not the reaction occurs depends on availability of the reacting elements, temperature, and other external factors, but what product is made is determined by the intrinsic organization of the reacting substances, that is, by their pattern. We do not know as much as we would like about how a liquid can emerge from a mixture of gases, but we do know that it does so under certain conditions and we know a great deal about the requisite conditions. The scientific problem is to discover the conditions which uniformly yield the observed result. When these relationships are known we have gone as far as science can take us in the search for causes.

These simple chemical reactions illustrate the sort of thing that is done by all mechanisms, natural and artificial. Their patterns are always actively determined; they are patterns of performance, which exhibit on one hand some constant features that give stability to matter and various types of organization, and on the other a capacity for change that makes nature a hierarchy of patterns of progressively increasing complexity. The first task of science has been the analysis of these patterns to discover their constant features, their uniformities. Their variable features, the novelties introduced by recombination of patterns, are everywhere apparent, but much harder to understand and codify. The chief concern of the physical sciences and of anatomy and physiology has been with the uniformities, the stable and recurrent features of things; but in the fields of evolution, embryology, psychology, and especially of behavior, interest centers in the variables, the nonrepetitive and irreversible changes that emerge within the flow of events. These unpredictables are not uncaused and their causes can be discovered by ex post facto inquiry. This synthesizing process is primordial, it is apparent at all levels of the operations of nature, it assumes greater significance as we ascend from the atomic level to the human brain, and it is the crucial issue in our present inquiry. I interpret Whitehead's ('29) dictum, "creativity is ultimate," to mean that it is something which science cannot explain or analyze further.

This is not a philosophical postulate. It is an observed fact that creative activity, or "formative process," is an intrinsic property of everything in the natural cosmos that is known to man. Nothing in nature is static, and the discovery of the laws of change is the cardinal problem of scientific inquiry.

Scientific explanation must be mechanistic. An acceptable biomechanics must be founded on a true understanding of the essential properties of mechanism as such. It must observe what mechanisms actually do and fit theory to facts. The popular conception of mechanism as passive structure fails to recognize mechanism's intrinsic activity which participates in the operation and sets its direction.

An even more serious trouble with the treatment of mechanism in classical physics is the failure to include the observer as an integral part of the mechanism *as it is observed*. Classical mechanics must be supplemented by the principles of relativity not only in subatomic physics but also in our consideration of every natural mechanism that comes under observation. What *we know* about any mechanism is inseparably bound to the observer and is restricted by his capacity to observe and to interpret the observations. "The knowing subject intrudes itself unpreventably into the objective scheme of things" (Margenau, '50, p. 52). This is a fact of critical importance in the search for mechanisms of all kinds and especially those of human motivation and of human social organizations.

Mechanical order and disorder

The living machine, like every other mechanism, works in an orderly way. No operations of nature are disorderly. An apparently random movement is random only within some particular frame of reference. Even the movements of electrons are not lawless. If they were, they could not be systematized statistically or treated scientifically in any way. The laws of probability imply order, not chaos. Accidents don't happen in nature. The novelties that constantly appear in nature do not happen by chance (Chapter 9).

The apparently random activities of electrons and rats and men are cited as evidence that natural events come by chance and hence that nature is disorderly. But no one has explained how the observed order can come out of chaos. So when Sir James Jeans writes ('43, p. 140) that quantum theory has disproved the principle of the uniformity of nature we wonder if he realized the implications of the statement. A chaotic or dismembered world could not be investigated scientifically, nor could any living thing survive in it. The apparent discontinuities result from gaps in our knowledge and as these gaps are bridged the integrity of our world is more securely validated.

We are told that quantum physics has demolished two pillars of the old science—causality and determinism. To this I reply that these pillars have not been destroyed or weakened; but we must change our ideas of their structure. All natural events have causes; the causes lie within the events themselves and change as the events change. Nothing in nature is indeterminate; but this does not imply that all is inexorably predetermined. The determination again is internal to the events as they go along. Einstein's faith in the order of nature was not tarnished by the revolutionary discoveries of current mathematical physics. He expressed the hope that the statistical methods of quantum physics would prove to be a temporary expedient (Engel, '55).

The theories of evolution that rest upon chance variations or random mutations have been critically examined by Simpson ('47, '49), who shows clearly that the concept of chance must be ruled out, and he gives illustrations of other explanations that are scientifically acceptable.

I repeat that the behavior of any class of things, whether electrons or people, which seems to us to be random is not lawless. We do not know all of the laws of these events, and Heisenberg has shown that in the nature of things there are some features of behavior that we never can know because of our limitations. But we do know that all apparently random events when studied statistically show certain uniformities which can be formulated as laws of probability. These laws do not enable us to predict with certainty the action of any individual, but they give us a measure of probability that is adequate for practical operations.

Because we have no absolute knowledge and every scientific fact and principle is at best a more or less probable approximation, we depend more and more upon statistical methods of measuring these probabilities. But when some of our eminent physicists go so far as to say "everything is statistical," we ask, just what do they mean by "everything"? Even though we grant that *our knowledge* of things is so incomplete that statistical methods give us our best measures of probabilities, we must remember that these methods are human inventions. In the methods now regarded as acceptable there are certain presuppositions, such as the number of odds against chance which may be regarded as "significant." The significant "critical ratios" selected may differ widely in various operations. The method, then, always involves some process of selection by the operator, and it has been claimed that the statistical methods now in current use are inappropriate for some large classes of data. This claim is supported by Bridgman ('56) in his discussion of probability concepts. Evidently, then, our statistical methods are imperfect instruments which deal with *knowledge about things,* not with things in their own right.

R. S. Lillie played up the contrast between random and directive activities. His remark ('45, p. 157) that novel conditions may originate through pure chance is unfortunate, and still more so is his further statement—"Chance is a real factor: the detail of nature is only partially integrated, and unforeseen conjunctions are sure to happen." Unforeseen by whom? By ignorant and fallible men. In speaking of "primeval chaos," a distinguished astronomer says: "No true chaos exists for one who knows all the laws. . . . We are not yet blocked by unknowableness" (Shapley, '48).

Because of our limitations, we use the concepts of chance and random activity *operationally* in lieu of adequate knowledge of causes; but the constant aim is to reduce this chaos to order by statistical and all other devices at our command. Statistics reveal results of natural processes in the mass, that is, as generalizations, but they tell us nothing about causes of the particulars. No two events result from the same combination of causal factors, and these particulars are often of more significance than are the generalizations abstracted from them. So let us set the goddess of chance aside in that pantheon to which Sam Weller assigned his Wenus and all other fabulous monsters.

If nature is only partially integrated and utterly random activity is anywhere prevalent, then every hiatus must be filled by some unnatural or mystical agency and the problems presented are scientifically insoluble. Those scientists and philosophers who deny the integrity of the order of nature reject the cardinal principle of science and have nothing with which to replace it but chaos and futility.

Set over against this postulated universality of law-abiding interrelationships is the uniqueness of everything that can be identified as a definable thing. Although science deals mainly with regularities and uniformities, it cannot be indifferent to the particulars whose properties are generalized. Indeed, what constitutes individuality is one of its major problems, an accessible problem because all the manifold relationships of the individual can be arranged in groups of similars that can be classified and quantified either by direct measurement or statistically. Professor Dewey in his *Logic* ('38, pp. 437 ff.) makes some pungent comments on the "dogmatic restriction of science to generalizations" and shows the fallacy of the current assumption that "institution of generalizations *exhausts* the work of science."

That nature so far as known to us is an integrated orderly system is the most important induction of modern science. How shall we square this basic law of nature with the obvious disorder that now threatens to destroy all that we prize most in our present cultural structure? This is a vital question, and the answer is very simple.

As we have seen, any definable mechanism—a solar system, an electric battery, a man, a family, or a nation—is a more or less well-integrated unit which maintains transactional relations with surrounding things. It preserves its identity just so long as its own integrating processes are dominant over the disintegrating agencies that act within it and upon it. Both the integrating and the disintegrating factors of the operation are lawfully ordered processes. The disturbing or destructive processes are disorderly only from the standpoint of the mechanism involved.

The laws of nature were not enacted by men to suit their own convenience, and if men disobey these laws the infraction carries its own penalty. It is fortunate for us that the man and his social group are endowed with intrinsic capacities for self-regulation and self-repair that are far more efficient than those of any other mechanisms that we know. We already know how to correct our own worst disorders, but we stupidly refuse to use this knowledge in the practical management of our affairs. Our dominant cultural policies are suicidal. How long will it take us to find this out and make the necessary corrections?

Summary

The behaving body is a mechanism which transforms material and energy derived from the outside and returns these to the environment in altered form. This is an active process involving expenditure of energy. These activities, like those of all other mechanisms, are directive. The ends toward which they are directed are, first, the survival of the individual and the species to which it belongs, and, second, the largest possible satisfaction of needs and desires. Living bodies have many properties in common with lifeless bodies, and other properties that are distinctive—the kind of mechanism employed, the patterns in which the materials are organized, and the patterns of their performance.

The popular conception of mechanism as inert structure acted upon by external forces is all wrong. The causes of mechanical action are intrinsic to the mechanism itself. An external agency acting upon the mechanism thereby becomes a part of the mechanism, for mechanical action is always a transaction of some sort. In the light of this fact we envisage the human individual and human society as natural products of an integrated cosmic mechanism that exhibits incessant change, differentiation, and growth in accordance with the laws of its own organization. The pattern of this cosmic evolution is self-sustained and self-directed, and so is the pattern of organic evolution and growth of the individual.

Chapter Six

Human Engineering

The human machine

If nature is machine-made, if man is a machine and all his works are mechanical products, shall we then worship the machine and bend all our energy and inventive genius to making more and better machines until all human enterprise is devoted to a gadgetry that can only make more gadgets which absorb all other interests at the expense of the esthetic and moral values that alone can give us those refined and fruitful satisfactions that make life worth living?

This indictment has been made against the mechanists—that by glorifying the machine they degrade and ultimately may destroy all the spiritual values that men cherish and the moral obligations that are essential for the survival of our civilization. We must grant that such an unreasoning glorification of the machine might happen—for indeed it *has* happened in the case of some individual people and some great nations, with catastrophic results.

In 1923 nine of the world's most prominent financiers met at a conference in Chicago. These were men of great wealth, each of whom had created a vast financial organization and mastered the art of making money. An insurance company has recently circulated a record of their later activities. By 1950, twenty-seven years after the meeting at the height of their power, most of them had died in bankruptcy, four of them having received prison sentences for fraud, and three of them having committed suicide. We have seen two of the world's most powerful nations, Germany and Japan, collapse in ruin after building extremely efficient political and military machinery for world conquest. The money-making apparatus of the financiers and the military equipment of the totalitarian powers were cleverly designed for their purposes, but they failed to deliver acceptable products. Why?

A moonshiner's still may be skillfully designed for economical manufacture of bad whisky, but we don't accuse the still of responsibility for the harm done. That apparatus is only an incidental part of a larger organization that has something radically wrong with it—wrong as gauged by the biological criteria of fitness as defined in our first chapter.

In the instances of the financiers and the nations a bad product was delivered because the machinery of production was itself inherently defective. It lacked a factor which is indispensable for successful human behavior, namely, a due regard for the social consequences of action taken. Such failure must not be cited as typical or representative examples of the way living mechanisms operate in human economy. They illustrate the inevitable evils that result from faulty design of the social machinery. They also show that the traditional conceptions of what mechanism is and how it works must be revised and expanded so that man's so-called spiritual values may be integrated with all other vital processes in a workable program of successful living. A practicable biomechanics must include the biosocial and the psychosocial factors or it fails utterly to meet the requirements of our times. This is not a personal opinion biased by ethical considerations but a biologically valid conclusion based on critical examination of various patterns of social operation and the actual consequences of their operation.

In this work we are dealing with behavior as a mechanical product. The somatic sensorimotor apparatus is our primary concern. Adequate treatment of the very important visceral and emotive factors and of the disorders with which psychosomatic medicine deals would require other large books, and since these topics are discussed in many other works there are few references to them here. Our attention here is directed particularly to factors of behavior that are operative in evolutionary development. The factors which are distinctive of the period of individual development present educational problems which are beyond the scope of this survey. It is, however, important that all educators understand the basic biological factors here under consideration, for they play an indispensable role in all learning and in the use which the individual makes of what he has learned.

Our scientific knowledge of behavior, its causes and its mechanisms, is of no practical use to us unless we do something about it and with it. And what we do is determined by the ends we want to reach, by what kind of people we want to be and what kind of life we want to live. These decisions should be and can be based on scientific knowledge. This indeed is what science is for—to teach us what it is good for us to do (pages 32, 147, 200, 222). It is good for us to be well fed, well clothed, and well housed, to invent labor-saving machines, to enjoy the beauties of nature and of man's creative art, to build efficient and stable social structures, and to enlarge and refine the satisfactions won by these creative activities. A comprehensive psychobiology embraces within its scope all human conduct, the causes which motivate it, and the material and "spiritual" consequences which ensue. To ignore the mentalistic factors of these biological processes is unscientific and indeed practically impossible. These factors are obviously present in the observed behavior and in the acts of observation and interpretation.

Mankind has not been endowed with his unique capacities for cultural advancement miraculously. Everything we have has grown up with us naturally in the course of human evolution, with recognizable origins in our subhuman ancestors. This is as true of our intelligence, of the verbal and other symbols employed in thinking, and of our finest values and moral standards as it is of our bodily structure and muscular skill.

Let us look again at the properties of the machine as mechanism. Every machine, natural or artificial, has a specific pattern of organization adapted to make a specific kind of product. You may say a dynamo delivers electrical current and a cat delivers kittens because that is what they are made for, or you may turn the statement around and say that electrical currents and kittens explain the structures employed. Neither statement makes sense without the other, expressed or implied. The machine is a means for reaching an end. The end (the product) cannot be made without the means (the mechanism), and the machine is meaningless junk if it does not deliver the appropriate goods. This is as true of every natural mechanism as it is of a dynamo or a corporation.

This evident fact has been lost sight of in much current theory of human behavior. In our search for the nervous mechanisms that regulate behavior, attention has been directed mainly to sensory experience which reports environmental conditions and to the central apparatus which arranges the perceived data in orderly systems of successive levels of integration. But really the key factors of both neurophysiology and psychoneurology are at the other end of the behavioral process. That is to say, the patterns of the central operations involved are determined primarily by the ends to be reached by the appropriate behavior.

The neuromotor features of the process, accordingly, are by far the most significant factors, for the behavior is futile or harmful if the resulting action is inappropriate. The motor components of both unconscious and consciously directed behavior give the clearest interpretation of the sensory and associative functions. This is emphasized and convincingly documented by Sperry ('52), who writes: "In a machine, the output is usually more revealing of the internal organization than is the input. Similarly in the case of our thinking apparatus an examination of its terminal operations and finished products may be more enlightening than any amount of analysis of the transport of raw materials into it." The primary concern of the mechanist, I repeat, is with the product made. His interest in the mechanism employed is incidental to this; but this interest may be very keen because we must understand the mechanism and the principles of its operation in order to control its action and improve its efficiency.

Mechanisms make everything we know anything about, and nobody can set a limit to the range of variety of things that natural mechanisms can produce. Man as a mechanism invents other mechanisms for his own convenience. Some of these are tools and other physical works of various degrees of complexity. Others are mental constructions of many kinds, including practical and scientific knowledge, creative art, and standards of social comity and morals.

Mechanists and humanists alike are working for the advancement of human welfare and satisfaction. The cultivation of spiritual values by the humanists can be vastly improved by paying more attention to the available scientific knowledge about the means which they must employ, and the mechanists must not be so preoccupied with the details of their apparatus as to be unmindful of the values created. The key to success in both fields is a judicious evaluation of the values for which we search. Many highly prized values prove in the upshot to be phony, and if the product made by any mechanism is shoddy or dangerous it is the province of science to show this up. The machine can then be scrapped or perhaps remodeled to correct the defect. It is of course a simpler problem to remodel a defective linotype machine than to reform the habitual criminal, but both of these things have been done. If, however, reform of an incorrigible, murderous bandit proves to be impracticable, he must be scrapped, if not by execution, by sentence to a scrap heap which must be securely guarded.

The manufacture of atomic bombs for mass destruction should by all means be prevented by concerted action and then the incalculable resources of atomic energy can be applied only constructively for the benefit of mankind. All the vast machinery of warfare is misdirected. We have to tolerate it as long as there are people who have not yet learned that aggression is no longer a profitable way to behave.

Experience is the best teacher, and we have about five thousand years of recorded human history to serve as a guide to show us what kinds of conduct have resulted in security, comfort, and progressive refinement of values sought and won. But human nature did not begin five thousand years ago. It is the product of hundreds of millions of years of evolutionary history—a history which can now be read in broad outline with reasonable assurance of accuracy. This record enables us to discover which factors of behavior have been biologically implanted in human nature by direct descent from prehuman ancestry, which have been subsequently acquired during the million years (more or less) since man emerged from apedom, and which are newly acquired by every individual during his growth from a fertilized egg. This knowledge is important because these three classes of behavior patterns differ radically, not only in origin, but also in the bodily apparatus employed and the measures that are effective to ensure their healthy growth and appropriate regulation.

It is repeated that the objectives of scientific study of behavior are, first, the recognition and precise definition of all factors of each of the three classes of patterns just mentioned and, second, the discovery of the laws in accordance with which the interplay of these diverse factors results in successfully integrated behavior of the individual and of the social groups of which he is a member.

The search for causes

If any mechanism is not working properly, we must find the cause of the trouble before we can cure it. So we want to know the causes of all kinds of behavior. We are not concerned here with the philosophy of causality in the abstract, but only to find out how causal processes operate instrumentally in vital activity.

When the laws, that is, the uniformities in accordance with which natural events take place, are adequately known we can discover causes. Our ideas about causality are derived from the observed contingent relations of things. We notice that a particular event, B, does not happen unless some other event, A, is present, and conversely if A is present it is always accompanied or followed by B. If we say A is the cause of B, this for the naturalist is simply a shorthand expression of the observed contingent relations between them. This uniformity is the basis of the cause-and-effect relationship. The "always" here refers, of course, only to the instances observed; it is not a universal. There is *always* an uncertainty factor in any causal situation.

There is no external causal agent which acts as a *deus ex machina* upon a natural process. The active agency exists, but it is within the process itself; indeed, it *is* the process. It is an inexact use of words to say that any cause controls its effect. The control, again, is there, but the control is exercised within the event, not upon it. An external agent may start a process and by that fact it becomes a part of the process, a factor in the causal situation.

In a causal situation as perceptually observed we usually recognize a linear succession of events, but this time factor is not an essential feature of the situation and in some instances is irrelevant and misleading. There are circular causal systems and feed-back systems which cannot be plotted on linear time. The principle of causality is essentially a timeless concept because it embraces the contingent relationships of a total situation, not merely a sequence of events. In classical mechanics causal relations are defined in terms of perceptual space and time, but quantum mechanics employs a different frame of reference which does not require precise description of the phenomena as a chain of events in space and time. Here causal relations are not abolished, but they cannot be expressed in the conventional terms.

The principle of circular causation, or a web of interrelated causal processes, is exemplified in biological functions. This is particularly significant in mental action and in social control by intelligent direction, for, as A. E. Emerson ('54) expresses it, it is quite possible for an individual who is the result of a process to influence the operations of the process and its effects. This theme is critically examined in two papers by Grünbaum ('52, 55).

It is the directive quality of the causal situation that gives to scientific principles their predictive value. This self-directive activity is what Sellars ('43) calls "immanent causality," which is nothing other than the directive constructive activity which is inherent in every mechanism and is the distinguishing characteristic of mechanism. Lancelot Whyte ('49) recognizes this and that causation is a one-way process. "Since the classical method was based on the equality of cause and effect, we require to find a more general cause-effect relationship which includes equality as a special case. The new method must therefore be based on *the inequality of cause and effect.*"

McCulloch (Frank *et al.*, '48, p. 259) mentions that Thales was responsible for the conception of immanent causality. "He was the first to insist that the Gods were in things and not behind them. To know the Gods, then, is to know how things work. . . . Fortunately for biology, the basic notion of function was, and remained, an operation whose end was within the operation." There is no *vis a tergo* in any natural causal situation, and there is no room for any extraneous and intangible principle of causal necessity.

We may accept John Dewey's conclusion that in science the conception of cause has no significance except operationally, and our interest in it here centers in the directive control which is inherent in a causal situation. Knowledge of causes may enable us to control the course of events, or, if that is impossible, to control our own conduct in adjustment to them. Man-made machines and human social organizations are designed for this purpose. In our programs of control we must envisage the causal situation in its entirety as an integral unit. This has been emphasized by Dewey in Chapter 22 of his *Logic* and by Arthur Lapan ('37) in a provocative paper. The integrity of this situation must not be impaired by the analytic processes employed in its investigation.

In natural processes there is no dissociation of things and their properties, matter and energy, mechanisms and what they do, organs and their functions, human bodies and human experience, or mind and the setup of objective conditions upon which it is contingent. What nature has joined together, let not man by artifice of logical or metaphysical analysis tear asunder. These things do not exist separately. To abstract one from the other is to annihilate both.

Efficient and lasting control of behavior, then, should so far as possible be exercised from within, not by external restraint. If we wish to direct behavior we must try to change the internal organization of the behaving mechanism so that it will spontaneously act in the direction desired. Errors made by a defective adding machine can be corrected only by readjustment of the internal mechanism. A dog can be kept from running away by tieing him up, but it is better to train him so he does not want to run away. So also successful social adjustments can be reached only by voluntary participation of the people concerned, not by decrees imposed by the police power of the state. This is recognized by the more enlightened leaders in government, industry, and labor unions.

In our industrial age men are inevitably geared to the machines which they operate. This is true of the physical machinery of industry and transportation and even more obviously so of the social apparatus of every local community and of national and international operations. Some of the engineering problems presented by this unavoidable feature of the industrial revolution are briefly discussed, with citation of sources, by Mead and Wulfeck ('52). They quote Admiral de Florez' complaint that now we have reached the point where the machine has dwarfed the man. The human machine, he

claims, has not changed for countless generations, from which it follows that "we must, therefore, consider man's capabilities as a constant in contrast to the unending progression of the machine."

This disquieting conclusion rests on the false premise that human
nature does not change. It may be granted that the rate of progress
of human evolution of both bodily structure and social comity has
been slower than the recent spectacular burst of inventive skill in
the domain of gadgetry. But the lag in the evolution of man's equipment of sensory and motor organs has been more than counterbal-
anced by invention of mechanical accessories which vastly extend the
range of his organs of sense and his muscular power.

This advance in mechanical engineering is the direct result of a
change in man's mental equipment, that is, of the increase in available knowledge. But we have not been equally successful in solving
the problems of human engineering involved in the adjustment of
man to the machines he has invented. This failure is alarmingly conspicuous in the prevailing social maladjustments. The remedy lies in
the men themselves. The slow progress of the evolution of human
nature must be accelerated in the direction of more efficient social engineering. This fortunately we can do now with resources available
if we make a concerted and well-directed business of it.

Summary

A mechanism is a means for getting a product. The most characteristic feature of any machine is described in terms of its product, of
the end for which the means are adapted. The living body, like every
other mechanism, has no meaning apart from the ends toward which
its behavior is directed. The vital problems of human behavior center
in the motivation of conduct, that is, in a judicious appraisal of the
values for which we work. The principles of conventional mechanics
are inadequate in the sphere of values. We must, accordingly, supplement these principles by others of wider scope. No mechanical
system can admit the possibility of uncaused action. Motives have
causes that can be discovered. The cause of an action, as this term is
used operationally in science, is intrinsic to the process under observation, including both the internal operations of the mechanism and all
its significant relations with other things. A scientifically acceptable

program of human engineering cannot be successfully carried out without attention to the value judgments involved in its operations, for these judgments have scientific standing equally with all other factors in the causal situation.

CHAPTER SEVEN
Patterns of Behavior

Classification of factors

The innumerable patterns of behavior have been variously classified for convenience of description. In terms of the observable overt movements made, the following kinds, among others, have been distinguished. Tropism is a turning of the body for orientation with reference to the source of a stimulus. Taxis is a locomotor movement in direction determined by the source of the stimulus. Reflex is a movement of the body excited by a specific kind of stimulus and expressed in a specific pattern of response. The term is usually applied only to well-differentiated nervous and muscular systems with parts so connected as to ensure continuity of conduction from the receptive organ to the organ of response by more or less well-defined pathways.

Instinct has been defined so variously and so loosely that its significance for behavior is equivocal (Schneirla, '49). The clearest and most fruitful definition has been given by Coghill ('30a), who distinguished partial patterns of behavior, typified by reflexes, from total patterns, which involve the body as a whole. The latter include most of the patterns which are commonly called instinctive, as explained below. In many instances it is impossible to distinguish instinctive behavior from voluntary behavior by simple inspection. Here, as also in all the other kinds of pattern just mentioned, the intrinsic factors of the pattern must be brought to light before explanation is possible.

The factors of behavior are classified variously according to the

[76]

purpose of the inquiry and the criteria adopted. All factors of human behavior may be grouped in three classes in terms of their historical development, namely, first, the biological factors inherited from our prehuman ancestry, second, biological and social factors which are distinctively human and may have different patterns in the various races of man, and, third, factors which are acquired by each individual in course of personal development.

The distinction drawn by Coghill between total patterns and partial patterns is basic and of far-reaching significance. Closely associated with this is the contrast between synthetic and analytic factors which is given special emphasis in this book. The relations between the factors which are strictly personal and the social factors show interesting variations among the different kinds of animals, and these relationships have played an important role in the evolution of behavior. The endocrine and visceral factors control a large part of the internal apparatus of regulation of bodily functions, and their influence is dominant in all behavior which is motivated emotionally. The factors which operate unconsciously and those which are consciously motivated are demonstrably different, and the relations between these two classes present the most interesting and the most puzzling problems of all.

This list of factors, of course, might be extended indefinitely. Some of the groups mentioned are examined critically in the following pages, others are mentioned casually, and others are passed by without comment. Most of the omitted topics are adequately treated elsewhere; the selection here made is determined by the author's objective and his experience as a biologist. A psychologist, a sociologist, or a psychiatrist would make a different selection and manipulate his data in ways appropriate to the problems under consideration.

At the beginning of the second chapter it was stated categorically that the crucial problems of behavior center in the behaving individual, and this thesis is defended in the following discussions. Some of the social scientists vehemently deny this, and, of course, it must be granted that no behavior is exclusively individualistic. Before debating this question further we must inquire what the biologist means by a person and how the individual so defined is related to other larger and smaller units of vital organization.

Wholes and parts

A mechanism must work as a whole, and what constitutes a whole and the pattern of the wholeness so constituted depend on the characteristics of the parts and the nature of the integrating agencies that bind them together. The properties of the whole change with every change in the pattern of combination of the parts. It is the pattern of performance that gives to every mechanism its distinctive properties.

The preservation of the integrity of the living body is the primordial requirement for survival, that is, for successful adjustment to the disintegrating agencies that are always acting upon it. This is true of every other separate thing, from atoms to galaxies, each of which has something distinctive about it. If it were not distinctive, we could not define it as a thing. No two things are exactly alike and nothing is ever exactly repeated. Most so-called repetitive processes are not circular in pattern; they are spiral. We want to know how this unique individuality of things has been brought about and how it is maintained, what holds the world together and preserves the integrity and the individuality of its constituent parts.

Although the qualities of the parts may be altered by the process of combination, they do not lose their identity as units of structure and behavior. If the whole were homogeneous, it could not operate as a mechanism. This holds true throughout the whole range of things from atoms to human social organizations. Without internal cohesion and co-ordination, production stops and the mechanism sooner or later disintegrates and loses its identity. Every material thing is such a mechanism. Even a heap of rubble has an individuality that is distinctive; otherwise it would not preserve its identity as a heap. It is held together by mechanical agencies such as gravitation, cohesion, and so on. It is not an inert thing; it is internally active.

In the biological field, investigation of the relations existing between a whole and its parts is complicated by the fact that there are so many different kinds of wholes. The individuals of some one-celled organisms propagated by fission live almost (though never absolutely) independently of others of their kind. Some are temporarily, though organically, united in conjugation, and there are all grades of permanent union. Motile individuals may fuse into an amorphous mass, as in the plasmodium formation of the slime molds, or many individuals may adhere to one another and co-operate in some vital functions without loss of their separate identities. There is some division of labor here, and there are all gradations from these simple colonial aggregations to well-integrated bodies composed of many cells of diverse kinds that retain their individuality as cells but can no longer be regarded as separate persons. These multicellular organisms, in turn, may be organically united in colonies, again with more or less division of labor among the persons, sometimes forming enormous masses as in coral reefs, and sometimes large and complex free-moving bodies like the Portuguese man-of-war, Physalia.

It is clear, then, that the individuality of the separate organism or person as biologically defined is relative; and even in the larger animals, where there can be no doubt about what we mean by a person, it remains true that each cell and each organ has a subordinate individuality of its own that is distinctive and definable. Each of these units is characterized by its own type of integration. At a still higher level each separate person may be related with others to form a more or less stable group, the members of which are tied together, not organically, but socially; and here again we find distinctive types and successive levels of social integration (Chapters 14 and 15).

In the development of the individual and in the evolutionary series there is increasing complexity of organization. Successive levels of integration emerge along with progressive differentiation of the parts; and if the integrity of the organism is not preserved in this process the individual splits apart, as happens in the fission of tapeworms, or the body dies and disintegrates, as we observe in some pathological processes. The integrity of the person is primordial, however relative and variable may be its manifestation. Its importance increases in the series from lower to higher levels of organization. The individual organism is the focal center of all vital activity. Improvement of personal efficiency and diversification of personal abilities are key factors in all self-culture and in all evolutionary and social movements.

There are, then, two series of progressive changes from simpler to more complex, both of which are indispensable, although they are in some respects antagonistic. The first is the multiplication and specialization of the parts, with corresponding division of labor; the second is the progressive elaboration and reinforcement of the unifying influences that preserve the integrity of the body and counteract both internal and external disintegrating agencies. The first is analytic, the second is synthetic, and for successful living these opposing tendencies must be kept in proper balance.

Total and partial patterns of behavior

The history of the evolutionary development of patterns of behavior is hard to read and easily misinterpreted. Fortunately the embryological development of the higher animals recapitulates the evolutionary history, with some distortion, it is true, but on the whole instructively. The embryology of behavior was systematized by the pioneer work of the late G. E. Coghill, and in my opinion the most important principles which he derived from his intensive study of the development of behavior and the correlated changes in the bodily apparatus employed are those concerned with the relations existing between local activities, which he called "partial patterns" of behavior, and the integrative functions, which he called "total patterns." The partial patterns in general are analytic and were termed by him "organismic." The class of total patterns he termed "non-organismic." The significance of this distinction is explained in the next chapter and in various other contexts.

Coghill's program was motivated by a desire to discover the bodily mechanisms that execute behavior at each of the successive stages from the beginning of motility to the attainment of the final adult pattern. It was his hope that from these facts some general principles might be drawn that would shed light upon problems of human behavior and particularly upon the still unsolved puzzle of the biological nexus between the physiological functions of the body and the psychological processes of the mind. In this search he was not disappointed.

This study proved to be practicable, though extremely laborious and difficult. His findings comprise the first and so far the most complete account of the growth of bodily structure and the correlation of this structural organization with the observable overt behavior. Obviously this is too big a program to be encompassed within the span of one man's lifetime, but

Coghill proved that the approach was sound. He lived to see the fruits of his labor in widespread interest in the program, much other investigation instigated or influenced by it, and a new school of thought developed around the Coghillian conceptions of growth, differentiation, individuation, and integration.

These correlated anatomical and physiological studies of the development of behavior have organized a large aggregation of details into a system that has meaning. His pioneer work has been further advanced by many people, using his and different methods of inquiry; and parallel with this program there have been others in experimental embryology, comparative anatomy and physiology, and evolution.

The salamanders were selected for intensive study by Coghill for several good reasons. They are among the most generalized members of the vertebrate phylum, and yet their simple structure and behavior can be readily compared with our own so that many of the most fundamental human traits can be investigated here in primitive form. The choice of salamanders was especially fortunate because they are abundant throughout North America, their eggs are easily collected, reared, and observed, and they are tolerant of a wide variety of experimental procedures.

I have collaborated with Coghill, my part of the program being an intensive study of the internal structure of the amphibian brain to learn the details of the nervous apparatus employed by these animals in late larval and adult stages, that is, to see the definitive form of those mechanisms of behavior whose development Coghill was investigating. A general summary of my findings was published in 1948, and this was immediately followed ('49) by a critical survey of Coghill's life and work.

The more important general conclusions drawn from this work were summarized in a series of three lectures delivered in London (Coghill, '29) and in many shorter papers published before and after that time.

The brilliant advancement of experimental embryology ran parallel with Coghill's program and in the main independently of it. It is obvious that the record of the normal course of development supplied by Coghill and his successors provides the indispensable background for those experimental interferences with the normal which are now yielding so much valuable information about the interrelationships of the parts of the body among themselves and of the parts to the whole. All of Coghill's scientific material and his voluminous unpublished records are now in the Department of Anatomy of the University of Kansas, where, under the direction of Dr. Paul G. Roofe, the Coghillian program of research is vigorously prosecuted.

Coghill's method has been applied by himself and others in similar studies of the development of the behavior of many other animals from fishes to man, with results that bring to light instructive resemblances and differences. A good summary of the earlier literature has been written by Carmichael ('54). The most comprehensive program of study of prenatal human development is that of Davenport Hooker ('36 to '52) at the University of Pittsburgh. Postnatal human behavior has been studied by many workers (Barker *et al.*, '43), most thoroughly at the Yale Clinic of Child Development directed by Arnold Gesell ('45). Hooker and Gesell emphasize the fundamental agreement of the pattern of early human development with the Coghillian principles derived from the life history of salamanders.

The partial patterns of behavior are concerned primarily with the analysis of experience and of the resulting action. The total patterns are synthetic, that is, they maintain the integrity of the individual and they co-ordinate all bodily activities in the interest of the most efficient adjustment to prevailing conditions. Integration is the typical and basic total pattern, and the distinction between those components of integration which are innate and those acquired by personal experience is of fundamental importance for behavior. The innate components are common to all members of the species or group, and are relatively stable and hard to change; those acquired by experience are different in all individuals, and are labile, modifiable, and less predictable.

Coghill's definition of instinct illustrates the way his observations were applied to the larger problems of analysis of the factors of behavior. On this topic he wrote ('30a) this paragraph:

"All reflexes emerge as partial or local patterns within an expanding or growing total pattern that normally is from the beginning perfectly integrated. They become partial or local only overtly. They are inherently components of the total pattern or they are under its dominance. An instinctive reaction, on the other hand, is the total pattern overtly in action. . . . The mechanism of the total behavior pattern is, therefore, the agency of integration which we seek in the interpretation of reflexes and instincts. This agency acts by means of its growth; and it grows according to its own intrinsic pattern."

This is clear-cut. Instinct may include all grades of total activity from tropism and taxis to the manifold elaborate unlearned impulsions of insects, birds, and men, although the term is usually applied to the more complicated innate patterns of behavior.

Coghill's study of the embryology of behavior led him to the general principle that the earliest behavior is an integrated total pattern from the start and the dominance of the total pattern over the partial patterns is retained throughout life. With the emergence and complication of local reflexes special apparatus of integration is differentiated in the higher centers of the brain, and in mammals the cerebral cortex is the dominant member of this integrating system.

These statements are supported by ample evidence in the reports of Coghill's investigations and many others, although they are opposed to the general trend of thought during the past century, notably to current doctrines of reflexology. The Coghillian principle demands radical revision of traditional doctrines of reflexology, and it has implications of so wide import for the interpretation of all animal and human behavior that his conclusions are here stated in his own words.

"Behavior develops from the beginning through the progressive expansion of a perfectly integrated total pattern and the individuation within it of partial patterns which acquire various degrees of discreteness" (Coghill, '29, p. 38). "The development of behavior primarily through the extension of the total pattern, rather than through the projection of primarily isolated parts to become integrated secondarily, means that the maintenance of the integrity of the individual as a whole is the elementary function of the nervous system. This function is performed in *Amblystoma* through the growth of functional neurones into nascent organs" (*ibid.*, p. 90).

"The determination of the primary attitude of the organism toward environment is intrinsic. When environment is brought to bear upon this intrinsic apparatus through sense organs, conditioning of behavior begins: the initiative of attitude is primarily within the organism. . . . Although the conception of the 'organism as a whole' may in a degree be mystical as used by some writers, the demonstration of a specific mechanism that at all times makes the normal individual a unit takes this conception out of the realm of mysticism or vitalism and places it on a scientific foundation. . . . The mechanism of the total behavior pattern is, then, a growing thing. Its reality as such gives scientific grounds for the interpretation of the development of behavior, or learning, in general, as the expansion of a unitary system within which partial systems arise as dependencies under its jurisdiction: an interpretation that rationalizes the phenomena of behavior as treated under the various accepted categories" (Coghill, '30, pp. 642-43).

The earlier opinion that the higher and more efficient patterns of behavior are developed by a secondary additive linkage of originally separate and independent reflex units is still current and supported by considerable experimental evidence. This evidence is regarded as equivocal by other competent workers. Our most exact knowledge of prenatal human behavior has been contributed by Davenport Hooker,

who has personally observed the behavior of about a hundred living
fetuses and compiled the published records of more than a hundred
and fifty others. His summaries ('43, '52) include the statement that
"the sequence of appearance of reflex activity is entirely consistent
with Coghill's principles of the development of behavior." The integrative capacities are primary and essential properties of all organisms. Theories that regard them as secondary acquisitions are fundamentally unbiological. Barron ('54) has reviewed these controversial
issues and presented a wealth of evidence that the principles of development which Coghill formulated for salamanders are applicable
also for mammals and birds. In embryonic sheep the development
of patterns of behavior was correlated with the growth of the nervous
apparatus involved. The early stages parallel those of salamanders
rather closely, with some deviations, and the later stages, as was to
be expected, show remarkable changes in the patterns of arrangement of the nervous elements correlated with the increasing complexity of the action system.

It is the relative stability of the instincts that is overemphasized in
the current and erroneous dogma, "You can't change human nature."
Of course, human nature is changed in every individual according to
the experiences he has and what he does about them. That is what
education is for, to change human nature, and it does so more or
less efficiently. If you can't change human nature, then our entire
educational program is an unconscionable fraud, all wasted effort. Although these acquired patterns are not directly transmitted to the children, their influence on the course of development of human cultures
is immeasurably great, employing a mechanism that has been called
social heredity in distinction from that of genetic transmission. Changing human nature is the most important and the most difficult thing
we have to do. This is the critical problem of human behavior, and
the answers will be found in part in the domain of our biological
heritage and the inexorable laws of nature with which our conduct
must conform and in larger part in the "domain of manners" (page
192) which we as individuals can and do control.

If we were birds the task of changing our nature would be even
more difficult, because in the action system of birds the instincts are
highly elaborated and dominate the behavior. There is far less in-

telligent control of these stable inborn patterns of behavior in birds than in mammals. It is believed by some psychologists that a man is born with more instinctive tendencies than is any other animal. This is denied by others, but certainly behavior is determined by these instincts less in man than in any other animal species, for our instinctive tendencies are always matured under the control of learned patterns of behavior. The potentialities of the instinctive tendency may be suppressed, or they may be repressed and masked by social pressures. From early infancy a man's life is, in fact, a constant struggle to keep his inborn impulses under the control of socially imposed restrictions and intelligent judgments. The interplay between the smoothly running uniformities of the innate patterns of behavior and the disturbing influence of the unfamiliar goes back to the very beginnings of life, and it is the seedbed from which all progressive developmental processes spring, including every kind of intelligent adjustment.

Summary

Adequate description of the countless patterns of behavior requires analysis of the factors of each pattern and the classification of these factors according to criteria appropriate for each study undertaken. Some of the groups of factors which are relevant to the present inquiry are listed. For the science of behavior the most significant unit is the individual organism. Preservation of the integrity of the biologically defined person is the basic requirement of the vital process.

A distinction is drawn between those factors which are inherited from near or remote ancestors, and so are common to all members of the species or group, in contrast to those which are acquired during the personal experience of the individual. Another fundamental distinction is drawn between "total patterns" of behavior in the interest of the welfare of the whole organism and "partial patterns" which are local functions of specially differentiated parts of the body. Some components of both hereditary and acquired behavior belong in one of these classes, some in the other. The partial patterns in general are analytic—analysis of sensory experience and of motor patterns of response. The total patterns are synthetic—integration of all bodily activities for preservation of the identity of the person and for increase of general efficiency.

CHAPTER EIGHT

Analytic and Integrative Factors of Behavior

Analysis and synthesis

As we have seen, every object is polarized against the field of its transactions. It is not a thing apart from this field, but rather it is itself a part of its field. There are, therefore, two classes of natural processes: first, those which face inward and preserve the identity of the object, and, second, those which face outward and maintain the interplay between the object and surrounding things and events. The first define the object; the second determine its extrinsic relations and its status in the orderly processes of nature.

In living bodies these two classes of functions are here called *integrative* and *analytic* processes. They differ in ends achieved, in the physical apparatus employed, and, in some situations, also in the basic principles of mechanics applied. This contrast, I repeat, is fundamental, and its significance for behavior is progressively greater in the higher ranks of the evolutionary series, reaching its culmination in the consciousness of self in distinction from the things of which the self is conscious. This contrast has long been recognized in all classes of animals and given various interpretations, some of which are cited below, and we shall find it significant in a wide variety of contexts.

Coghill put particular emphasis upon a distinction between two types of vital process which he called "organismic" and "nonorganismic." The former, if I understand him correctly, corresponds fundamentally, although not in all respects, with his class of partial patterns and my class of analytic factors. The latter is clearly another name for his total pattern and my integrative factors. Actually, the terms organismic and nonorganismic are inappropriate, for his discussion clearly shows that both types are organismic in the ordinary meaning of the word. The distinction drawn between these two kinds of vital activity, however they may be designated, is basic and illuminating.

Notwithstanding the fundamental differences between the analytic and the integrative factors of behavior, it must be emphasized that the two classes of factors are never dissociated in operation and that many organs of the body may, on occasion, serve both analytic and integrative functions, the endocrine and nervous systems being notable examples.

In the most primitive animals the apparatus of analysis has no obviously specialized organs. In the ameba every part of the flowing stream of protoplasm may perform sensory, motor, or integrative functions, yet the two patterns of behavior are clearly distinguishable. As we pass from lower to higher animals, structural differentiation of specialized organs becomes increasingly diversified and complicated. Both analytic and integrative apparatus are progressively elaborated in the course of phylogenetic history and also during the development of the individual person. The analytic series culminates in human perception, the integrative series in human conception, rational thinking, sentiment, and volition.

In all except the most primitive animals the nervous system is the supreme regulator of behavior. In the brain the biological factors here under consideration are manifested in some peculiar ways which cannot be understood without more detailed and technical description than is here advisable. In the second part of this book the neurological and especially the psychoneurological factors are discussed and the peculiar structural and physiological characteristics of the nervous organs are described without going into the intricate technical details that can be understood only by specialists. This survey leads to some principles of psychobiology to which frequent reference is made here.

The analytic factors

The analyzers are sorting mechanisms, and the various kinds of sense organs are adapted to respond selectively to the different patterns of energy that act upon them. In the higher animals the sense organs and the related peripheral and central pathways of conduction and centers of correlation comprise the analytic system of Pavlov. The sensory projection centers of the cerebral cortex are the highest members of this system.

It is evident that the neuromuscular mechanisms comprise a similar analytic system, although this is not generally recognized and the idea meets curious resistance in some quarters. This was Coghill's opinion, and he made it clear that the motor analytic system includes both central activators and peripheral organs of response and also an elaborate system of inhibitory mechanisms. Every normal behavioral act involves both a selection from among all possible movements of those which are appropriate to the situation, as this is reported to the brain by the sensory analyzers, and the inhibition of the inappropriate movements.

The neuromotor apparatus comprises a structurally stable system of motor centers, conductors, and end-organs, and in addition to this a more labile central organization adapted to inhibit all motor components of the total pattern except those of the particular action called for. What the appropriate action is may be determined automatically by a central adjusting mechanism that is radically different from those employed in the artificial electronic computing machines, although the results achieved are in some instances closely similar.

The sensory and motor analyzers and the central adjustors which are interpolated between them comprise the analytic nervous system in the broadest meaning of that term. This apparatus is adequate for all reflex and much other automatic behavior that is done unconsciously. The patterns of these activities are, for the most part, determined by inherited structure, that is, they are reflex or instinctive. If these innate patterns of behavior are interfered with in any way, as by simultaneous activation of incompatible patterns, by conditioning of reflexes, or by voluntary choice, then the analytic apparatus no longer determines the outcome, although it still plays a necessary part in the process. What is actually done under these circumstances is determined by a superimposed integrative apparatus of quite different kind.

The analytic nervous apparatus consists of relatively stable structural arrangements of nerve cells and fibers that are approximately the same in all members of any particular species of animals. They can be identified with precision and, in fact, by far the larger part of the literature of neuroanatomy is devoted to their description. This is natural and fitting because these tissues are more easily seen and interpreted than are those of the integrative apparatus and they must be accurately known before the integrative organs can be identified and their functions explored.

Integration

Integration is the most fundamental property of everything there is, for no thing can preserve its identity as a thing without it. Integration, of course, has no significance apart from the things integrated, but its importance in behavior is pre-eminent. This section is devoted to some general considerations, and, because there is so much controversy about what integration is and the laws of its operations, it includes also considerable commentary upon selected samples of the literature.

First of all, it should be noted that in the extensive literature dealing with this subject confusion is introduced by failure to distinguish two conceptions of the meaning of the word that are very different. One of these is a normative concept, the other is an operational definition based on what we observe to be the relations between any existing whole and its parts.

The normative conception of integration is well expressed by the definition in the *Oxford Dictionary* of 1901—"the making up or composition of a whole by adding together or combining the separate parts or elements." This additive process finds its most perfect expression in mathematical integration in which the specific qualities of the parts are neglected when they coalesce to form a homogeneous whole. This normative concept is a useful tool in mathematical operations, but it has no counterpart in actuality. None of the wholes which we really encounter in nature are composed in this way, and none of them are homogeneous.

Here we must distinguish homogeneity from continuity. The structure of a complicated mechanism is heterogeneous, but the diverse parts are held together by internal processes that are continuous. Any interruption of the continuity of process results in impairment or disruption of the mechanism. One of Einstein's greatest contributions is the demonstration that the universe is a four-dimensional space-time continuum which is an integrated whole of heterogeneous structure.

Among the integrating agencies of living bodies are many mechanical factors, such as movements of body fluids with their contained chemicals, thermoregulators, electric generators, and so on. Three physiologically specific integrating mechanisms are of special importance for behavior, namely, the physiological gradients, the endocrine systems, and the nervous system. All plants and the lowest classes of animals lack nervous systems, and in them the gradients are important integrating agents.

During growth and evolution, as living bodies become more complex, with local differentiation of structure and division of labor, their parts differ in amount and kind of vital activity, or metabolism. The total metabolic rate, that is, the rate of living, can be measured in terms of consumption of food, water, and oxygen, excretion of waste products, heat generated, changes in electrical potential, susceptibility to injury of various sorts (e.g., by toxic chemicals), and in other ways. The various parts of the body differ in metabolic rate, and, in general, regions with high rate are dominant over regions of lower rate. Thus arise the physiological gradients which exert a controlling influence over all bodily activities and are especially important in regulation of the processes of growth, for regions of most rapid growth are usually dominant over all surrounding parts.

In embryos of higher animals the head grows faster than the rest of the body and so there is a "head dominance" over other parts in early stages of development. During the differentiation of the nervous system in succeeding stages, this dominance persists and is an important factor in shaping the growth of the nervous system and all behavior regulated by it. In other parts of the body there are subordinate centers of dominance, each with its own system of physiological gradients, so that the body may be conceived as a dynamic system of interacting gradients so organized as to maintain the integrity of the body and the appropriate co-ordination of all local activities in the interest of the organism as a whole.

In the evolutionary series these principles are equally evident, and in higher animals they have their most conspicuous expression in what is known as "cephalization," i.e., the progressive increase in the dominance of the head in the control of all bodily activities and especially of overt behavior. The endocrine system is enlarged and diversified, with chemical control of many bodily functions acting through the body fluids. This control also is regulated by the brain and so is subject to head dominance.

The ways in which behavior is directly influenced by the gradients are most clearly seen in plants and those lower animals which lack the nervous system or have only dispersed and generalized nervous tissues. Similar physiological gradients are present and they play a significant part in the economy of all higher animals, but their role is masked by the presence of highly specialized endocrine and nervous systems, which here comprise the dominant apparatus of integration.

We owe to the researches of C. M. Child our most comprehensive knowledge of the physiological gradients and the part they play in biomechanics. The significance of these facts for behavior was summarized in his book *Physiological Foundations of Behavior* ('24), and at the same time I published a companion volume entitled *Neurological Foundations of Animal Behavior* ('24). Some details of my application of the principles of the gradients to the nervous functions require modification in the light of subsequent work, and Child ('41) has made a critical survey of the entire field.

The endocrine functions to which reference was made above play a very important role in the regulation of the internal organs of the body, especially in the higher animals. The integrative action of this very complicated system is fully described in other works and will not be further considered here.

The apparatus of integration is never separable from the analytic apparatus, for integration uses the products of analysis; but in the brains of vertebrate animals we can follow in the evolutionary series the progressive differentiation of nervous structures which are specialized for particular classes of both analytic and integrative functions. The analytic functions use fixed and stable nervous centers and conduction pathways, with precise localization in space of the several functional systems. But the integrative apparatus is organized on different principles; its functions, wherever situated, are more labile and not so firmly bound to definitely localized arrangements of nerve cells and fibers. They are "field" functions which can be served by any tissue which has the requisite plasticity or flexibility without a high degree of specialization for a particular function.

In the brains of primitive vertebrates the simplest integrative apparatus is a nervous feltwork (termed "neuropil") that is undifferentiated and relatively, although not absolutely, equipotential in function. This is the parent tissue from which in higher vertebrates all the complicated apparatus of synthesis of behavior patterns has been derived. An outline of this process of differentiation is given in Part II of this book.

Most of the stimulus-response patterns of behavior of the analytic series can be adequately described and quantified in terms of classical Newtonian mechanics, and they are so described in our manuals of physiology and physiological psychology. This is true of some of the integrative processes also, but others are functions of dynamic fields, the nature and limits of which are determined by patterns of interactions of the energies released and not by any arrangement in space of stable structures. These field functions must be treated relativistically (in a broad sense), and it may not be possible to quantify them in terms of either Newtonian or quantum mechanics.

The contrast between analytic and synthetic factors of inorganic, vital, and mental processes has been emphasized by many writers and expressed in various ways. This distinction was drawn a hundred and fifty years ago by Bichat in his contrast of "organic" and "relational" spheres of vital manifestation. Another typical instance is Lloyd Morgan's description ('43) of protozoan behavior. He distinguished two qualities which he called "percipience"—activities directed outward toward environment —and "sentience"—internal processes that satisfy the physiological needs with no external reference. Although these names, borrowed from human psychology, were inappropriate because, as he said, they carry no implication of consciousness in this context, yet the distinction was clearly drawn in terms of objectively observed behavior.

About a quarter-century ago Ogden ('25) clearly stated the characteristics of natural integration as here outlined, and he showed that this conception of the process can serve as a common denominator for all phases and all types of research, since integrative processes are essentially similar in the inorganic, organic, and mental domains. Many years earlier C. O. Whitman ('88) defined organic integration in these words: "So in the development of a germ, in the repair of injured parts, and in the regeneration of lost parts, the fact is irresistibly forced upon us, that *the organism as a whole controls the formative processes going on in each part* [italics by Whitman]. The formative power then belongs only to the organism as a physiological whole, and it does not represent a sum or aggregate of atomic, molecular and other forces; and it disappears as such the moment the nexus is destroyed."

Whitman's profound analysis of vital processes in this paper led him to conclusions which were not acceptable to most of the experimentalists of the succeeding decades but are now receiving due recognition. This may be illustrated by some additional extracts: "Biological problems have been brought more and more under the influence of mechanical conceptions, which regard all phenomena from an objective standpoint. Science has vindicated this method, and as a *method* it is unassailable . . . but the biologist is reminded at every turn that the method is not exhaustive. . . . It is just here that we see the foundation for those *qualitative* distinctions which, in the mind of the biologist, must ever overshadow in importance the physicist's factors of quantity and motion. . . . Is it rational to conclude that, because vital conditions have arisen from non-vital, the exclusive study of the latter will reveal the former?"

In the unitary principle of Whyte ('49) integrative process is implicit in the "formative property" that he attributes to all natural things. His "normalizing process" (pp. 47, 51) is an integrative mechanism which leads to self-regulation (p. 125). Time-integration and space-integration in the nervous system are briefly discussed (pp. 131–40). These topics are treated in terms of field theory rather than particulate analysis.

Some of the current doctrines of organicism fail to come through with adequate solutions of the problems of integration because they do not recognize the total irrelevance of the normative concepts of integration to the practical adjustments actually made by living bodies. Thus Whitehead's "organic theory of nature" postulates certain "primary eternal objects" which somehow coalesce to form the complex natural things that we experience. Throughout his discussions normative categories are juggled with empirical data and the results are confusing, as I have elsewhere illustrated ('29, '30). When he says ('26, p. 111), "The only way of mitigating mechanism is by the discovery that it is not mechanism," the naturalist questions whether the philosopher has really caught the spirit of current science. Mechanism and organism are not in conflict, and organism is still mechanism. But mechanism cannot be evolved by additive integration, i.e., by the secondary aggregation of "primary eternal objects" or anything else. The integrative agencies are as "primary" as are the constituent "objects" and they are inherent properties of the objects themselves. I cannot agree with Whitehead that intelligently directed voluntary control is necessarily nonmechanistic; for I have a different conception of mechanism from his, a conception that embraces all that is recorded in classical mechanics and a great deal more.

A similar philosophy of organism is developed by Agar ('53), who bases his interpretation of integration on an atomistic conception of "the metaphysical nature of the world" that leads to the conclusion that the unity of the living body is not primary but arises by concrescence (Whitehead's term) of postulated metaphysical atomic elements. "Thus," he says, "the unity of a complex organism . . . is not primordial to the organism as a whole." His conception of the "incurably atomic" character of natural processes "has to be reconciled with the continuity of character" which we find in them. This he accomplishes by an involved dialectic which is wasted effort because his basic normative postulates are contradicted by all that we know about the organization of both living and nonliving mechanisms. The atomists, ancient and modern, have never succeeded in explaining the integrity of a whole.

The experimental evidence adduced by Agar in support of his additive conception of integration (composite embryos made by uniting separated parts, the formation of a living sponge by agglutination of artifically isolated fragments, etc.) seems to me to be misinterpreted. His analysis of these experiments leaves out the essential factors of "continuity of character." The formation of a living sponge by accretion of isolated fragments could not occur unless each of these parts had a pattern of integration determined by the whole from which it was derived. The agglutinated fragments of a sponge cannot make a sea urchin. In Agar's subsequent chapters the missing factors of "continuity" are supplied dialectically by postulation of a "central agent" which must always be present, so that he finally arrives at conclusions that have much in common with those of Montgomery and Coghill. The unrealistic normative postulates are in the upshot discarded in his interpretation of the data secured by actual observation. These three investigators, starting from radically different presuppositions and working with different materials by different methods, finally reached similar interpretations of what they actually observed about integration, because they were keen and honest observers.

There is one group of organisms, the slime molds (Myxomycetes), which do give the appearance of the formation of an integrated whole by the concrescence of separate individuals. This seems to be an additive process as postulated by the atomists. But this appearance is illusory. In this case freely moving independent unicellular spores, or zooids, flow together to form an amorphous mass of protoplasm, known as a plasmodium. The cells lose their identity as cells, though their nuclei persist and float freely in the protoplasmic fluid, but this mass of protoplasm, which may be very large, is not homogeneous. It actively crawls over exposed surfaces by an ameboid creeping movement which is directive under the influence of both internal and external causal agencies. None of the several spores which coalesce to form the plasmodium is a completely integrated biological unit, because it cannot complete the life cycle and reproduce itself. The plasmodium is such a unit, and ultimately it passes into a very complicated fruiting stage which is of characteristic structure and behavior in every species. The thousands of spores produced by each one of these fruiting individuals again have size, form, and internal organization which are characteristic of that species, and so the specific features are transmitted from generation to generation. The incomplete units (motile spores) which unite to form the plasmodium retain their specific pattern of organization and by interaction with one another they produce an integrated living body that can reproduce itself; and they cannot produce the body of any other species of organism. The materials and energies represented in this body are all derived from the surrounding environment, but the integrating agencies are intrinsic and the patterns assumed by them are determined internally.

In a similar way the fertilized eggs of the higher animals are formed by the fusion of two incompletely integrated individuals. The sperm is incapable of completing its development independently of the ovum. The same is true in general of the unfertilized egg, though in some exceptional cases (parthenogenesis) the ovum can be activated for completion of the life cycle without fertilization. Some of the details of the apparatus of integration in these cases have been discovered, but much remains obscure.

A well-known neurologist (Riese, '42), who is versed in modern philosophy, has undertaken the impossible task of squaring dualistic ontology with modern science. In his inquiry into the nature of integration, empirical data are interlaced with normative abstractions, the result of which is a neat *reductio ad absurdum*. His history of the growth of the principles of integration is well conceived and very instructive, but his own conception of organismic integration is derived from the normative mathematical integer which is "a homogeneous whole within which the various elements no longer appear." He grants that this cannot be realized by a heterogeneous structure, the unity of which is only relative. "No structure whatever can realize the building up of an organism out of structures." His appeal, accordingly, is not to the observed facts of structure in action, but to a *logically* prior factor which no longer has to deal with matter in space as we experience it. "This means that the organism as the material counterpart of this indivisible whole has to be considered as a continuum; thus, as homogeneous in itself." The fact that no living body, or any other body, is actually homogeneous disturbs him not at all, for, as he says, "The question, whether the organism is a whole or an assemblage of parts, cannot be answered by empirical methods. . . . In other words, integration is not a fact which has to be stated empirically; it is a principle." To regard this antecedent and extraneous metaphysical principle as "the definite unifier of the organism" involves a confusion of categories that cannot be tolerated in science.

The reader must not infer from the preceding comments that I have no understanding or appreciation of the metaphysicians' search for ultimate realities that lie beyond the reach of human experience and of which our phenomenal world may be an integral part or aspect. The naturalist, like everybody else, may wonder what lies behind our world of experience and is responsible for the orderly quality of the cosmic process. He extends his search for integrating agencies with all available resources, but these resources are limited and he can never hope to reach the absolutes postulated by metaphysics. Philosophical research may give valuable guidance in this quest, but it must be remembered that "the real world of metaphysics is not the starting point, but the goal of all scientific endeavor." In the brilliant chapter from which these words are quoted the late Max Planck ('49) pointed to the "gaping chasm, unbridgeable from the point of view of exact science, between the real world of phenomenology and the real world of metaphysics." Natural science deals only with the former.

Those philosophers who employ such normative concepts as Whitehead's "primary eternal objects," Agar's "metaphysical atomic elements," and Riese's principle of the "indivisible whole" as the "unifier of the organism" are trying to explain the known in terms of the unknown, which is a reversal of proper scientific method. What we know about the properties of all structure, whether it is lifeless or living, is enough to make it clear that the stuff of which the world is made is organized stuff and that this intrinsic organization is mechanistically self-contained. No hypothetical mystical agencies of control are needed to keep it going or to direct the course of its activity. As mechanism it is creative and its own patterns of "immanent causality" determine the changes in organization that emerge at the transition from one level of integration to another. In natural science we gain nothing by appeal to the unknowable noumena postulated by the metaphysicians. We do not live in a world of "pure reason" in the Kantian or any other sense. What we actually observe is natural phenomena. If we say with William James ('04) that we live in a "world of pure experience," we must recognize, as he emphasized, that our experience includes both perceptual knowledge and all the reasoning we do about it.

It is now clear why the nature and mechanism of integration is the basic biological problem. The most significant fact to be drawn from this inquiry is that integration as a total pattern of action is to be sharply contrasted with all partial patterns of local activity. This contrast is fundamental. Integration is not an analytic process in the same class with the differential sensitivity of sense organs, the conductivity of nerves, the contractility of muscles, or the secretion of glands.

The integrative processes are not so directly concerned with the spatial and temporal relations of things as are the partial patterns, because the primary function of the latter is adjustment of a body fixed in space and time to external things and events. The synthetic processes have a quite different frame of reference. It is true that the organs of synthesis have locus in the body and some parts of the central nervous system are concerned primarily with integration, but the pattern of this localization is radically different from that of the analytic apparatus. The space-time relations of these central integrative processes are different from and relatively independent of those of the external environment. These differences between the synthetic and the analytic processes are everywhere apparent, and they have their clearest expression at the highest level of integration as we experience it in our conscious life.

In Sherrington's discussion ('52, chap. 7) of integration at lower and higher levels he wrote: "The finite mind appears to be an outcome of the integration of the individual. Not, however, of integration merely in general. It seems to be the concomitant of one only of the several kinds of integrative processes combining the individual's whole. . . . Integration by the nervous system is *sui generis.*"

Disintegration

From the beginning of embryological development the differentiation of the apparatus of local reflexes and other partial patterns tends to weaken the integrity of the body, to break up the whole into parts with an individuality of their own. If these local independencies are sufficiently strong, the result may be a fission or separation of the body into two or more separate individuals, as occurs in the budding of polyps and the segmentation of tapeworms. In higher animals this is prevented by strengthening the apparatus of integration so that it normally maintains sovereignty over all partial patterns of whatever sort and keeps them in subordination. If this dominance of the total pattern over the local pattern is for any reason weakened or if there is excessive development of any local apparatus, "that sovereignty may give way to the dominance of parts that are normally its subjects, and, as a result of this, behavior may cease to serve the individual as a whole appropriately; that is to say, it may cease to be normal" (Coghill, '33). Such a disturbance of the normal balanced relation of parts to the whole may result in bodily deformity or tumors, or it may be manifested only as abnormal behavior.

There is always some rivalry or conflict between the interests of the local members of the body (the partial patterns) and the integrity of the body as a whole (the total pattern). These conflicts are resolved in normal growth and normal behavior by the dominant control of the total pattern. In the development of human behavior there is an analogous conflict between the inherited patterns of self-preservation and self-gratification and the demands of the social code of the community. Normally these conflicts are resolved by a subordination of some of the personal prerogatives to the requirements of the larger total pattern of the social organization of the time and place. If this adjustment is not successfully accomplished, psychic conflicts persist and are accentuated. The result is erratic or irrational behavior, and perhaps eventually mania, schizophrenia (split personality), or double or dissociated personality of the Dr. Jekyll–Mr. Hyde type.

Most mental and social disorders result from frustration of one sort or another. Normal behavior is goal-directed. If the goal cannot be reached, the motivation is lost and the usual well-integrated course of conduct is disorganized. All activity may be inhibited, or the behavior, lacking an objective, is erratic or pathological. An illuminating analysis of the mechanism of these conflicts is given by Nina Bull ('51, chap. 2). The symptoms of human mental disorder are so various and the contributing causes are so complicated and obscure that the search for curative treatment has been for the most part empirical and not very successful.

Pavlov discovered that it is possible to produce in the dog an "experimental neurosis" that closely resembles human psychoneurosis. These studies have been confirmed and extended by many other psychologists working with various species of animals. It has been found to be possible to set up experiments with rats, sheep, cats, dogs, and monkeys in which, after the animal has been trained to solve a difficult problem, if the difficulty is increased to a point just beyond the animal's ability, the resulting frustration disrupts the normal patterns of behavior with symptoms that are quite like those seen in human psychoneuroses. For description and discussion of these experiments see the works of Anderson and Parmenter ('41), Masserman ('43, '50), Hunt, ed. ('44), and Fulton ('43, pp. 515-20).

In these experiments the observers have two advantages that clinical psychiatrists cannot have in their examination of human patients. First, the animal's mental processes are simpler, so that the variable factors in the problem are relatively few. The second and far more important advantage is that the animal's behavior may be controlled in a large variety of experimental situations so as to isolate particular factors and subject each of them to rigorous tests.

A long series of experiments at the University of Michigan on abnormal behavior of rats (Maier, '48, '49) shows that the neuroses of rats and men are essentially similar and that analysis of the rat's behavior brings to light some general principles which have important applications in the prevention and treatment of abnormal human behavior. Professor Maier finds "that behavior elicited during a state of frustration has certain unique properties, and that these properties make frustration-induced behavior different in kind from that produced in a motivated state." These differences are listed, and the conclusion is drawn that the recognition of this fundamental difference between motivated behavior and frustrated behavior clarifies the problems of prevention and cure of many forms of human aberration, delinquency, crime, compulsive behavior, and psychoneurosis. The same principles are applicable in the treatment of all antisocial disorders of individuals, social institutions, and national governments. Masserman ('50), after inducing neurotic states in cats, investigated various forms of curative therapy, with some success.

The great advances in successful treatment of mental disorders in recent years have resulted in large measure from skillful investigation of the subconscious factors of mentation. These very complicated submerged integrations are indispensable precursors and accompaniments of all mental processes, and they may determine the entire habitus of a person's mentality. If for any reason these unconscious factors are organized in patterns that are maladapted or abnormal, the resulting mental disorder may be remedied by methods of treatment which reveal these abnormalities to the patient and show him how to correct them. Current practice of psychiatry and mental hygiene aims to bring out into the open those subconscious factors of repression, conflict of motives, and exaggerated autism that distort the reasoning processes and disrupt the personality. This mental therapy, of course, should always be accompanied by thorough physical examination so as to bring to light any organic disorders that may be contributing factors.

Rivalry between the totalizing agencies and the individuation of local independencies is characteristic of all normal development, the actual course of which is the resultant of the interplay of these conflicting processes. The integrating agencies normally are dominant, thus preserving the unity of the person. In postnatal human development this takes the form of cortical inhibition of the innate reflexes and instincts in problem situations until intelligent analysis gives appropriate direction. This delay of the response is an essential factor in conditioning of reflexes, learning, and all rational processes. As Dewey has emphasized, intelligence germinates in problem situations—"Conflict is the gadfly of thought"—for consciousness enters into behavior only when the simpler unconscious adjustments are inadequate.

Summary

Some vital processes face outward and keep the body in harmonious adjustment with its surroundings. These are called *analytic* because the process of adjustment requires two kinds of sorting operations. The first is an analysis by the sense organs of the heterogeneous agencies that act upon the body and incite it to response. A second sorting operation is done by the motor system of analyzers, which selects from among all possible movements those which are appropriate to the situation as this is registered by the sensory analyzers.

Another series of vital processes faces inward and its operations are synthetic. These are called *integrative* functions because their primary concern is with the maintenance of the body and the regulation of its internal affairs, with no external reference.

These two kinds of vital processes differ radically in the kind of mechanism employed, in the laws of the operation of this apparatus, and in the behavior which results from their action. Both of them are primordial and essential components of the action systems of all animals from the lowest to the highest. They do not act independently of each other, but are always intimately interrelated in everything that the body does. These are the "partial patterns" and the "total patterns" as defined by Coghill, and the partial patterns in normal behavior must always be kept under the control of the total pattern.

Integration is not a unique property of living beings, for everything in nature exhibits it. Nothing that exists could retain its individuality as a definable thing were it not for intrinsic integrating agencies that hold it together. Natural integration is not an additive thing, like mathematical integration. It is a formative process, and the whole has properties other than the mere sum of its parts.

Disintegration may result from failure to keep the partial patterns in harmonious relation with the total pattern. This may be brought about either by impairment of the integrative apparatus or by abnormal development of some local tissues or partial patterns of action. Such a disturbance of normal balance may result in bodily deformity, tumors, and other diseased conditions, or it may be manifested as abnormal behavior or mental disease.

CHAPTER NINE

Levels of Organization

Levels of analysis and integration

The vital processes of both analytic and integrative systems can be arranged in a series of successively higher levels of complexity, with obvious changes in the patterns of organization. The analytic series culminates in human perception, and the integrative series culminates in the nonperceptual mental processes of mankind—rational, emotive, and volitional.

Similar levels of organization are obvious in the inorganic realm also, and in the aggregate they comprise the integrated order of nature as this is known to science. Some of these levels of the rising scale of cosmic patterns of process seem like isolated plateaus separated by deep chasms. In others the continuity of process is evident. Where apparent gaps appear, we must believe that there is a concealed connection, that is, some sort of a mechanism that effects the transformation from one pattern to the other. This hidden nexus can be discovered by patient search. The properties of each level must be fully explored to discover that level's distinctive features and the processes by which these features have been brought about. At the transition from atoms to molecules, from lifeless to living bodies, from apes to men, from the neurophysiologic to the neuropsychic, to mention four examples, the change of level does not happen by chance. These are directive processes with natural causes that can be found—and some of them have been found.

[103]

In both inorganic and organic realms there are so many different kinds of levels that it is difficult to name any general criteria by which they may be distinguished. Needham ('43, '46) has given us a graphic description of the integrative levels that are manifest in all natural processes and particularly in organic and social evolution, with a summary of the general features of the successive stages in the rise of complexity and efficiency of organization. In this chapter we shall define the levels under consideration in terms of the patterns of performance. The changes observed at the transition from one level to another may or may not be measurable quantitatively, but the change in pattern is easily recognized.

In a steam-powered dynamo, heat energy undergoes successive conversions until it emerges as electrical energy. In this case all the transformations of energy involved are measurable in terms of conventional numerical units; but also involved are factors of pattern of performance which are usually ignored because with presently available techniques they cannot be expressed quantitatively. At the transition from the neurophysiological to the neuropsychic level this change in pattern takes the anomalous form of the emergence of awareness as one of the properties of the psychic pattern. This statement, of course, explains nothing about the mechanisms at work or the mechanical principles of their operation at the moment of conversion from one pattern to another; but it does set the process within a frame of reference which is congruous with that of all other kinds of conversion of patterns of energy manifestation.

Because the intrinsic integrative functions are the primary factors that determine the distinctive characteristics of every individual animal and play so large a part in the regulation of his behavior, they are given special attention here. The general principles of integration are the same in the inorganic and the organic realms of nature, but in the animal world these factors are organized in very distinctive patterns which show a remarkable series of changes in complexity and efficiency as we pass them in review from the lower to the higher ranks of animals.

In a general survey of integrative processes in both the inorganic and the organic realm, Novikoff ('45) gives graphic demonstration of the saltatory character of the changes in patterns of organization as we pass from one grade of complexity and efficiency to another. He develops the general concept of levels of integration, with this summary: "Each level of organization possesses unique properties of structure and behavior which, though dependent on the properties of the constituent elements, appear only when these elements are combined in the new system. . . . The laws describing the *unique* properties of each level are qualitatively distinct, and their discovery requires methods of research and analysis appropriate to the particular level." In a recent essay ('49a) I have discussed these principles as they are actually manifested in the evolution of behavior.

Especial emphasis has been put on Novikoff's last point by Northrop ('47), who writes that "there are different scientific methods for different stages of inquiry, and . . . the method which is scientific for one stage may be quite unscientific at a different stage. . . . It is the problem that designates the method, not the method which designates the problem."

It seems to be obvious upon even casual inspection of our world as a whole, and especially of the living beings in it, that, however abrupt the transition from one level to another may appear to be, the process is continuous. The chain of "immanent causality" is unbroken. At each successive level of change a new pattern of integration emerges, so that things preserve their individuality and at the same time are interrelated in such a way as to cohere in a unified whole. And yet these principles have been so generally ignored or given merely lip service that people condone their ignorance of causes by appeals to chance, randomness, accident, or chaotic disorder, as if these could explain anything.

The course of organic evolution is not a simple linear series. It is best pictured as a widely branching growth, the so-called phylogenetic tree, with progressive increase in the number of branches. The evolution of these separate phyla has advanced in accordance with some general biological principles which are common to all of them, among which Darwinian natural selection is of major importance. But each major branch of the animal series follows its own distinctive lines of specialization independently of the others, and the terminal twigs of these branches which now survive have no direct genetic relationship. They may have separated from a common ancestry hundreds of millions of years ago.

In our search for the evolutionary (i.e., the genetic) factors of animal behavior the ancestry of the species of animal in question must be taken into account. Its phylogenetic history must be known, because very similar patterns of behavior have been evolved independently in various branches of the phylogenetic tree. This is called convergent evolution, of which many examples are known.

Structural features which are genetically related in the evolutionary series are called homologous regardless of the functions performed. Thus the human hyoid bone is homologous with one of the gill arches of fishes, although their functions are totally different. Structures of different phylogenetic origin which have come to resemble each other by convergence are analogous. The eye of the octopus resembles the vertebrate eye in many respects, but each eye originated quite independently of the other and they are not homologous. The wings of insects are not homologous with those of birds, for the two organs have nothing in common except the function. They were evolved independently and the mechanisms employed are radically different. The skeletal parts of the wings of birds and bats are homologous, but most of the other parts of these wings are analogous.

In a similar way various patterns of behavior which resemble each other may be homologous or analogous or a mixture of the two. In human social organizations by far the most important factors of behavior are unique developments within the genus Homo, with no homologous counterparts in subhuman animals. The symbols employed in language, mathematics, and art, the higher intellectual and esthetic values, and all moral judgments are distinctively human perquisites.

Yet it must be recognized that these unique capacities did not originate fortuitously. They are products of evolutionary development just as truly as is the human skeleton. We must be careful not to homologize the distinctively human patterns of social organization with the superficially similar patterns seen, for example, in insects, for there is no genetic connection between them. But there are some biological factors which these two series of evolutionary development have in common, and the specifically human traits have arisen naturally by further elaboration of simpler patterns of performance of the primate ancestors of the human race. We can find the precursors of all human symbolisms, human values, and human ethics in the behavior of other animals, although at a much lower level of organization and vastly inferior in efficiency.

We are searching here for these genetic relationships. This field has been very incompletely explored, but, as we shall see, enough has already been found to justify further exploration. The genetic, that is, truly homologous, relationships of human behavior are more fundamental and instructive than are the adventitious analogies, and what we want to discover is the actual mechanisms employed in this evolutionary process and the laws of their operation.

It is unfortunate that in stressing the qualitative uniqueness of each level Novikoff indulged in some polemic which weakens his argument. In the higher organic levels, particularly where social relations of animals are involved, he is caustic in his criticism of those sociologists who have been led astray by misleading analogies and anthropomorphism. It is a fact, however, that every unique emergent has primordia which may be recognized in the next lower level of integration. What Needham calls "mesoforms" can be recognized at transitional levels and these give clear evidence of continuity between the levels despite the apparently jumpy character of the changes. Those who recognize these primordia of high-level integration at lower levels are not all mystics or visionaries, as clearly shown by the discussion of Novikoff's paper by Needham ('45), Gerard and Emerson ('45), and Novikoff ('45a).

In this connection reference should be made to Needham's book ('43), Gerard's survey ('40), "Organism, Society and Science," and Schneirla's essay ('49) "Levels in the Psychological Capacities of Animals." The symposium edited by Redfield ('42) includes chapters on integration at all biological levels. In two recent papers Kroeber ('48, '49a) gives a critical analysis of the concept of levels as a working tool of science with especial reference to the status of the individual, the social structure, and the culture as these are interrelated at the higher levels. Wheeler ('28) treats the subject concisely and clearly, with references to other literature. A valuable source book by Allee *et al.* ('49) and several recent papers by Emerson are especially recommended, notably "Dynamic Homeostasis" ('54).

The successive levels of organic integration are open to inspection in two continuous series, the embryological, or ontogenetic, and the historical, or phylogenetic. The time span of the first is short and every detail of it can be observed if and when we learn how to do it. Some of the principles so discovered are mentioned in the preceding chapters. The second series is spread throughout the hundreds of millions of years of evolutionary time and we have no authentic record of the actual behavior of any of these animals except those which survive to our days. Fortunately these survivals include representatives of every grade of organization from virus to man, so that it is possible to reconstruct with a fair degree of probability the salient features of each level of organization in the evolutionary series. Existing species of animals can be arranged in graded series from simple to more complex, and these can be assigned to their approximate places in lines of phylogenetic descent if one uses available data with sufficient industry and skill.

It is again fortunate that the characteristic behavior of every living species of animal is correlated with equally characteristic structural features, so that the presence of the structure can be taken as a safe indicator of the colligated behavior, provided our knowledge of both behavior and structure is adequate. The structure of the fossilized skeleton of an extinct animal will reveal to the comparative anatomist a wealth of information about that animal's behavior—the food eaten, method and efficiency of locomotion, relative size and probable acuity of the organs of smell, hearing, and vision, the size and shape of the brain, and so on. The presently available knowledge of fossil remains has given the paleontologists a sufficient volume of actual historical records to enable them to reconstruct the main lines of phylogenetic descent with all needful accuracy. Comparison of living species with these extinct ancestral forms yields reliable evidence of their own phylogenetic history. Thus by an indirection the history of the evolution of behavior can be read. The embryological development of the individual recapitulates some features of this phylogenetic history more or less closely, and this provides an additional check.

Viewed from the standpoint of evolution, most of the simpler groups of animals are primitive and the more specialized kinds have been derived from them or from comparable types, though some of the simpler forms, notably among the parasites, have been secondarily degraded by degeneration from higher species. In each of the spreading branches of this tree of life larger or smaller groups of animals of like kind naturally fall into a series of successive modifications of structure and behavior. Correlated with this hierarchy of successive grades of specialization there is a hierarchy of levels of integration, for the method by which integration is maintained necessarily differs according to the patterns of the activities to be integrated. These levels of integration cannot be arranged in a single linear series, for each major branch of the phylogenetic tree has its own characteristic pattern of organization with which the integrative functions must conform.

We may, then, expect to find a different series of integrative levels in each existing phylum of the animal kingdom, in the evolutionary history of each phylum, in the patterns of embryological development of the individuals within each phylum, and in the postnatal educational progress of every individual. Each of these series must be separately examined and analyzed, and this analysis must include the factors which maintain the individuality of the persons and also those which preserve the integrity of the groups to which they belong and with which they have contacts.

In this analysis especial pains must be taken to distinguish between homology and analogy as these are defined above. Both types are present in most behavioral complexes, but their significance for evolutionary theory and especially for solution of the practical problems of human adjustment is different and this difference must never be overlooked. The details of pattern which characterize the several integrative levels are not systematically surveyed here. Only a few samples of them are mentioned in connections where they clarify general principles.

The history of the differentiation of successively higher levels of integration is registered in the adult organization of the brains of the higher animals. The human brain has been described as a series of levels of progressively more complicated structural and functional organization.

In the behavior of all animals, and in larger measure in those that we call higher, there are significant social relations which play a major role in behavioral adjustments. There are other nonsocial assemblages of animals which are defined biologically. These are the species and smaller or larger groups of animals of like kind which are distinguished from other groups of different kinds. These groups will receive special consideration in the following chapters.

Laws of structure and laws of change

The uniformities of nature which are codified as laws include those of stable structure and those of directive change. The first are typified by the principles of anatomy, the second by those of embryology and genetics. None of these disciplines can attain full stature without intimate partnership with the others. Unfortunately the laws of nonrepetitive and irreversible change are much harder to codify than are those of the uniformities of structure, and the processes of growth and evolution belong in the former category.

We cannot clarify the mysteries which now baffle us at the transitions from one level of organization to another until the mechanisms employed are fully understood. This is illustrated by the rebirth of chemistry which occurred when the mechanics of the process by which molecules are made from the constituent atoms was discovered and by the equally revolutionary advances in biology when experimental genetics in partnership with cytology revealed the mechanisms of growth and heredity.

Analysis of the factors operating in the evolution of behavior requires at least a brief survey of the general principles of organic evolution, to which attention is next directed. Fortunately for us some of the evolutionary factors reappear in the growth of the individual body and the mechanisms of growth from egg to maturity can be directly observed while in process. Experimental zoology and especially experimental embryology have brought to light many principles of developmental mechanics that are applicable *mutatis mutandis* in evolutionary development also.

Summary

Both analytic and integrative vital processes can be arranged in series of levels distinguished by obvious differences in patterns of performance. The integrative series is of special interest here because of the dominant part played by these intrinsic functions in the development of the distinctive personal qualities of every individual. In the higher animals, and especially in mankind, these personal qualities are very important factors of the behavior patterns. The mental processes comprise the higher levels of the integrative series and their status in the hierarchy of vital functions must be clarified.

The transition from one level to another, as from lifeless to living and from unconscious to conscious action, may appear to be abrupt and discontinuous, but underlying this appearance of saltatory change there is an unbroken series of causal connections.

Chapter Ten

Trends in Evolution

General principles of evolution

There is nothing haphazard about the evolutionary process. Since Darwin's time random variability has generally been regarded as the foundation upon which the doctrine of natural selection rests, but Darwin himself was not satisfied to let the matter rest there. He said that one of the most urgent problems of his time was search for the causes and laws of variation—and that is still true today.

The urge to live and to live as abundantly as possible is a high-level exhibition of a property that seems to be characteristic of our cosmos as a whole. The formative process that is manifest throughout nature is signally accentuated in animal growth and evolution and it reaches its culmination (so far as now known) in the creative or inventive capacity of the human mind.

In the flux of change some patterns of structure and performance endure with little alteration and others show successive modifications that go on in unbroken sequence without sacrifice of the individuality of the structure or impairment of the integrity of the larger dynamic system within which it is set. This type of change may be called *evolution* in the broadest meaning of that term. Cosmic evolution may come to expression in galaxies, river systems, mountain ranges, animal phylogeny, or the growth of a particular organism. These changes are all creative, and the creative agency resides in the natural system as one of its basic properties. Organic evolution, then, is one sector of a general movement which has a directive quality. That this is the way nature works is an empirical fact. Why nature works this way, that is, what first cause may lie behind the observed facts, is a question which science has not answered. But there is nothing mystical about the facts.

The levels of integration to which reference has been made emerge during the development of the individual body in a sequence that is evidently directed toward the efficient action and self-sufficiency of the adult. There is ample evidence that during the hundreds of millions of years during which life has existed on this planet there have been similar changes involving a hierarchy of successive levels of integration. These evolutionary movements have come to expression in more complicated devices for adjustment of the animals to their environments, a larger measure of control of environing conditions, and increased capacity for self-control and self-culture with resulting richer satisfactions.

There are trends toward increasing specialization of structure in adaptation to various ways of life. The control of environment may change the physical features of the terrain, as illustrated by the growth of coral reefs which reshape the configuration of the oceans and create vast areas of fertile land, by beaver dams which divert the courses of streams, and by enterprise of man which may revolutionize both the topography and the flora and fauna of a continent through the replacement of forest and prairie with farms and the construction of canals, irrigation projects, and great centers of industry. In the higher ranks of animals this control of environment is brought about by means of, and in the interest of, increase in the self-sufficiency of the individual persons. Environmental control and self-culture go hand in hand. At all levels of vital organization there is some social control within the groups and from group to group. At the higher levels the social relations play a progressively larger part in both environmental control and the development of personal competence and initiative.

These directive movements take an astonishing variety of forms. Some of the trends lead to a wide range of diversity among closely related species, each of which is highly specialized for survival in some particular situation. There are innumerable insects and these are classified in many thousands of species, each of which has a very restricted habitat and a very limited range of possible ways of behaving; but these species in the aggregate are so diversified that some kind of insect is found in almost every environment that can support life. Other evolutionary trends lead to diversification, not of species as a whole, but of the capacities of the individual members of the species, giving each of them a wider range of ability to adjust to diverse situations and unexpected exigencies. These two trends— the one toward diversification of species, the other toward greater competence of the individual animal for independence and versatility—take different directions which result in radically different patterns of behavior, as explained in Chapter 14.

Some other evolutionary trends are regressive, that is, they involve dedifferentiation of structure and simplification of behavior, as in some parasites. In still other cases there is a trend toward overspecialization in some direction, which may go so far as to be injurious, resulting in death of the animal or final extinction of the species.

All these evolutionary and developmental trends are significant for behavior, for the conduct of every animal is influenced more or less by its past personal and racial history. Whether any of these trends may be regarded as progressive depends upon our definition of progress. Evolutionary progress of some kind is implicit in any ranking of animal species as higher and lower, so some attention must be given to the principles of classification.

Factors of organic evolution

Among the recognized factors of evolution those of special significance for us here are mutations, recombinations of the genes in fertilization of the ovum, and natural selection. The factor last mentioned is unquestionably of major importance in setting the direction of the "genetic drift" or trend of most evolutionary processes, but Darwin took special pains to emphasize that it is only one of many evolutionary factors.

The importance of natural selection as a directive factor in evolution, although for a time discredited in some quarters, is now more firmly established than ever before. In Darwin's time, little was known about the nature and causes of variations. They were accepted as "given by nature," and the principle of natural selection was thought of as a negative process—the elimination of the unfit—which could produce nothing new. Now the emphasis is different. It is recognized that variability and selection are not independent factors. They go hand in hand. New species arise because favorable variations are actively preserved by selection, not because the unfavorable ones are eliminated. Natural selection, then, is a positive creative process (Simpson, '49, p. 223). New forms are produced by a natural selective process in essentially the same way that the breeder creates a desired characteristic by a positive selection of the individuals that fit the specification chosen. In nature the specifications for fitness are set by two factors: (1) the internal organization requisite for "intrinsic viability," and (2) adaptation to existing environmental conditions (Holmes, '48, '48a).

Although natural selection originates no mutations or other modifications of the germinal protoplasm, it does determine which of these changes in the hereditary organization shall persist from generation to generation, and so it sets the direction of the evolutionary process. The details of the mechanisms employed in this synthetic process we cannot go into here. Two of them may be mentioned. Progressive evolution, that is, the enhancement of fitness, may be brought about by selection of favorable mutations of the genes or by the selection of favorable recombinations of the genes in the fertilization of the ovum.

The human ovum contains forty-eight chromosomes, twenty-four from each parent. The number of different genes in these chromosomes is believed to be of the order of about thirty thousand. The genes of each parent differ from each other and are differently arranged. In fertilization the paternal chromosomes are paired with the maternal, and in this rearrangement the chance against two individuals having exactly the same pattern of combination of chromosomes is about 300,000,000,000,000 to 1. So we see why no two people in the world (except identical twins) are exactly alike genetically, and these innate differences are accentuated by the diverse cultural influences to which they respond. (For further discussion see the works which we cite of Dobzhansky, Julian Huxley, S. J. Holmes, George Gaylord Simpson, and Arthur Keith. Julian Huxley's "Vindication of Darwinism," Huxley and Huxley, '47, pp. 153 ff. is especially recommended; see also the symposium edited by J. Romano, '49.)

Some evolutionary movements have been called orthogenic, and this is merely a descriptive name for the trends observed (for a review of these theories see Osborn, '17; Huxley, '43; and Simpson, '49). The important questions about orthogenesis are, what initiates the trend, what sets its direction, and what holds the movement to its course—in short, what is the cause of orthogenesis? This is a biological term and the explanations sought must not overstep the boundaries set by acceptable scientific method.

No unnatural or mystical agencies may be invoked for control of the process, though this has repeatedly been done by eminent men of science and philosophy. Several paleontologists have advised that, because the word "orthogenesis" has so often carried mystical implications, it is better to replace it by such a term as "directive evolution."

Natural selection involves incessant interaction between a changing environment and a changing internal organization of the animals inhabiting it. The latter series of changes must be kept in appropriate adjustment to the former if the animals and the species to which they belong are to survive. The chief factors of this process of internal readjustment are now well known, although many details of the operating mechanism are still obscure. The early attempts of Lamarck and his followers to explain the process of adaptation of organism to environment by direct inheritance of bodily changes acquired by exposure to changed environing conditions or by change in habits have been discredited by much patient research. The Lamarckian principle, stated in its original form as inheritance of acquired characters or use-inheritance, has no scientific standing, although this does not imply that inheritance of environmental influences in a less direct way is necessarily excluded. Current research in genetics has discovered the mechanisms of heredity and of the acquisition of new hereditary traits and revealed the principles involved with great clarity and in remarkable detail. These details we cannot go into here.

The innate components of behavior and those that are acquired in postnatal life constantly play into each other's hands. It is evident that the acquisition of new patterns of behavior through experience must start with the use of the already available inborn patterns and that the process of learning will necessarily be profoundly influenced by them. Though the learned behavior may subsequently dominate and control the inherited reflexes and instincts, there is little evidence that learned behavior or any other personally acquired characteristics can be directly transmitted to the next generation.

Much confusion has arisen from failure to recognize that not all congenital or innate characteristics are inherited. The baby on the day of birth is about nine months old. His inherited traits were irrevocably fixed at the moment of conception, and during the forty weeks of prenatal life the genetic traits with which he was then endowed mature in an environment which is the mother's body. This short period of very rapid growth is the most critical part of a person's life, and the course of development is influenced by the mother's health and way of life, how well she is nourished, and a thousand other factors which modify the pattern of fetal growth.

The only way to be sure which traits are strictly genetic and hence heritable and which have been acquired during prenatal and postnatal development is to conduct scientifically controlled breeding experiments continued for several generations. This has been successfully done with fruit flies and the farmer's domestic animals, but such experiments are not practicable in a human population. By indirect methods, such as, for instance, critical comparison of pairs of fraternal and identical twins reared together and reared apart under diverse conditions, some inherited traits have been clearly defined. Eye color is hereditary, but body weight at birth depends mainly on the mother's diet, the duration of pregnancy, and other factors that have nothing to do with heredity. Many of the so-called racial characteristics have been shown to be due to environmental influences and not to heredity. In fact, a genetically pure human race does not exist.

The controversies that have raged for centuries over the inheritance of acquired characteristics have not been finally laid to rest, though the problems are now discussed on a different level. Geneticists are in substantial agreement that the Lamarckian principle can practically be ruled out, yet current research indicates that Weismann's doctrine of the complete segregation of germ plasm from body plasm must be qualified or reinterpreted. It seems to be now well established that hereditary traits can be transmitted not only by the genes of the chromosomes but also by organized bodies in the cytoplasm. These so-called plasmagenes are usually in reciprocal relation with the nuclear genes, though they may arise and propagate themselves independently of nuclear structures. The plasmagenes provide a possible mechanism for the inheritance of acquired characters under certain restricted conditions. Sonneborn ('49, '50) has outlined the evidence for this in untechnical language. His conclusions are that "under identical environmental conditions, organisms and cells that possess identical genes may inherit and transmit to their progeny different traits. These hereditary differences, observed in microorganisms, higher plants, higher animals, and among the tissues of higher animals, are beyond doubt controlled by the cytoplasm. . . . In sum, the cytoplasm, as well as the genes, plays a decisive role in determining hereditary traits."

Dobzhansky ('50) in a concise summary of the relations existing between genetic and environmental factors remarks: "In last analysis, every mutation is caused by environmental influences, and there is no theoretical reason why geneticists could not eventually learn to induce at will specific mutations in specific genes." For fuller discussion see his larger work ('51).

The organism as a whole is in transactional relations with its environment. There is reciprocal chemical interaction between the cytoplasm of its cells and surrounding tissues and fluids and between the cytoplasm and the chromosomes of the nucleus. By this indirection, agencies of the external and internal environment may change the physical and chemical structure of the genes and so provide a possible (but restricted) mechanism for the inheritance of acquired characteristics. This field is as yet so incompletely explored that no dogmatic statements are justified.

It should be mentioned in this connection that the Lamarckian type of inheritance can be simulated by the now well-established principle of "organic selection" advocated by C. Lloyd Morgan ('08), J. M. Baldwin ('02), and others. Useful acquired modifications which cannot be inherited may be reacquired generation after generation, thus favoring survival. During this time mutations which are similarly favorable may occur and be transmitted in successive generations, so that ultimately the adaptive modifications are replaced by heritable mutations and so fixed in the genetic organization of the stock. Natural selection in this way perpetuates and reinforces first the acquired modifications and subsequently the inherited traits that replace them.

In the early stages of human evolution, while the recently enlarged cerebral cortex was in a nascent and therefore plastic stage of organization, organic selection probably played a very important role in setting the pattern of the definitive heritable structure of the brain and of the correlated mental capacities. When man first began to use tools and to invent other new devices for extending the efficient range of his own bodily functions, these acquired habits were doubtless decisive factors in his struggle for survival, as they still are. In a tribe already proficient in the use of tools, mutations which favored in any way the development of this inventive skill would be more likely to be incorporated into the stable genetic structure than in a similar tribe with a less advanced culture.

In a provocative paper by an anthropologist (Greenman, '48), appeal is made to the biological principle of neurobiotaxis in a search for the neurological basis of evolution by preadaption and organic selection. Whatever the biological mechanisms employed, it is clear that in some way the invention and use of tools, signs, symbols, and other extraorganic apparatus have played a major role in directing the course of human evolution from its beginning until now (Pannekoek, '53; La Barre, '54; Howells, '54).

The invention and use of tools to supplement the organic equipment of the nervous and muscular systems unquestionably has been a major factor in the acceleration of human evolution. In a competitive society the success of any population, in peace as in war, is directly dependent upon the elaboration and skillful use of two kinds of tools—mechanical devices of ever increasing complexity and social structures (government, police and military organizations, corporations, labor unions, etc.) of greater power and efficiency.

Classification and biological rank

From the earliest times animals have been classified in various ways according to their appearance, way of life, structure, utility to man, and other arbitrary features. All these methods of systematization have significance for behavior, and the classification of species and of social groups merits special attention here. Consideration of the latter is now deferred. Here we must ask what is meant by a species and by a "natural" classification of animals.

Systematic zoology (taxonomy) is a highly developed specialty. The classification of animals now in current use by systematists is based chiefly upon their structural resemblances and differences, because their bodies can be preserved for leisurely study but their internal physiological processes and their overt behavior are evanescent. All kinds of animals are arranged in phyla, classes, orders, families, genera, species, subspecies, and races. Of these successively smaller units, the species is of special interest from our present point of view.

Any classification of animals is, of course, an artificial logical construction; its form will depend on the postulates and criteria chosen. In current practice the aim is to arrange animals, as far as possible, according to their genetic relationships; but since those which are now living represent terminal twigs of a widely branched phylogenetic tree which has been growing for hundreds of millions of years and most of the members of which are now extinct, this ideal can be only approximated. The ultimate court of appeal here is the fossil record of actual historical sequence in the transformation of one form into another, and fortunately this is now sufficiently complete to show the relationships of most of the larger units with a high degree of probability.

No one has succeeded in framing an acceptable definition of a species in terms of any single criterion, for species arise in many different ways and the characteristics by which they are distinguished differ according to the conditions prevailing. Nevertheless there is general agreement that species are more definite biological units of classification than any smaller or larger groups. For an up-to-date discussion of the species problem, see J. Huxley ('43) and Simpson ('53). In a critical review of the taxonomists' problems van der Horst ('47) tells us that biological classification as of today is a compromise between two incompatible aims. The ideal is to express accurately the genetic relationships of the various living and extinct animals and plants, that is, to depict "evolution at work" in our system of classification. Perfection we cannot hope to reach, and the closer it is approximated the more complicated the system becomes and the named groups merge with no definable limits. The ramifications of the phylogenetic tree are genetically continuous and for practical purposes of classification arbitrary lines must be drawn. For cataloguing we need a system of superimposed categories each of which can be sharply defined. Such categories do not exist in nature, so arbitrary rules must be formulated by competent authority. This has been done by international commissions.

It must not for a moment be overlooked that few, if any, existing lower species are actually ancestral to any higher species. These animals are all terminal members of their respective branches of the phylogenetic tree and any inferences drawn about their relationships to extinct transitional ancestral species must be carefully checked in every possible way.

A caution has been emphasized by Tilly Edinger, our most competent student of paleoneurology, in a paper ('49) entitled "Paleoneurology versus Comparative Brain Anatomy." After much personal research and study of more than five hundred reports of features of neurological interest recorded by other paleontologists (which are listed in her previous publications) she writes:

"Comparative anatomy generally presumes that the hierarchy of living vertebrates, from the lowest to the highest, reveals the ways of evolutionary development. The living representatives of the vertebrate classes, and among mammals those of the lower and higher orders, certainly constitute an ascending series of evolutionary levels. These levels are, however, characteristic of each class, and not connected; no living animal represents the form which gave rise to the next higher class. Such forms lived millions of years ago. In their living descendants the evolutionary levels of the different organ systems are correlated, but today's patterns were not rules at all times. This has become apparent in studies of the only organ accessible to study in fossil vertebrates besides skeleton and teeth—the brain."

It has been mentioned that in current classifications animal species are arranged in divergent phyla in accordance with their probable phylogenetic relationships. The species of each phylum are often graded in ranks of higher and lower, and the several phyla are similarly ranked. In this ranking various criteria are employed, with confusing results. Certainly the members of the animal kingdom cannot be graded in a linear series from low to high, because that is not the way evolution works. The phylogenetic tree is widely branched and in each branch the direction of change is determined by processes of specialization and integration which are distinctive and peculiar to that branch.

The several species cannot be ranked in terms of the lapse of evolutionary time, for some species which in very early time were adapted to an unchanging environment have survived unchanged until now. There are lampshells of the genus Lingula in our present oceans whose fossilized ancestors from as far back as Ordovician time have been found, and during this period of probably about four hundred million years there has been no obvious change. The time scale is not a valid criterion of biological rank. Any surviving species may be of high or low rank when compared with related species, living and extinct. (A convenient summary of present knowledge about evolutionary time is given by Simpson, '49.)

The most generally used criterion of rank is structural complexity. In a series arranged from generalized to more specialized bodily structure, the species with more advanced differentiation of parts are ranked as higher. This is convenient because most of the systematists' work is done with dead bodies preserved in museums, where structure is all they have to work with; but it leads to some curious contradictions. The birds are much more highly specialized than the mammals, yet the class of birds is generally ranked lower than the class of mammals, even apart from man and the higher primates. The fossil record reveals many lines of evolutionary change in which specialization in some direction went so far that the species was no longer viable under changed conditions. A specialization that leads to extinction cannot appropriately be used as a criterion of rank.

The trouble with this anatomical criterion of rank is that structure has no biological significance apart from how it behaves. It is the pattern of performance that counts. We must look, then, for criteria of rank that can be functionally defined in terms of survival value and efficient living.

Animals may be ranked according to the perfection of *adaptive* specialization shown, a criterion which is at basis functional. Every species of animal must, of course, be well adapted in structure and mode of life to its particular habitat or it could not long survive. Not all behavior is adaptive, yet successful adaptation is an essential requisite in the struggle for survival, and if the adaptation is adequate for survival in all cases, how is one to judge which sort of adaptation is higher? There are many parasites that succeed in maintaining themselves in enormous numbers and some of them are highly specialized. In extreme cases the adaptation involves a complicated cycle of transfer from one specific host to another, to each of which adjustment is made by appropriate changes of structure and behavior. The role of mosquitoes in the transmission of malaria and yellow fever and of snails in the complicated life cycle of the liver fluke are familiar illustrations. In the pinworms and tapeworms the specialization for assimilation of predigested food and for reproduction is accompanied by total degeneration of most of the other bodily organs. We do not like to call this sort of regressive specialization progress, and we do not rank any parasites very high notwithstanding their successful and sometimes spectacular adaptation to a restricted way of life.

Survival value is basic; but obviously it cannot be used as a criterion of biological rank, for the most numerous organisms are those which are classed by everybody as the lowest—bacteria and other unicellular forms.

The naïve idea that mere propagation and survival are the primary goals toward which all vital activities are directed has been defended in some high places. Bertrand Russell ('27), for instance, claims that both the behavior of all living things and the whole course of evolution flow from this simple impulse to increase the amount of protoplasm. His conclusion is, "When we ask ourselves, from the standpoint of an outside observer, what is the end achieved by all these activities, we find that it can be summed up in one very simple formula: to transform as much as possible of the matter on the earth's surface into human bodies." If this philosopher had even a little firsthand knowledge of biology, or if he had been able to make a judicious biological appraisal of the activities of Bertrand Russell himself, he would not have fallen into that trap. We do not measure progressive evolutionary movements or human cultural movements by that yardstick.

This is another illustration of the fallacy of the claim so often made by mathematical experts that only quantitative data are significant in natural science. In biology the quality of the living stuff is more significant than its quantity, and it is these qualitative differences in pattern of performance to which we must devote our attention in the study of behavior.

Progressive evolution

If it is admitted that animals can be ranked in a scale from lower to higher, then it is permissible to speak of progressive evolution from lower to higher rank. But this expression is meaningless without further specification of the criteria of rank and progress—progress toward what? Progress has, in practice, been so variously defined and so often debated without definition and with covert transfer from one connotation to another in course of the argument that much of this dialectic is futile. It is not profitable to debate the questions whether progress is something inherent in any natural process or whether progress is desirable in any event, as some have done with very disquieting conclusions, before we have decided what we are talking about (Moog, '47; Roofe, '48).

An evaluation of some sort is necessarily implicit in the idea of progress, and those who insist that the concept of value must be rigorously excluded from science are inclined either to deny that there is such a thing as progress in nature or to search for an objective formulation in terms of directive trends without reference to their worth to the organisms under consideration. This, as already indicated, I think is not good biology—and can the biologist afford to be indifferent as to whether his own work is good or bad? If an animal succeeds in satisfying a need, he wins an advantage that is good for him. This is a value from the standpoint of the animal in question, whether or not the animal himself or the observer recognizes it as such. Further consideration of these natural values can be deferred now. Let us start with the admission that in evolution and in embryological development we can recognize directive trends and the consequences toward which they lead. This objective knowledge, of course, does not indicate which, if any, of these trends are progressive. It all depends on what the observer means by progress—a trend toward what?

A series of species of worms can be arranged which begins with free-living forms, like the earthworm, passes through slightly modified forms, like the leeches that are parasitic only while feeding, and culminates with obligate parasites, like the tapeworm. There has been an evolutionary trend toward more complete parasitism, which may be called progressive if parasitism is the end in view. But we humans do not prize this kind of progress.

The question, What is progress? then resolves into a matter of definition, and all definitions are made by human minds, not by the parasites that we study. All other scientific judgments are similarly subjective. It is only the observed facts that are objective. The scientific worth of any naturalist's opinion about what can properly be called progress can be gauged only by its operational utility in the interpretation of the known facts. This is what we must look for in our selection of definitions, criteria, generalizations, and explanations.

Sixty-five years ago, when I was a pupil of my older brother, the late C. L. Herrick, he gave me a definition of biological progress and of the criteria to be employed in ranking animals that I later amplified in a discussion of grades of behavior ('24, pp. 13, 221). The conclusion reached was that "in the broad view advance in evolution involves adjusting the whole organic realm, including the plant and animal kingdoms, to an increasing range of natural conditions." Similar ideas have been expressed by others in various contexts, most convincingly by Julian Huxley ('43) in his comprehensive work *Evolution, the Modern Synthesis* and by Simpson ('49, chap. 15) in his book *The Meaning of Evolution.*

Huxley on page 387 defines evolution "as the process by which the utilization of the earth's resources by living matter is rendered progressively more efficient." There is obviously an evaluation implied here, and further on (p. 562) he writes: "The distinguishing characteristics of dominant groups all fall into one or other of two types—those making for greater control over the environment, and those making for greater independence of the environment. Thus advance in these respects may provisionally be taken as the criterion of biological progress." The interest of the behaviorist in these definitions centers in the idea of control. That is what behavior is for— self-control as a means of gaining better control of environmental resources in order to win a larger measure of satisfaction.

Progressive evolution may be defined, for our present purpose, as change in the direction of increase in the range, variety, and efficiency of adjustment of the organism to its environment and of environment to the use of the organism. This involves increase in the complexity of bodily structure, which ensures sensitivity to a greater variety of environing energies and more refined sensory analysis, elaboration of more varied and efficient organs of response, and more complicated apparatus of central control—nervous, vascular, glandular, etc.

Progress in the development of the career of any individual may be gauged by similar criteria, that is, by his success in meeting the emergencies of life with strength, skill, and versatility that yield more and richer satisfactions. There is universal craving for satisfaction of needs and desires. The needs and desires may be very simple or of unlimited complexity. If a man is content with shoddy satisfactions, his life is degraded to an unworthy level of integration with corresponding sacrifice of the more satisfying values.

The conclusion is that in the higher animals the life of the individual is enriched. There is enlarged capacity for diversified living, for more varied and satisfying experiences in flexible adjustment to changing conditions, and for control of environment and of personal culture. The individual lives a fuller life, that is, he makes a better living as measured by satisfactions achieved.

The dominant line of progressive evolution has culminated in man, whose better brain gives him advantages not available to any other animals, despite his inferiority to some of them in other respects. The advantages accruing to man from his endowment with better brains are accompanied by a shift of the evolutionary process from the physiological to the psychological level of integration, with a corresponding change in the criteria of progress and the technique to be employed in its attainment. Whether in this domain the human race is capable of further progress as gauged by our biological criterion, or even of holding its present position of supremacy, only the future can reveal. There can be no progress unless we can keep the peace, and the key to this problem is obvious and simple, as stated by Bath ('48): "A recognition of the essential partnership of everyone in a capitalistic society is the keystone of industrial peace." This formula is equally applicable in the wider domain of international relations.

Evolutionary movements in general are accessible to observation. Their causes and the laws of their operation can be discovered; many have already been discovered. The "new evolution" in the domain of purposive planning for more efficient management of human affairs is a lawfully ordered process, but our knowledge of its laws is still pitifully inadequate. For these laws we are searching. We must know what they are before intelligent control of the further course of human evolution is possible. This is the most urgent problem with which the sciences of man are now confronted. We can adjust our conduct to orderly natural processes only if we understand how they operate. We cannot adjust to chaos or chance.

Summary

Those natural formative processes that show continuous directive change are evolutionary. Organic evolution is a high-level manifestation of this formative process, which is repeated in similar form in the personal development of every animal. The evolutionary processes show trends in various directions. Some are directed toward increased independence and efficiency of the individual animals, with a wider range of capacity for flexible adjustment to diverse conditions. Some result in diverse specialization of species, each of which is rigorously adapted to a restricted type of environment and way of life. Others lead to specialization that is so extreme as to be inflexible and incapable of readjustment to changing conditions, with resulting extinction of the species. Among the factors which influence the course of evolution, natural selection is given special attention.

Animals are commonly ranked from lower to higher, and this implies that there is progressive evolution; but this expression is meaningless without clear definition of what we mean by higher and by progress. From the standpoint of the behaviorist, progressive evolution may be defined as change in the direction of increase in the range and variety of adjustment of the organism to its environment resulting in more efficient control of behavior and of surrounding conditions.

Chapter Eleven

Adaptation: Means and Ends

Adaptation

The trends which are recognizable in evolution and individual development and the obviously directive quality of behavior have many causes. Of these the one most generally identified and emphasized is adaptation. This is a name for a biological process which has been so variously defined and evaluated that some attention must be given to it here.

In biology adaptation means adjustment of the organism—its structure and behavior—to existing conditions. In this broad sense it is, of course, everywhere evident, for without this adjustment no organism could survive. What is not so clear is how the existing adaptations came to be and what their significance is for the future course of development. This is a time-linked problem: when adaptation is viewed as process it has a past reference and a future reference which must be looked into. There are adaptations of the parts, adaptations of the whole organism, and adaptations of various kinds of groups, all of which are significant for behavior.

Some adaptations which are acquired by experience are tremendously important for the individual; but, since these are not inherited, they are generally regarded as of no significance in the evolution of behavior. Adaptations which are patterned by the composition of the germ cells are results of untold generations of past evolutionary history. It must be recognized, however, that in human societies acquired knowledge and skill may be transmitted by what has been called social heredity and so may play an important part in shaping the pattern of social evolution. Adaptation is an integrative process and the mechanisms employed may be radically different at successive levels of integration.

Everybody recognizes that animals do discriminate between beneficial and injurious situations and that they tend to select the one and to avoid the other. This is the fundamental feature of adaptation. The mechanisms employed in these selective adjustments are of many kinds and none of them are well understood.

Schneirla ('49, p. 260) mentions one factor that can be recognized at the lowest levels of behavior. A weak energy of stimulation is typically followed by approach, intense stimulation by withdrawal. Thus the seeking and avoiding reactions occur in response to quantitative factors of the stimuli, and this factor is correlated with differential thresholds of excitability of the muscles and other organs of response. In the earthworm, for instance, the circular muscles which elongate the body are first activated by weak stimuli, but strong stimuli of the same sort activate the longitudinal muscles which contract the body with backward movement of the entire animal. Innumerable modifications of this principle of differential sensitivity and responsiveness are known among the invertebrates, and in the higher animals similar principles of adaptive threshold systems can be recognized in the cerebral mechanisms of adjustment. At all levels of behavior these heritable mechanisms are influenced more or less by individually learned patterns of response—more in the higher animals than in the lower.

Inborn or genetic adaptations arise by mutations, that is, by spontaneous or induced modification of the structural organization of the genes. Most mutations are not adaptive, many of them are injurious or lethal. It may be regarded as now well established that the most important instrumentation employed in the production of successful adaptations is the preservation of favorable mutations by natural selection, though Darwin's original formulation of this principle has been modified and amplified in the light of present knowledge, as has been clearly explained by Simpson ('47; '49, chap. 16; '53).

It cannot be claimed that every act of each of the known kinds of behavior is adapted to preserve the life of the actor, to enhance his welfare, or to conserve the species. It does not do the moth any good to sear its wings by flying into a flame. It does not do mankind any good to go to war over issues that can be settled more economically and more satisfactorily by diplomacy. In view of the innumerable instances of maladjustment found in all ranks of animals and of the fossil record of total extinction of many large phyla due to failure to make successful readjustments, some naturalists have claimed that, though adaptation exists, it plays no part in the evolutionary process.

It is true that some behavior is nonadaptive, or neutral, and that many injurious acts are performed; but if an animal's behavior in the aggregate is not to his advantage he perishes, and if in the course of evolution of a species there is an irreversible trend toward differentiation of unsuitable features of structure or behavior, that species is eliminated. This elimination of both individual and species has happened many, many times, and yet in the struggle for survival adaptation is the key factor—because, as Julian Huxley expresses it ('43, p. 417), "the problem of adaptation is merely the problem of functional efficiency seen from a slightly different angle," and he concludes (p. 413) that "adaptation has been all-important in evolutionary progress," for the selection of appropriate adaptations, however brought about, is the cardinal method of the evolutionary process. A similar conclusion is reached by the paleontologist Simpson ('47, '49), who writes: "Adaptation is real, and it is achieved by a progressive and directed process. This process is natural, and it is wholly mechanistic in its operation. This natural process achieves the aspect of purpose, without the intervention of a purposer, and it has produced a vast plan, without the concurrent action of a planner." Another paleontologist (Romer, '49) adds his confirmation in these words: "Evolution as seen in the fossil record is in its entirety a study of continual adaptive processes."

In both living bodies and inorganic machines adaptation of means to ends is effected in accordance with well-known mechanical principles, if any consciously purposive factors that may be present are left out of account. This is the thesis of a recent work by W. Ross Ashby ('52), a theme which he documents with a detailed discussion of these mechanical principles supported by mathematical treatment of the data.

The adaptive quality of vital processes has been acquired during past evolutionary history and it has also a future reference. In other words, it has survival value and it has predictive value. Artificial machines that can predict are in current use. Information about past and present weather if properly coded can be fed into an electronic computing machine which in a few minutes will deliver a prediction of tomorrow's weather. Natural predicting machines are as old as life itself, for vital processes are oriented toward the future—that is, toward the preservation and enrichment of life.

Means and ends

What is the relation between means and ends in goal-directed behavior? Philosophers have seriously debated the question whether the end may control the means, whether the future may determine the present. To common sense and to Newtonian mechanics an affirmative answer has seemed impossible, because time has been regarded as a simple unbroken linear dimension of our perceptual world. Current relativistic conceptions of space and time and spectacular advances in mathematical theory and engineering technique have opened new vistas which require reinterpretation of many familiar facts.

At the beginning of a scientific inquiry we must rule out the metaphysical conception of "teleological causation," with its implication of some occult influence acting upon material bodies. We must recognize that in a causal situation the control is intrinsic to the situation as a whole, and the causal situation is not necessarily a linear sequence. The cause is not an external agent acting upon an inert mechanism. "Immanent causality" does not act at a distance in either time or space. The end-product of both adaptive behavior and directive evolution is an emergent arising within the process as such. This is especially clear in some examples of biological adaptation and instinctive behavior.

Buds of trees are cleverly protected and the beaver's fur is thickened in preparation for winter's frost, but the tree and the beaver do not plan it that way. The adaptation is done "naturally," as we say, not with foresight. These devices were developed during past evolution and were implanted in the genetic organization now in operation. These adaptations face backward in perceptual time, not forward, for they have been determined during the past history of the race and of the individual.

During this past an internal organization was established which is a factor in the determination of present behavior and of the further course of evolution of the behavior patterns. Both the past and the future course of events may be directive, and what is now acting is not an end as yet unattained but ends which have been achieved and are now incorporated within the organization of the behaving individual. The directive quality of the behavior is evident, but "pursuit of the end" is not a proper description of it.

It is true that there is a "forward reference" in directive evolution, embryological development, tropism, and instinct; but this is only our interpretation of a course of events with a trend which has been determined by previous events. An end not yet reached has no causal significance in the situation, nor is the metaphysical principle of teleological causation admissible here. The concept of teleology has, accordingly, been in disrepute among naturalists, taboo in science, for the reasons just mentioned and especially because so often it carries with it mystic notions that run counter to accepted principles of causality (Köhler, '38, p. 378; Romer, '49).

Notwithstanding this, the directive trend of many evolutionary processes and of all adaptive behavior insistently calls for explanation. A trend is directed somewhither. What determines the direction taken? Adaptive evolution and adaptive behavior have no meaning apart from the ends toward which they are directed, and they cannot be executed without an appropriate mechanism. The problems of teleology cannot be solved simply by banishing the word from our vocabulary.

Here we are reminded of Ray Lankester's attempt to recast the concept of teleology into biologically acceptable form. In the *Encyclopaedia Britannica* (11th ed., 1911, 28:1024) he wrote: "Darwin's theory had as one of its results the reformation and rehabilitation of teleology." The revised teleology was described as "the study of the adaptation of organic structures to the service of the organisms in which they occur." His principle was rejected by most naturalists as a pseudoteleology; but the fact remains that adaptations do have a forward reference—the survival and satisfaction of the organism—and it is now widely recognized that teleology is a good name for this fact and the theory associated with it. A few examples may be cited.

Montgomery ('07, pp. 391–95) wrote: "Genuine teleology in the manifest products of nature is found unmistakably operative in the existents we are perceptually aware of as living organisms. . . . From the very start vitality involves teleology." Assimilation and dissimilation, anabolism and katabolism comprise the cycle of life. "This complex process, which constitutes enduring vital activity, involves all the teleological characteristics of the living organism in all stages of development."

The literature on emergent evolution (page 53) implies a natural teleology of the sort just described, and still more recently the concept has been enlarged to include all directive processes, both inorganic and organic. The mechanisms involved in directive action, or goal-directed behavior, are under investigation. Northrop ('48) makes some interesting conjectures which are based in large part on data reported in a recent symposium (Frank *et al.*, '48) and other related papers. There is general agreement that the present search is for new approaches and more comprehensive formulations of problems and methods. In the symposium last cited, Frank writes (p. 191): "The concept of teleological mechanisms, however it may be expressed in different terms, may be viewed as an attempt to escape from these older mechanistic formulations that now appear inadequate, and to provide new and more fruitful conceptions and more effective methodologies for studying self-regulating processes, self-orienting systems and organisms, and self-directing personalities. . . . We are moving toward a conception of a 'natural teleology,' as Woodbridge suggested in 1911."

A similar view was expressed by G. H. Mead ('36, p. 271): "There is, then, no real conflict between a mechanical and a teleological account of the world or of the facts of life." Science needs both for the solution of problems. "You get a statement which starts off in teleological form, and then you give a mechanical account of it." This teleology does not imply the presence of any factor which is independent of structure. It does recognize that every directive process has a restricted finalistic character defined by the end-state toward which it is directed and actually implemented not by the end-state but by the existing trend toward that end.

The most fruitful of the available mechanical principles employed in these researches is the "feed-back," a servomechanism of interaction by which the behavior of the mechanism is controlled by an object toward which the behavior is directed. A simple illustration is the now familiar device by which a guided missile may be directed toward a moving target by sound waves, light rays, or other emanations from the target. Much animal behavior is similarly controlled by signals from the goal toward which it is directed, as in the pursuit of prey. This "feed-back" from the goal has been characterized as teleological, a mechanical teleology which involves no action of a future upon a present. Here the end does control the means, but the action is here and now, even though the goal to be reached is at a locus in space and future time as yet undetermined. There is, then, a natural teleology which is nothing other than an expression of the principle of circular causation mentioned on page 72.

None of the directive processes so far considered can be called purposive in the ordinary meaning of the word "purpose," but there is evidence that we may find in them an integrative process from which at a higher level human purposive behavior has emerged. It should also be mentioned here that human purposive behavior may be examined either objectively, as set in a frame of perceptual space and time, or subjectively, and in the latter case the frame of reference is radically different. A genuine teleology can be recognized in purposive action, when the idea of the end motivates the conduct, but even here there is no teleological causation, for having an idea of the future is a present act. This teleology, too, is mechanically determined and the nervous mechanisms involved are now under investigation.

When Whitehead, Lillie, and other naturalistic philosophers speak of directive action and other purpose-like processes as extraphysical, they do not mean that they are extranatural or supernatural. These are processes at higher levels of integration than are those which are codified in conventional physical science in their spatial and temporal relations. These higher dimensions may even transcend the four-dimensional space-time of relativity. Even so, I insist that they should not be regarded as extraphysical. Proving that a light ray is not a stream of solid particles did not make the ray an extraphysical entity, but it did necessitate the reformulation of some classical principles of physics.

Roy Wood Sellars once remarked to me, "In purposive action with ends in view we have a determinative sort of immanent teleology which is no more than directed control." This idea of immanent teleology he has expressed ('43) in print:

"What I am arguing for is a teleology of self-direction rather than a teleology of finalism, a teleology intrinsic to an economy which is both spatial and temporal. In such immanent causality traditional ideas of pushes from the past or pulls from the future are transcended. A high-order substance makes its own time in terms of its economy. In all this I am not forgetting that such immanent causality must be adjusted to the play of transeunt causality, for the organism must act in relation to its environment. But to the extent there is self-direction there is escape from blindness and chance. As I see it, the brain-mind is an organ for the highest type of self-direction."

A recasting of the problems of behavior as conventionally formulated is called for. These problems may be formulated in terms of perceptual space and time, as is usually done in physiological research, or they may be formulated in a different frame of reference derived from introspective experience which conforms with a different system of laws. In this reformulation some conventional principles must be discarded, but few naturalists will accept Sir James Jeans's radical assertion ('43, p. 145): "So far as our knowledge is concerned, causality becomes meaningless." In science we can discard notions of final causes, mythical causal agents, and causal necessity; but we cannot get along without causes and consequences. So also we need the principle of teleology, divested of any mystical accessories.

Summary

Adaptation as defined biologically is adjustment of the organism to existing conditions. It is a time-linked process with a past reference and a future reference. Two classes of adaptations are significant for the evolution of behavior. The first are those which are innate and heritable because they derive from the organization of the germ cells. The second class includes acquired skills which, though not inherited, can be transmitted from generation to generation by social mechanisms—by so-called social heredity. The second class plays an important part only in the higher animals and especially in mankind.

The idea of "teleological causation" must be rigorously excluded from science. Yet the fact remains that all adaptations do have a future reference. There is an end to be achieved, and this implies some kind of natural teleology. Active search is now being made for the mechanisms of this forward reference of adaptive behavior and human purposive action.

CHAPTER TWELVE

Evolution of Value

The natural history of value

The introduction at this stage of our inquiry of so controversial a topic as the scientific status of value may surprise and puzzle the reader. In the preceding discussion, the term "adaptation" was defined as successful adjustment of the organism to the conditions prevailing so as to secure functional efficiency. These adjustments are beneficial, which is another way of saying that they are of value to the animal. There are, then, some values which can be defined biologically, for they are the ends toward which successful behavior is directed.

All behavior is somehow motivated and the end sought is the satisfaction of the motivating conditions (page 18). Human motives generally stem from values. Things that people need and desire are regarded as valuable, and the value resides in the satisfaction of the craving. Since all animals have needs and are more or less successful in their quest for satisfaction, it is possible to recognize the values that motivate their behavior and to express these relations in biological terms. Our search here is for a natural history of value.

Because most human conduct is motivated by ideas of value and because these ideas comprise the data that are used in our thinking about values, most of the voluminous literature on this subject is on the psychological or philosophical level; that is, the values considered are strictly conceptual. But underlying these concepts there is a vast domain of organic needs and satisfactions that never emerge into consciousness, and these biological factors play a much larger role than is commonly recognized in determining what values we seek and what steps we take to get them. The evolutionary development of these unconscious factors of motivation can be investigated because they are biological processes that can be discovered. Because values motivate conduct, consciously or unconsciously, we may agree with Patrick ('29, p. 161) when he said: "The mechanist indeed might, so far as one can see, even regard the whole evolutionary movement as a process of achievement of successive levels of value." And so, it may be added, "biology is the logical place to begin any study of values" (Muller, '43, p. 119).

An inquiry into the biological origins of human motivation may start with our conscious experience of motives and the investigation of their bodily instrumentation and then work backward into successively lower ranks of animals in the search for evidence of recognizable stages of progressive differentiation. Before such an inquiry into the evolution of value is undertaken we must formulate an acceptable definition of human values in biological terms. Concepts of value in terms of metaphysical universals or normative absolutes of perfection have no utility in this search, for vital processes are fluid and all biological principles are relative. Let us, then, examine some samples of human values, state their distinguishing characteristics in biological terms, and then look for evidence of these values or their simpler precursors in the behavior of other animals.

Admiral Byrd ('38) with rare insight and still more engaging frankness has given us a glimpse into the secrets of his own motivation. He makes it clear that the decisive factor in his determination to risk the hazards of four and a half months of solitary life less than ten degrees of latitude from the South Pole was the craving for a personal experience impossible elsewhere. The scientific observations recorded were sufficient justification for the financial outlay, yet it may be questioned whether these values would have induced him to take the risk in the absence of this other motive which was intimately personal and could make no appeal to any of his associates and supporters, who in fact attempted to dissuade him from the enterprise.

So it is with distinguished achievement in every other field, and especially in scientific research. Without this inner motivation of craving for new experience of some particular kind, not only new to the individual but new to the race, to stand where no human foot has trod, to see what no one before has seen, to know the unknown— without this urge for gratification of a strictly personal desire, all exploration and all pure science would languish.

Professor Michelson played with light waves and mirrors all his life because, as he said, "it is such corking good fun." That was, for him, a sufficient reason; but it was not a good enough reason to induce a group of hard-boiled businessmen to pay him a substantial salary for doing it. One of us might get fun out of using a mirror to throw a beam of sunlight into the eyes of motorists on a trunk highway, but businessmen are not likely to pay him for doing it.

Clearly the conduct of both Byrd and Michelson was motivated by values of two quite different kinds. One class of values is strictly personal and is defined in terms of the private satisfactions won. Another class is defined in terms of its worth to the community and so is open to public inspection. This second class of values, however, would have no motivating influence if the individual himself did not derive satisfaction from public service.

We conclude, then, that true values are always personal perquisites. They have no objective existence apart from the persons who cherish them. A valuable object or enterprise is valuable only because people want it. If nobody wants it, its value is nil. Values, then, cannot be divorced from the individuals who seek them. They reside neither in the objects sought nor in the persons who seek them but in the relation existing between the thing sought and the satisfaction it gives, or may give, to the seeker. There are impersonal standards of value, but there are no impersonal values.

This does not mean that values are entirely internally determined, for there are always at least two parties in a relationship. Where many people like the same things these things are commonly regarded as intrinsically valuable. But a good picture, for instance, commands a high price only if there are many people who appreciate its good qualities, that is, who have similar standards of value. These standards vary. Some pictures which received awards in recent exhibits are regarded by other competent critics as childish scribbling of no value whatsoever. The relational definition of value does not allow any divorce of the two members of the relationship.

This is the conclusion to which we are led from an examination of the human pursuit of values which is intentionally directed. The value of the material and social profits which accrue from scientific research is everywhere recognized and acclaimed, but the scientific status both of the objective values and the private satisfactions achieved is equivocal. The traditional code of procedure in natural science rigorously excludes both classes of values from its legitimate domain (page 31). The profits to the public are regarded as by-products and as such are handed over to technology, while the satisfactions are either left orphaned or given asylum in the normative disciplines. Yet all these values are real things that motivate behavior, and science must not shut its eyes to them.

Moreover, both the extrinsic and the intrinsic components of human motivation can be recognized also in all animal behavior, which is similarly motivated by sensorimotor experiences involving adaptive adjustments to the surroundings and also by those internal processes which we have assembled in the class of integrative experiences. This is clearly stated by Yerkes ('43, p. 171), who writes, "Meanings or values determine the scope and quality of an organism's adaptive and constructive life. This is as true of chimpanzee as of man. In both, hereditary—that is, structurally established—meanings abound, and in both there is also large and varied capacity for the acquirement of new meanings through racial tradition and individual experience with animate and inanimate, social and nonsocial environment." The implication in the last sentence quoted is that these meanings and values may or may not be consciously recognized as such by the animal experiencing them.

In that interplay between organism and environment which is the process of living, the pattern of the performance is determined primarily by the nature of the living person, though this pattern is constantly modulated or inflected by what is going on around. The animal's needs are internally determined, but the means of satisfaction are for the most part outside. The value to the organism of these means resides in the use made of them. This is as true in the vital economy of an ameba as in that of a man.

The ameba, it is true, has a very simple action system, with few needs and few ways of satisfying them. But there is one value it cannot do without—what the biologist calls survival value. The urge to stay alive and to enlarge and enrich life in every possible way is the basic property which distinguishes living things from inanimate objects and which gives to organic evolution a quality different from any other phase of cosmic evolution known to us.

With progressive elaboration of animal bodies and their social aggregates there is a parallel increase in needs and enlargement of the range of attainable satisfactions. The honeybees live richer lives than the ameba, richer in both wealth accumulated and satisfactions enjoyed. To survival value they have added social values and many others. A rat has a code of values which is very satisfactory for the rat, however objectionable it may be to the man whose wealth is devoured.

So we recognize a hierachy of biological values which are in organic relationship with enlargement and diversification of bodily structure, social organization, and ability to learn by personal experience. There is a similar progressive enhancement of values achieved in the growth of every human child. In the lower ranks of animals and in early infancy of a man most of these values are built into the hereditary structure and are biologically defined in behavioristic terms. In the higher animals and in the growing child there is an increasing proportion of learned skills and consciously recognized satisfactions which can be evaluated both biologically and psychologically.

As we have just seen, there is good evidence that some of the higher animals seek for values in the same way that men do, with conscious apprehension of the objective desired and of satisfaction won. But this behavior cannot be distinguished by any unmistakable objective signs from that of the most primitive animals, which so far as we can tell have no awareness at all of what they are doing or why.

Accordingly, in this search for the biological origins of human values our attention will be directed to those factors of motivation which can be recognized objectively and to principles that can be formulated in biological rather than psychological terms.

Human values

If now we examine the literature dealing with human values, we shall find that some of the experts in this field of inquiry have formulated their conclusions in propositions that are equally applicable in the domain of human purposive motivation and in the wider field of animal behavior. A review of some samples of this literature leads me to the conclusion that there is a natural hierarchy of values that begins with life itself and culminates in man's finest aspirations for self-culture and social service. Our search for the biological evolution of value is not a vain quest.

It is fitting to begin our survey with a stimulating book entitled *The Evolution of Values*, written by Professor Bouglé ('26) from the standpoint of the social sciences. The subject is treated naturalistically, and Bouglé begins with a sound biological principle: "In the beginning is action . . . action tends to arouse thought" (p. 151). He quotes Aristotle's phrase, "Man thinks because he has a hand" (p. 180), and he makes it clear that, though human values are largely conditioned socially, the germs of these values go back in evolution to a period long before there were men with hands or thoughts.

As a sociologist, Bouglé did not inquire further into biological origins. If he were writing today in the light of what we now know about sociobiology, he would perhaps have formulated his basic postulate differently. He wrote that human values are objective facts because they are socially determined and are collective, and "values present themselves to me as given realities, as things." Values so defined are denied to all subhuman animals, though antecedents of these values can be recognized in animal societies.

To this criterion of value as a socially determined objective thing I object, because the whole history of biological evolution gives clear evidence that all animals achieve true values as these are defined by Bouglé himself in his subsequent discussions. It is true that most human values are set in a social frame, that "judgments of value have for function to formulate, not the natural properties of things, but the desires of men living in society"; but the social frame within which these desires are set is a secondary feature. This appears in his further definitions: "Judgments of value—whether of the esthetic, religious, economic or moral order—express, not the relations of things among themselves, but the relations of things to human tendencies"; and again, "True values are the things men set their hearts upon"; and in still another place, "Wherever found, a value is a permanent possibility of satisfactions."

These extracts put the emphasis where it belongs, upon the *relation* between desires and needs and the things that give satisfaction. This is a biological criterion which is applicable throughout the whole range of animal life, for all animals have needs and most of their behavior is concerned with the satisfaction of these needs.

As explained below, we must be on guard here against the errors of the social positivists. The desires of men and the needs of all other creatures arise as expressions of their own inner natures, however much they may be inflected by social and other environmental conditions. This sets the most significant criteria of value within the organism, and our search for the biological antecedents of the desires of men must be directed to the intrinsic properties of the organism as such, its needs and satisfactions, and not primarily to the things that satisfy the needs. This postulate is basic for a biological analysis of values as motivators of behavior.

Coghill's study of the development of behavior ('30) let him to this conclusion: "The determination of the primary attitude of the organism toward environment is intrinsic. . . . The initiative of attitude is primarily within the organism. . . . Any theory of motivation, therefore, which ascribes the activation of behavior wholly to the environment is inadequate." His argument in defense of this thesis I have quoted ('49, chap. 15) from his unpublished manuscripts and it need not be repeated here.

It is granted that in mankind, where social relations are highly developed, the environmental factors of our values are especially important and distinctive. But even here social values are gauged in terms of personal satisfactions sought and found. The external adjustments are essential for the satisfaction of needs, but only as means to ends. The satisfaction sought is personal. The environment may provide wealth, but whether this wealth is of value depends entirely upon the use made of it. When a wealthy person is called "a man of means," the phrase is exactly right. Whether his means are of any real value to him or anybody else is quite another matter.

In our human affairs means and ends are curiously interwoven and interchangeable. The end achieved becomes the means for the next enterprise. The merchant makes money and immediately spends it for enlargement of his business. The miser who makes money only to hoard it makes of his means an end. Each gets the kind of satisfaction that he craves, and that craving is determined by his own nature, not by the nature of his business.

Our scientific analysis of value puts the emphasis on the internal factors. It is even more obviously true that this is where the emphasis belongs in the case of artistic values. Edmund Burke's classic essay *On the Sublime and Beautiful* illustrates the futility of the most refined logical analysis of objects regarded as beautiful. In his search for "the real cause of beauty" he finds it "in the natural properties of things," and these he examines in detail. The qualities of beauty are found to reside in things that are comparatively small, smooth, delicate, and so on. It is true, as the distinguished author says, that the breasts of women are by common consent beautiful and they do possess these qualities; but it is a travesty of common sense and of logic to look for the cause of their beauty entirely apart from the attitudes and appetencies of the observers. Beauty, like value, resides in the relation between the object of regard and its meaning in terms of the response of the subject to it.

The involved dialectic of Wolfgang Köhler's *The Place of Value in a World of Facts* ('38) seems to me to include a similar fallacy. Köhler makes it clear that the procedure of science involves evaluation at every step. In certain phenomenal contexts we recognize a relationship of "requiredness," and this is correlated with certain other "transphenomenal realities" that in the objective realm we characterize as "organic fitness." Requiredness and fitness are equated with value. This is all to the good, and I maintain (contrary to Köhler's opinion) that these relationships can be validated biologically, because our biological criterion of fitness is the satisfaction of the needs of the organism.

Nor can I follow Köhler when, in this work and in his later

exposition ('44), he ascribes value to the things that satisfy needs, and this in their own right. The value does not reside in these things nor in the organism that craves them, but only in the relation between the need and the things that satisfy.

Despite his logical argument (with postulates that I cannot accept) against the doctrine that "the essence of value is valuation," I believe that this doctrine exactly describes all values that we recognize phenomenologically, whether the valuation is done consciously or biologically. As elsewhere pointed out, the acquisition and possession of a value is an experience and every experience (conscious or unconscious) is an act, not an attribute of a thing. If a dress looks elegant, the elegance does not reside in the dress per se. It looks elegant to somebody, and to somebody else it may look ugly. If an ameba ingests an animalcule as valuable food and rejects a piece of sand, the value resides in the fact that one is good for the ameba and the other is not. There is no value apart from such a relationship. The value resides neither in the individual having the experience nor in the object of regard. The awareness factor may or may not be present.

This is a relationship within a definable "field," a feature which Professor Köhler himself emphasizes in the conclusion of his paper of 1944. The implications of this concept, whether viewed phenomenologically or otherwise, seem to suggest that the definition of value should be stated relativistically, and when it is so conceived no elaborate dialectic is necessary to demonstrate that value is inherent in all organic nature.

It is a far cry, of course, from the biological adjustments of an ameba or an ant by which these lowly organisms extract a precarious living from a ruthless world to the satisfactions experienced by a railroad magnate, an inventor, a poet, or a philosopher while they do the constructive work to which they have set their hands and minds. Yet the ant's behavior is a succession of reactions which "satisfy the motivating conditions." Whether the ant knows that she is doing this we have no way of finding out. We should not begrudge the ant any values that she has, for these seem to be genuine as measured by the definition adopted. Many of our own satisfactions are achieved just as blindly.

In discussing human values Santayana ('05, p. 222) wrote: "Satisfaction is the touchstone of value; without reference to it all talk about good and evil, progress or decay, is merely confused verbiage, pure sophistry in which the juggler adroitly withdraws attention from what works the wonder." And in another passage (p. 236): "In spite of all logical and psychological scruples, conduct that should not justify itself somehow by the satisfactions secured and the pains avoided would not justify itself at all."

To this we may add the conclusion reached in a concise critical discussion of "Value Judgments and 'Objectivity'" (by Cantril *et al.*, '49): "Because value judgments play so important a role in scientific thinking, ways and means must be discovered of making value judgments themselves the subject matter for scientific inquiry."

The relational nature of value

If as Dewey ('25) says there is "no room for a theory of values separate from a theory of nature," then it is incumbent upon the naturalist to adjust his own values and those for which he searches in harmony with that order of nature within which they have emerged. A survey of the literature shows that one can find authority for almost any definition of value that he may require for dialectic. These definitions are as various as the philosophies of their designers. It would be presumptuous for the naturalist to propound a comprehensive theory of values, but he has a legitimate interest in pointing the way toward a scientific approach to it.

For such an approach it is important that distinctions be drawn between (1) values achieved and experienced (satisfactions sought and won), (2) things regarded as valuable, (3) the act of evaluation (an intellectual exercise tinged with emotion), (4) scientific study of values and things of value as factual data and of the processes and results of evaluation (psychologically, sociologically, economically, and in all their other relationships), and (5) the objectively manifest results of the preceding activities (such as patterns of behavior and social organization, commercially valuable inventions, and so on). In rule-of-thumb practice and in scientific investigation these various aspects and relationships of values are blended in ever-changing patterns.

Fortunately for us naturalists there are many experts in this field who, however they may differ about everything else, are in agreement in accepting a relational theory of value that is naturalistic in conception and readily tested operationally by scientific methods. The study of relationships is a cardinal feature of natural science, and much of that science's technique has been elaborated for just this purpose. This conception of value as a relationship is so fundamental and illuminating that a few illustrative passages may be quoted in addition to those already cited.

Ralph Barton Perry's comprehensive study ('26) yields this concise definition, "A value is any object of any interest," which he explains by a quotation from Professor S. Alexander: "In every value there are two sides, the subject of valuation and the object of value, and the value resides in the relation between the two, and does not exist apart from them. . . . Values arise out of likings and satisfy them." E. L. Thorndike ('36) writes, "Values are functions of preferences."

These authors, and many others who might be cited, are examining values in terms of human experience of them, but their statements are framed in general terms which embrace, as explicitly stated, similar relations wherever found. Professor Perry, for instance, uses the word "interest" with biological implications, defining it "in terms of the behaving organism." The relationships here under consideration are accessible to observation and experiment in both human and subhuman fields of behavior. The worth of the value is judged in terms of resulting satisfaction. The satisfaction may be appraised subjectively or objectively. When examined objectively the philosopher's formulations are seen to be essentially the same as Professor Carr's biological formula ('25) previously quoted, that all vital adjustments as expressed in animal behavior involve "the satisfaction of the motivating conditions."

There is no fallacy of dialectic here arising from ambiguous meaning of terms. The philosophers and the biologists see eye to eye and speak the same language. The satisfaction of needs is a common function of all living things, indeed it is the essential vital process. It follows that the basic value is life itself, as was recognized by Dewey when he said ('25, p. 252), "Empirically speaking, the most obvious difference between living and non-living things is that the activities of the former are characterized by needs, by efforts which are active demands to satisfy needs, and by satisfactions."

Because the basis of all value is life itself, what the biologist properly calls "survival value" is primeval and unescapable. It can never be outgrown, however much may be added to it. From this primordial value all others have been individuated in a hierarchy of values that culminates in man's most refined intellectual, esthetic, and moral satisfactions.

The goodness of value

The traditional view has been, and still is, that the question "What is good?" is not a scientific problem and cannot be answered by science. Here, as in every other inquiry, we must start with some postulates and definitions.

By common consent transcendental categories of goodness must be excluded from biological consideration, for biology recognizes no absolute standards of good and evil, of right and wrong, or of anything else. We start with the proposition that it is biologically good to be alive. Without vitality there can be no biology, good or bad. What preserves and enriches life is biologically good, that is, it is good for the organism. It is biologically good to enlarge and diversify the organism's capacity for productive behavior and to enhance the satisfactions won. If, in the broad view, the good did not outweigh the evil, then the urge for life would disappear, no living thing would long survive, and biology as a science would not exist. In biology there is no uncertainty about the meaning of the word "goodness." With this connotation of the word, what is good and what is evil is a factual question to be answered by appeal to actual experience.

Goodness as science views it is not something inherent in things, persons, or acts as such. What is good is a judgment which cannot be made apart from the questions good for what? and good for whom? The cow that gives the most milk may be the best cow for a dairy, but she may be the worst member of a herd of beef cattle. If science is good for anything, it should be at its best in helping us to make such choices.

There is general agreement that what is good is valuable. Since life is intrinsically valuable to the organism that has it, whatever is good for the organism is a value. Having so defined goodness, science can tell us what is good *for us* under specified conditions and, if we must make a choice of goods, may help us to decide which of them is most likely to prove most desirable in the end, that is, which will give the most acceptable satisfactions.

Whether such judgments have ethical significance depends on the definition of ethics adopted. If the standards of good and evil, of right and wrong, are based on transcendental absolutes of perfection, then such an ethic belongs in metaphysics, not in science, and Lundberg ('50) is perfectly right in his insistence that "injecting ethical judgments into generalizations about behavior and claiming that these judgments, as well as the generalizations, are arrived at by scientific methods" is illegitimate. But here and in another paper ('50a) he overlooks the fact that there is a naturalistic ethic which is defined behavioristically and is derived from behavior by acceptable scientific standards. These ethical standards are relative, not absolute, and they must accord with actual experience of the relative worth for human welfare of the values which men cherish.

The moral laws of naturalistic ethics are not decrees of some extranatural power. They are the laws of nature and as such they are self-executing. Transgression of these laws brings its own penalty. No prosecutor is required. If you drink whisky to excess, your health is impaired. If you drink wood alcohol, you die. In so far as our personal and social codes of moral law conform with the scientifically validated principles of biological values they are right, and any deviation from these principles brings disaster. The wages of sin is death, if not of the person, certainly of his richest values and satisfactions. And ignorance of the law excuses no man. To succeed in life we must conform our moral codes to nature as it is, in just the same way that we establish our codes of personal and public hygiene.

That there is available for our guidance a code of practical morals that has scientific standing is obvious from the fact that at the present stage of human cultural evolution some of the moral issues have actual survival value. Without some generally acceptable moral standards civilization crumbles beyond repair and the people perish. Furthermore the ultimate test of value is satisfaction, and, since morality yields higher satisfactions than unmoral or immoral conduct, it follows that self-control in accordance with moral standards marks the highest level yet attained in the course of human evolution.

Experience shows that in business honesty is the best policy. Big business, and little business too, have found that the maxim "the public be pleased" yields larger dividends than the older slogan "the public be damned." In our culture business solvency is a social value. If success in business is acquired dishonestly, it does not pay out in the long run, as illustrated by the examples mentioned on page 66. This principle applies to management of one's personal affairs and to social movements of all kinds, including international diplomacy. People have been slow to recognize that this elementary moral code, which is older than the ten commandments of Mosaic law, cannot be violated with impunity because it is the expression, at the human level of cultural evolution, of the basic law of the survival of the fit. In this domain the satisfactions sought and won go beyond mere survival value to esthetic and moral appreciations which no brute can achieve.

All values are relative. What is good in one situation may be fatally bad in another. Sugar is "good," but it is not "good for" a diabetic. What is good must be good for something. Otherwise the word has no meaning, and it is the business of science to find out what things are good for. Our criterion of goodness here is, as stated by Murphy ('43, p. 98), "things are discoverably good or bad, not in their intrinsic characters, but in their capacity to satisfy interests and desires." Our biological concepts of the good, if they have any practical significance, are of particulars, not of universals. We want to know what is good for a particular individual or class of individuals or group under specified conditions, and facts of this sort can be discovered by appropriate inquiry.

Survival value may be good enough for the countless swarms of bacteria, worms, and ants, which, indeed, may have few other values. But not for men. Our values are as various as are the needs and desires that generate them. They are not normative abstractions detached from human interests and actions. They are natural products of our ways of life. As I have elsewhere written ('36, '46), these values are inherent in the vital process. They belong to us and to every other organism that holds its own in the struggle for existence, each according to the measure of his ability to create them. For they are made, not found; they grow up with us and are part of us. They can be no better than we are. What they are, with each of us, depends largely on our own efforts, for they are what we want them to be. They are ours because we make them each for himself, and no one can transmit his values to anybody else.

The evaluation of values

Improvement in control over the forces of nature yields greater wealth, for wealth is the external member of this vital correspondence with environment. It can be held in common, bought, sold, entailed, and measured quantitatively in various ways. But value as the internal and personal member is a private passion; it is the mainspring of the personality. Its measure is personal satisfaction, and for this we have no convenient measuring rule. We gauge our satisfactions qualitatively, as do all other animals.

Although human satisfactions cannot be measured in numerical units with any technique at present available, yet they can be arranged in a graded series of preferences, and methods have been devised for dealing quantitatively with these preferences. These methods can be applied also in the objective study of animal behavior. We really get along practically very well without these numerical measurements. All we need to do is to rank our preferences judiciously in the order of their real worth in our efforts to master what Robert Louis Stevenson so happily called "the continent art of living well."

From these considerations it follows that the practical issue involved in a natural history of value is a judicious selection of standards and criteria for the *evaluation of values*. This, as just explained, is essentially a scientific problem, to be solved (if at all) by critical study of the process of evaluation and of the results which follow from the successful pursuit of various kinds of value. The relative worth of a value is gauged by the quality of the satisfactions which it yields.

Measurable data and quantitative statements of conclusions expressed in form favorable for mathematical analysis are the ideals that we try to reach in all factual inquiries. In many fields, especially in the biological sciences, this goal is not even in sight within presently accessible horizons. Here we are limited to descriptions in terms of qualitative differences for which no numerical expressions have been found. Thus, observed behavior may be used as an indicator of internal states that can be described only in vague general terms. To take an extreme case, in the realm of values tokens of value can be measured (in dollars or some other convenient unit), but the satisfactions which they yield cannot.

Having a preference is a mental act which is based on judgments of relative values. These personal preferences are real facts. Their significance for the science of economics can be expressed statistically in terms of what people buy and what they are willing to pay. But their full significance for introspective psychology, sociology, and ethics cannot be so expressed. We can investigate scientifically the biological and social factors which have established these preferences; but however successful we may be in quantifying the physical, physiological, and social expressions of subjective processes, the latter cannot be manipulated with the same units of measurement, and for some subjective nuances no metric at all has been devised. Nonetheless, practically we use our minds in social adjustments and these mental processes can be investigated scientifically with or without numerical measurements.

In the present state of knowledge we are confronted with serious difficulties if we attempt to convert statistical or numerical ratings of symbols and indicators of value into quantitative measures of the real values. We can measure distance in miles and wealth in dollars, but these units do not stand in any obvious simple or uniform mathematical relation with the satisfaction that I get out of walking a mile or earning a dollar. The first whole dollar that I ever earned stands out in my memory as one of the high spots of my career. I really earned it by picking strawberries for a neighbor at one cent a quart, and the big silver coin that I held in my childish hand gave me more intense pleasure than any monthly pay check that I have ever received since that time.

For further discussion of these controversial questions the reader is referred to Birkhoff, '33, p. 13; Cohen, '31, pp. 93–99; Johnson, '36; and Troland, '28, p. 283. Brief mention is made by Cushen, '55, of a more recent attempt by N. M. Smith and colleagues to develop a mathematical theory of value especially applicable in programs of operations research.

Morris and Jones ('55) report the results of a study directed toward the development of a scale for the measurement of value which gives promise of a method for getting records of personal preferences of people of five nations with widely different cultural patterns. These data can be used for both psychometric scaling analysis and factor analysis.

The profit motive

The significance of biological values for behavior lies in their motivating influence. This was our point of departure here. The profit motive has long been a controversial subject, but no dialectic can refute the fact that people normally work for profit and are likely to continue to do so. This led me to make a biological appraisal of the profit motive ('38), which came to the conclusion that profit of some sort is the end toward which most behavior, human and other, is directed. For personal profit of some kind is the basic biological value.

Progressive evolution as we have defined it (page 125) involves successive enrichments of the intrinsic values of life and refinement of their quality. Or, otherwise expressed, biological progress is gauged by the profits that accrue in the business of living. This is the criterion employed when we rank animals as lower or higher in the scale, and the same test is used when we judge the worth of our fellow men. It is important to note in both cases that this criterion is stated in terms of values, not of wealth, as these were defined above. If one is content with shoddy values his life is improverished regardless of any accumulations of property, power, or fame.

It is illogical to label as hedonism the principle that satisfaction is the fundamental biological value and then reject that principle because it bears that label. If the quest for biological profit as gauged by satisfaction is called hedonism, then that concept must be stripped of the Epicurean dogma that carnal pleasure is the source of our highest satisfactions. Human culture at its best derives from satisfactions of a higher order. The esthetic and moral values which give this culture its pre-eminence are, like all other mental processes, generated as biological functions of human bodies and as such they can be analyzed and evaluated scientifically. They are integral parts of human experience and, as explained in the next following chapter, the evolution of experience can be described as a biological process. In this process the evaluation of experience, at first physiologically and later rationally, plays a leading role, with the result that at our present stage of cultural evolution moral integrity and altruism have actual survival value. These, as well as all the other refinements of cultured humanity, yield profits that can be gauged in terms of biology, economics, esthetics, or ethics.

We see now that the evolution of values takes a natural and important place in the general scheme of organic evolution, and that the prevailing social codes are emergent products of a life in which evaluation of experience is an indispensable ingredient. In subhuman experience most of this evaluation is done automatically and unconsciously. In human cultures much more of it is done intentionally, and if the values which motivate behavior are unwisely chosen the social unit is impaired or destroyed. Most sociologists seem to have been unwilling to face this fact and its significance for social science.

A plea for "a social science that has become intelligent enough to extend its scope from social facts to social values" was expressed by Jensen ('41). Subsequently Cantril ('49) emphasized the part that values in general and moral values in particular have played in the evolution of human cultures and that "a system of ethics and a code of morality are not only emergent co-products of man's evolution but become themselves directive agencies in the evolutionary process itself." The last point is a key factor in the solution of many problems of social adjustment.

It is also clear that in subhuman animals values as biologically defined have similarly played an active part during the whole course of organic evolution. This was stated by Kroeber ('49), the anthropologist, in this form: "Recognition of the functioning and capacities of an organic species in [is] a sort of formulation of the values genetically inherent in that species. At any rate, it *can* be that, even if biologists usually are not aware of the fact and might resent the imputation of any concern with values." His conclusion is: "It follows that if we refuse to deal with values we are refusing to deal with what has most meaning in particular cultures as well as in human culture seen as a whole."

Is truth a value?

The answer to this question may give us a crucial test of the validity of the traditional dogma that science has no concern with values. In science we are searching for the truth, searching with singleness of purpose, with all our might, and with large expenditure of time, effort, and money. Why? My demand ('44) for recognition of the incentives and satisfactions of scientific work as integral components of the scientific method is here repeated.

We are taught that science must not be contaminated by human interests and values, that these are mere by-products of the scientific assay to be thrown out in the flux as dross or turned over to technology. Now, when the technologist makes a fortune out of this slag, as he may in a cement factory perhaps, is science consumed with jealousy? Not at all. Science has what she went after—a truth—and she is content, perfectly satisfied. But the satisfaction, as we have seen, is a value. So when science in her disdain of values finds a truth, she automatically creates value in spite of herself. This interesting dilemma is resolved very simply by frank acknowledgment that the incentive which motivates the search and the satisfaction which eventuates with success are integral components of the search itself, without which it would be meaningless.

It was shown on page 32 that evaluation is an essential feature of scientific method, and now it is manifest that the values sought and found have scientific status as such and not merely as useful or decorative by-products. Indeed, we may go further and say that science has a code of moral values that again are inherent in the organized structure of science and essential for its existence. Science is motivated by passionate desire for the truth, and any violation of the code of faithful and honest recording of observations made destroys science inevitably. Honesty, which is a moral virtue, is essential in science because success in science is not possible on any other terms.

This situation seems to imply that truth is a value, and the resulting questions like everything else in this obscure domain, have inspired much controversy, in which I have participated ('36a). If

value must be expunged from science, which is a human achievement, then the scientific career would offer no allurements beyond
those of an artist whose faith in esthetic values has perished. No
cogency of dialectic can shake the faith of the scientific investigator
in the intrinsic worth of his labor—not merely as a value which may
be realized secondarily by applications in industry, but as a value
realized during the research as it goes along, value which is inherent
in scientific method as a process yielding vital satisfactions. For, as
Lessing said, it is not the possession of truth, but the successful struggle for it that rewards the scientist with satisfaction.

Truth as an object of interest is a value in the same sense that
other things that yield satisfaction are so regarded. The value lies
in this relationship. Of course, truth has other relationships; it is
not identical with the interest which fosters its growth. Truth as we
use it instrumentally is not an independent normative category. Each
truth is a generalization from our experience, cast in the form of a
proposition that can be verified in all subsequent experience that falls
within its scope. It is a product forged in the flame of vital experience, and its full meaning cannot be realized apart from the history
of its fabrication.

If we supplement this instrumental conception of both truth and
value by appeal to the correspondence theory of truth—congruence
with a previously accepted body of factual knowledge—we arrive at
the same conclusion. The congruence which is sought, the harmony
in which we have an interest, is not mere logical consistency of
propositions—formal consistency. It is correspondence with actual
experience as embodied in verifiable propositions.

A truth is not a proposition. It is a judgment which may (or may
not) be embodied in a proposition. If so embodied, the proposition
must have certain characteristics; it must be congruent with all relevant experience and with all other propositions which correctly record that experience. As experience widens, truth is enlarged and
rectified. We may, then, grant that there are some aspects of truth
that are not functions of interest, yet from this it does not follow
that truth in some of its other aspects is unrelated and incompatible
with interest. The proposition is a static object; it is an inert symbol

of a momentary phase of a living and growing achievement, an expression of its designer's present judgment. A proposition which is true today may be false tomorrow.

In our search for truth we may take comfort in the knowledge that in so far as our efforts are successful we have acquired real values and that these values not only enrich our own lives but also propagate themselves like enzymes. A truth is a vital thing that may grow indefinitely in ever wider circles and that outlasts the mortal who first made it known. The time has come when we see the fulfillment of that prophecy that was expressed by Murphy ('43, p. 101) when he wrote: "Science, after all, is remaking the world, and will doubtless get around to values in time, if they turn out to be really important."

The current slogans "Truth for Truth's Sake" and "Art for Art's Sake" are meaningless verbiage. The great artists are not motivated by these abstractions. They live their art. Their productions are expressions of this way of life. The secret of their enduring vitality lies in the formula Art for Life's Sake. In a similar way the scientist's search is not for a body of static dogma. Science too is a way of life in a quest for Truth for Life's Sake.

Summary

There is a natural history of values which can be explored scientifically if value is defined as the relation existing between an interest, desire, or need and the thing which satisfies the craving. This relationship motivates human conduct which is intentionally directed toward a desired objective and also animal behavior which may or may not be consciously guided toward an appropriate adaptive adjustment. All animals have needs which they strive to satisfy, and this satisfaction is a value whether or not it is recognized as such. The quest for satisfaction may be triggered by external events, but the satisfaction sought or achieved is a personal perquisite.

Mankind has no monopoly of values. There is a hierarchy of natural values parallel with the progressive enlargement of the action system of animals in the evolutionary series. We can recognize an evolution of value in phylogeny and a similar growth of value judgments in the development of every child. Value as here defined is immanent in the organic realm as an objectively verifiable phenomenon. Animal behavior is permeated with values and motivated by them.

Human motivation now takes its place among the other biological functions; and the problem of its nature and apparatus faces two ways, outward toward environment and inward toward the need or the desire and its satisfaction. The conscious components of the process are seen to be parts of the causal complex of vital activities, for they have natural causes and these relationships are not inaccessible to science. Much of the motivation arises below the threshold of awareness and is unrecognized as such; indeed, some of it would be vehemently repudiated if recognized, as psychoanalysis so often reveals.

Biological values can be ranked in terms of the worth of the satisfactions experienced, but they cannot be measured in numerical units. The search for truth is a quest for value, for all truth is instrumentally useful and it satisfies a human craving. The goodness of value is relative. The vital questions are, good for what and for whom? There are no absolute standards of what is good and what is right, but there is the unescapable obligation to choose what is right in every particular situation and to make this decision in the light of all available evidence.

CHAPTER THIRTEEN
Evolution of Experience

The natural history of experience

As we saw at the beginning of this study, both natural science and all the practical adjustments that precede and follow scientific inquiry are based on experience. The naturalist, accordingly, must attend to experience as such, its growth, its method, and its limitations, and not merely to things experienced. He must have some understanding of himself as an experiencing subject before he can interpret and evaluate the data experienced, for, as everybody recognizes and as I have illustrated ('47a), naïve experience is often unreliable and misleading.

The naturalist's interest in experience is strictly operational. He needs to know how it works and what it means in terms of behavior and the resulting satisfactions and frustrations. The general principles of ontology and epistemology lie beyond his horizons, though his operations in the practice of knowing and the philosopher's theory of knowledge must be consistent if both are true to the facts of nature. Furthermore, the philosophical analysis may suggest profitable topics and methods of inquiry—as, it is apparent here, it so suggested to me.

We naturalists need not be perturbed by the philosophers' failure to come to an agreement about the definition of experience. For our purpose we may accept the description of experience ascribed to John Dewey by Sidney Hook ('49): "For Dewey experience is an objective, dynamic transaction between a live thing and its environment, not a private possession of an isolated and insulated mind." We have all had experience, and each one of us knows what it means to him. This knowledge is a private possession, but the experience itself as a transaction has wider relationships. We also know that other people and other animals have experiences more or less like ours; otherwise we could not succeed in getting along with one another, our household pets and domestic animals, and the wild animal life of our surroundings.

We generally accept our experience as given. We take it for granted and ask no questions about its inherent nature. But the behaviorist cannot let the matter rest here. He must understand the tools with which he works, and his operational analysis of human and animal experience must be thorough and radical. Accordingly, in an essay "The Natural History of Experience" ('45; cf. also '49, chap. 19) I attempted to trace the growth of experience through successive levels of integration. Some extracts from that paper are included here and in subsequent passages (page 303). From this survey it was concluded that experience is a personal matter, that is, it pertains to an integrated unit of some sort and in biology that unit is the person. It is also an active process, not merely something that happens to a passive body. It is a personal adjustment to some change in the situation, and the word itself denotes this total adjustment viewed from the standpoint of the experiencing subject. This means that it is a total pattern in the Coghillian sense.

In an inquiry into the biological properties of experience it must not be overlooked that the reasoning process involved in the inquiry and the accompanying pulses of emotion and impulse are themselves experiences. These subjective processes and all our experiences about the objective world are natural events; they are things that we do with our bodies; and this capacity for sensorimotor experience and for reasoning about it has been acquired, again naturally, during the long history of prehuman and human evolution. The psychobiologist may approach the subject from the genetic side and ask, What are the biological roots of human experience and in what soil do these roots grow?

Any examination of the enlargement of experience in the individual or in evolutionary history must of necessity start at the top level, that is, with our own adult human experience; for if there is no awareness of the events under consideration they cannot be considered scientifically or in any other way. In the behavior of the adult man conscious control sets the pace and the direction, but in the fetus and in the more primitive animals unconscious control clearly predominates. Accordingly, if we are looking for the early precursors of human experience, attention must be directed primarily to the unconscious components of it, for these are all that are open to inspection at the lower levels, and the search for the precursors in lower animals of these unconscious components must be pushed to the limit. We find (page 59), that this limit is not reached at the level of the simplest animals known, for some rudimentary precursors of mentation can be recognized throughout the whole realm of inorganic nature. I prefer to give these early precursors of mind some noncommittal name—mind-stuff, if you like, but not mind.

The psychobiologist may start at the beginning and observe the successive steps by which animal experience and the experience of the human fetus and infant are enlarged and diversified. These two series of events show striking uniformities and instructive parallelism up to a certain point. The critical stage at which human development passes beyond that attained by any other animal is, of course, the focal point of interest. This inquiry will be clarified by examination of the nature of animal experience in the prodromal stages, following the advice of Dewey ('17): "Any account of experience must now fit into the consideration that experience means living; and that living goes on in and because of an environing medium, not in a vacuum." To this Whitehead's statement ('29) may be added: "The principle I am adopting is that consciousness pre-supposes experience, and not experience consciousness." Awareness arises within experience, and when conscious experience reaches the level of knowledge then the process of knowing must be analyzed on its own terms. Perception and reasoning are experiences of higher order than reflexes, and these psychological processes cannot be adequately described in physiological terms.

The nature of experience

Our conscious experience is one manifestation of a larger organic process which may be examined objectively. In our search for the earliest precursors of the human type of experience we must, I repeat, of necessity ignore the conscious factor, for at the lower levels we have no recognizable criteria for it.

All animals have experiences of some kind, and so do inanimate things. The engineer says that a cantilever bridge experiences certain measurable stresses when a train of cars passes over it, and it reacts to this strain in measurable ways. The bridge experiences the strain but, so far as we can tell, it has no knowledge about it. The engineer upon completion of his measurements and computations has scientific knowledge about the situation, though he lacks the first-hand experience that the bridge has. An ameba experiences the satisfaction of hunger when it devours a smaller animalcule. A man has experience when he winces from pain of a pinprick. This is common usage. In each of these cases the object reacts to a change in the situation and the reaction is part of the experience; in fact, I think it is safe to say that the reaction is the experience. The exciting agent is, of course, an integral factor in the situation, but the quality of the experience as such is determined primarily by what the organism does about it. If the creature has no visual organs, light is not an adequate stimulus and the animal does nothing about it. How he does respond to an adequate stimulus depends on the structural organization of his body. There may be no awareness of the experience in any of these instances, but if the man is conscious of the pain this awareness is part of his reaction. His experience is different and different parts of the brain are acting if the awareness component of the experience is present. The experience is a property of the individual that has it, or, better, that does it; for an experience is an act, not a passive receptivity, merely something that happens to an inert body. This is true equally for the bridge, the ameba, and the man. The experiences just mentioned are instigated by external events. Those other experiences which are internally activated are perhaps of larger psychological significance; but since these are more difficult of access, we begin our examination with experience of the familiar stimulus-response type which is simpler and more easily analyzed experimentally.

Beginning our analysis, as we must, with human conscious experience, we find that the events in this realm fall into two categories which are radically different introspectively and in their significance for behavior. Because they differ in the second respect, that is, objectively, their properties can be investigated also with the conventional methods of biology. The categories in question are, first, experiences about things and events in the external world that are acquired perceptually and so may be termed *perceptual experiences;* and, second, those internal intellectual and emotive processes that have no direct external reference and so may be called *conceptual experiences.* Both classes of experience are, of course, apprehended subjectively but, since knowledge acquired perceptually is always referred outward to external things set in particular places and times, this kind of experience may be called for short *objective knowledge,* in contrast with *conceptual knowledge* acquired by strictly internal mental processes which use abstract symbols without any external reference or temporo-spatial relations. We may, accordingly, speak in more general terms of *extraspective experience* and *introspective experience.*

This contrast is fundamental, yet it does not carry any implication that the contrasted members are independent of each other, for the processes designated are complementary and neither has meaning apart from the other. Dewey ('48) characterizes them as "transactions," and in every transaction there are two reciprocating members, here the experiencing subject and the things experienced.

This familiar antinomy of the subjective and the objective realms of experience has been analyzed and interpreted by Sellars ('38) in a way which has given me some suggestions for an application of the philosopher's epistemology to fundamental biological problems. He analyzes the double knowledge of ourselves that we have—i.e., behavioral, physical external knowledge in which mind is disclosed in what mind does, and opposed to this a self-knowledge in which the knower is internal to himself—and this analysis can be recast to fit into a psychobiological frame where it has operational value.

Professor Sellars points out that mind can be studied in both of the ways just mentioned. First, there is mind as an object of regard, comparable with the physical objects and events of our external world. We know mind by what it does, just as we know stars and tides and men. This is the method of conventional behaviorism. Consciousness does not enter into this function of knowing except as means to an end; it has no place in the objective picture. This knowledge is public and scientifically verifiable. Second, we know mind by personal awareness. This knowledge is private and incommunicable except by indirection with the aid of symbols which can be recognized objectively. We thus have two systems of knowledge, both of which are lawfully ordered but incommensurable by any system of measurement so far discovered. We know, however, that they are not actually incommensurable, for they are organically related and integrated in the living body. The professor of philosophy devoted his inquiry to "the philosophical problem of coalescing the results of two ways of knowing the same reality." The naturalist may approach the same problem from a different standpoint and with different technique.

It is repeated and emphasized that this classification of patterns of experience must not be rigidly interpreted, for it is becoming increasingly clear that human sensation, perception, and reasoning have many characteristics in common. In actual operation these and the emotive and volitional factors are inseparable. It remains true, however, that these processes show recognizable differences which have significance for behavior.

Three characteristics which distinguish perceptual experience from conceptual experience merit special mention here because they have objective indicators which are recognizable in overt behavior. In the first place, perceptual knowledge is always projected outward away from the perceiving self; conceptual knowledge is experience within the self, with no outward projicience. Second, perception is essentially analytic; the building up of concepts and reasoning about them are synthetic, i.e., essentially integrative. This distinction, it should be mentioned, is drawn in terms of ends achieved, not of means employed, for perception always involves some synthesis, and analytic processes are employed in reasoning. In the third place, perceptual knowledge is always framed in three-dimensional space and linear dimensional time; conceptual processes may disregard these limitations.

Now let us see whether we can find in the behavior of subhuman animals any evidence of a similar twofold quality of experience as judged by the criteria just mentioned. It is at once apparent that all animals in their adjustments to environing conditions have *sensorimotor experience* which is comparable with human perceptual experience except for the lack of any evidence of a conscious component in the lower species. The vital process is an interaction between organism and environment, and the living body is at the focus of a polarized dynamic system. The sensorimotor reactions have the same kind of external reference that is experienced in human behavior of stimulus-response type, whether conscious or unconscious, but the internal regulatory activities do not, being *self-centered* and *self-contained.* Even the simplest animals show this contrast (page 92).

Sir Charles Sherrington's researches in mammalian physiology ('52, p. 325) led him to draw the same distinction between "sensual perception" with a spatial reference and "awareness not derived from sense" which has no spatial projection. Goldstein's ('40) psychological analysis of behavior is similar to that of Sellars. He distinguishes "concrete" behavior, determined directly by a stimulus, from "abstract" performances, in which action is not initiated by any external agent but by the account of the situation which the individual gives to himself. These, he says, are totally different activities of the organism. "Even in its simplest form . . . abstraction is separate in principle from concrete behavior." Margenau ('54) draws the same distinction between two dominating poles of cognitive experience which he calls the "immediate" and the "rational."

The second pair of contrasted characteristics of human perceptual and conceptual experience—*analytic experience* versus *synthetic experience*—is also recognizable objectively throughout the animal kingdom. In addition to the polarization of organism against environment just mentioned, there is an internal dynamic polarization of different sort in which the whole is set over against the parts, the totalizing synthetic activities at one pole and the local activities (partial patterns of behavior) at the other. This polarization is a key factor of our problem. Sensorimotor behavior is essentially analytic. This is true whether the stimulus-response reactions are excited from without or within the body, whether they are exteroceptive or interoceptive, to adopt Sherrington's terms. The self-contained activities concerned with the maintenance and integration of the body are essentially synthetic. They satisfy needs, not merely of the parts but of the whole.

In human experience we recognize a third pair of contrasted characteristics. Perceptual knowledge is organized within the frame of space and time. Things perceived are here and now or there and then, and these dimensions are oriented with reference to the perceiving body as a fixed point of reference. But our concepts, sentiments, and fantasies are set in a different frame of reference. These abstractions and their verbal and other symbols may be devoid of any spatial or temporal reference. These nonspatial and nontemporal qualities of human ideation cannot be identified in other animals than ourselves by direct observation because space and time are indispensable tools of sense perception. We may, however, be able to find some objective indicators of the precursors of conceptual processes that are identifiable in behavior. To this topic we shall return.

The growth of experience

It now appears that the search for primordia of human perceptual and conceptual experience in the behavior of lower animals is not a hopeless quest. It is particularly significant that we find a succession of progressively higher levels which seem to provide the seedbed of the human type of conceptual thinking.

These contrasted types of experience are primordial. All animals exhibit them. Here in behavior which, so far as we can tell, may be unconscious we find the germinal stage of that distinction between extraspection and introspection which we recognize consciously. In its most elementary form, as seen for instance in the ameba, the structure is labile but its performance exhibits stable patterns which evidently are determined by intrinsic organization. The stimulus-response type ensures adjustment with environment and the integrative type preserves the individuality of the person and provides for orderly co-operation of the parts of the body in the execution of appropriate vital activities.

As the evolutionary series is passed in review, beginning with this primordial stage, we see progressive complication of the action system. There is a corresponding specialization of bodily structure and further accentuation of the fundamental distinction between the analytic operations of the sensory and motor systems and the synthetic operations of the integrative apparatus without external reference. The details of this process cannot be reviewed here; but it should be kept in mind that consciousness is essentially integrative and that most conscious acts are recognizably related (directly or indirectly) to implicit or explicit behavioral expression of some kind.

This twofold quality of experience and of things experienced, as manifested in external relations in contrast with internal relations, is everywhere observable, from atoms to galaxies, from ameba to man. In the series of living things it is the key factor in determining the distinctive characteristics of every individual organism, and beyond this of every social group also. The character of organism and group is determined primarily by their internal organization, but survival and growth depend on the maintenance of successful external adjustments.

In the development of the individual body we see a sequence of events which is similar to that of the phylogenetic series. The researches of Coghill have contributed our most valuable information on this subject. The "total patterns" which he recognized in growing salamanders are the behavioral expression of what is here termed integrative experience, and his "partial patterns" are, for the most part, expressions of sensorimotor experience. He found convincing evidence of the primacy of the total pattern of action as an over-all integrating agency. The growth and differentiation of the bodily organs employed in these types of behavior were described in sufficient detail to permit correlation of the growth of behavior patterns with that of the related structures.

In the development of the human individual the phylogentic history is recapitulated in its broader features, much foreshortened and with notable deviations from the time schedule of the evolutionary sequence. The development of some organs is accelerated, of others retarded, but through the whole period of growth the body responds appropriately to its environment in the interest of nutritional and other needs, and it maintains its own integrity as an organism. During the forty weeks of prenatal life the patterns of growth and activity are determined mainly by intrinsic agencies, that is, by the inherited organization and the interplay of part with part. At birth the sensorimotor experience is abruptly amplified and its organs rapidly mature to full efficiency. Experience of integrative type at the physiological level holds its position of dominance in the control of all processes of growth and, as the higher suprasensory apparatus of the cerebral cortex slowly matures, the integrative functions assume greater importance and new patterns on the psychological plane. Out of the preconscious integrative processes and the primitive sensory-motor-affective type of mental process a new type of experience emerges. The child learns to talk, to count, to read, and to think in terms of these and other symbols of ideas. The life of reason is born.

The claim that experience is the foundation of all human knowledge must be interpreted with due caution. Conceptual knowledge is acquired by reasoning, and the process of reasoning involves not only analysis but also synthesis. It is creative; and an original idea, like every other product of biological integration, is not built up by simple summation of factual data. It is an emergent, a new product. This is why Einstein said that induction alone could not lead to the fundamental concepts of physics. The demand is for induction plus creative imagination. This gives us those norms of logic, mathematics, and philosophy which are indispensable tools of scientific investigation, and these theoretic norms may go beyond experience by extrapolation.

Summary

Since "all experience is an arch wherethrough/Gleams that untraveled world" and since all our knowledge of this world must come through this arch, we must have a critical understanding of this experience. The genetic approach may help us to win this understanding. We must start with human experience because this is the only kind we know at first hand. The conscious components of human experience cannot be identified with certainty in the lower ranks of animals, but a conscious experience is not an isolated event; it has antecedents, accompaniments, and consequences which are objectively manifest, and when these unconscious components of human experience are adequately known their antecedents can be recognized in all other classes of animals. This provides a practicable technique for a comparative psychology. The conclusion reached is that an experience is a personal adjustment of a living body to some change in the situation. It is not a passive reception. Experience is a total pattern rather than a partial pattern as Coghill defined these terms. An experience is not an isolated fact. It is a bodily process and as such has a wide range of relationships which can be investigated scientifically.

Our conscious experiences are of two sorts, distinguished as *perceptual* and *conceptual*. The former are projected outward. They give us our knowledge about the spatial and temporal relations of things in the objective world, and they are analytic in method and results. The knowledge so acquired is public and impersonal. Conceptual processes, on the other hand, may disregard the relations of things in external space and time as these are sensed perceptually. Conceptual experience is strictly internal and private, but it can be communicated by means of gesture, language, and other objective signs. It is essentially integrative. There are objective indicators of both classes of experience, and these can be studied comparatively in all animals.

CHAPTER FOURTEEN

Social Factors in Evolution

Social organization

Our attention up to this point has been directed primarily to the behaving individual and the surroundings to which he must adjust. The adjustment to living neighbors involves some physiological and psychological factors that we call social. We recognize two major classes of animal assemblies, the social group and the species. The latter is the result of evolutionary change in the course of which animals of common descent change their structure and habits in adaptation to different surroundings and ways of life. When this divergence goes so far that the separate populations are no longer able to interbreed they are classified as different species.

The species is not a social group, but the patterns of animal societies are so dependent upon the characteristics of the several species that the behaviorist is interested in the mechanism of both speciation and social organization. The human species is of special interest in this connection, for Homo sapiens has developed social patterns that are unique and distinctive characteristics of mankind as a species. "Culture," as this term is currently defined by the anthropologists, is patterned behavior at a higher level of organization than has been attained by any subhuman animals. The diverse cultures of human communities have arisen by virtue of capacities that only man possesses—language and normative codes of behavior expressed as distinctive folkways, legal enactments, moral standards, and so on.

The social groups, in general, are functional assemblies of two or more members of the same species for mutual advantage. They may be transient or very stable and enduring for many generations of the individual members. We are told by W. C. Allee, a competent authority, that no species of animal is known that does not possess some kind of interindividual relations within the species. The groups are of so many diverse kinds and the bonds which hold them together are in many instances so intangible and fugacious that definition of the social unit is difficult. In a biological survey of social relations we may take into consideration all these diverse sorts of relationships within the species and attempt to discover the factors of their operations and their evolutionary significance. Only a few samples of them can be mentioned here.

The social groups generally have no distinguishing structural features, although there are exceptions, such as, for instance, the differentiation of the sexes and of the castes of insects. In human societies some social groups have distinctive physical characteristics but the trend is toward different patterns of behavior and ways of thinking. Many groups wear distinctive dress or insignia. Others are distinguished by cut of hair or beard. Army and navy training tends to develop a characteristic carriage and physique and the members of some trade guilds and vocations can be recognized by bodily signs. Social aggregates are distinguished, as a general rule, by their patterns of behavior, and in higher animals psychological factors of several distinctive kinds play the dominant role.

The social group as a biological unit plays a major role in determining the behavior of all higher animals which live in communities, large or small, transient or stable. Each individual of the group is influenced by the other members of his group, both those of his own kind and those who are aliens. The alien members of the group may be commensal or parasitic, or they may be forcibly subjugated slaves. The group as a whole has contacts with other groups of the same or different species, and individuals of any group may encounter groups of the same or different kind as enemies, prey, collaborators, or casual companions. Illustrations of these social adjustments are found widely distributed in all ranks of animals in endless variety.

The relation between parent and offspring is the primitive source of social organizations of various kinds. Even in one-celled organisms which reproduce by fission there is a transient relation of daughter cells to parent. In conjugation a different kind of temporary relationship exists, and this marks the beginning of those elaborate systems of familial social organization which are highly developed in some of the insects and in mankind.

Totalitarian and individualistic social patterns

In the now generally accepted classification of animal kinds, most of the species except the lowest are arranged in two series which represent divergent lines of evolution. The fossil history, supported by much other evidence, shows that these two main branches of the phylogenetic tree separated from the parent stem in an early evolutionary stage at about the level of organization of the surviving jellyfishes. One of these lines of evolutionary change leads through the worms to the insects, the other through a series of transitional forms to the vertebrates. Both lines are biologically successful and efficient, though their efficiency is expressed in radically different ways. Attention is again called to the fact that the rank of a species is not measured by the numbers that manage to survive and propagate, though this is one of the factors that must be taken into account in a biological evaluation of successful living. Judged by this criterion the insects are more successful than the vertebrates, for there are many more of them.

The contrasts between these two great divisions of the animal kingdom are more conspicuous at the higher levels where they are accentuated, and the differences in social organization are so great and so instructive that we shall examine them critically. Our attention, accordingly, is next directed to the behavior of the animals which have reached the highest level of efficiency in these divergent lines of evolution, namely, the social insects and civilized men. The social organization in the higher ranks of the first line may be characterized as predominantly *totalitarian,* that of the second as more *individualistic.*

This distinction is drawn graphically and convincingly in two interesting books by Haskins ('39, '51) to which the reader is referred for amplification and documentation of my argument in this and the next following chapter. Haskins divides all animal societies into three broad classes—the family, the integrative, and the associative. The family type, as he defines it, is primitively relatively temporary and simply organized, but in its most highly developed form it gives rise to the integrated type, represented at its climax by the stable and complicated colonies of the social insects. The associative type is a loose and evanescent flock or herd, the members of which are frequently not closely related genetically and this sort of animal association is the seedbed from which modern democratic governments have been developed.

Among the mammals the familial and associative social patterns are characterized by considerable freedom of the persons, that is, they are predominantly individualistic; the closely integrated society of insects is much more rigid in a pattern that we here call totalitarian for reasons to be stated shortly. In highly developed societies all these types may be represented, but usually one or another of them is dominant. Let us adopt this classification and see how it works out in the two great branches of the animal kingdom to which reference was made above.

Examining first the insects, we find very many species, each of which is nicely adapted to some particular niche of the environment. Many of them have elaborate social organizations within which several castes are specialized—workers, drones, queens, etc. In all these social groups the welfare and autonomy of the individuals are subordinated to the supremacy of the colony as a whole. The group is the cardinal unit; the individuals serve the group as automatons, motivated, for the most part, by blind impulsions; their behavior is stereotyped in patterns which are biologically determined and in general the same for all members of the species, colony, or caste. This totalitarian type of social organization reaches its highest stage of development in the beehive and the ant colony.

This sort of specialization has succeeded to the extent that the world is populated with more insects than any other class of multicellular animals. There are more than 3,500 species of ants, for instance, and the leading authority on the life of ants, W. M. Wheeler, estimated that there are now more ants in the world than there are individuals of all other terrestrial animals in the aggregate. The several kinds of ants are adapted to almost every possible environmental situation. Each kind has several castes with refined division of labor, and the castes are differently specialized in each species. Each species and each caste shows amazing perfection of adaptation of both structure and behavior for the performance of specific and very exacting duties which are rigidly defined and from which any deviation is usually fatal. The characteristics of the species and castes are established by a considerable variety of biological methods, including stable genetic, nutritional, and other factors, in the interest of the colony as a whole. The individual ant has a very limited range of abilities. Although there is some freedom of choice about how it performs its particular duties and some ability to learn by personal experience, these deviations are narrowly restricted and most activities are standardized. Every member of the colony must conform most of its behavior to a predetermined pattern of stereotyped reflex and instinctive action—or perish. Countless numbers do perish, but their places are immediately taken by others, for any wastage of antpower is compensated by great fecundity.

This type of social organization reaches its highest development in the army ants of the tropical rain forests, of which more than two hundred species have been described. Some of these species have been under close observation for twenty years by T. C. Schneirla, so their social structure and biomechanics are now well understood. They live in enormous colonies with closely knit organization, which may comprise 100,000 individuals or more. The compact social structure is well exhibited by the amazing physical structure of their nests. The nest, as described by Schneirla and Piel ('48), "is a seething cylindrical cluster of themselves, ant hooked to ant, with queen and brood sequestered in a labyrinth of corridors and chambers within the ant mass" (cf. Beebe, '21).

Such a colony is a perfect example of a communistic *totalitarian* social structure. It has high survival value, but this is achieved at the cost of other values that in human society are more highly prized. We all want to stay alive, and we want much else besides; we want to enjoy advantages won by personal competence and freedom from regimentation that are necessarily sacrificed in a totalitarian community. Those sentimentalists who have held before us such an ant colony as the utopian model of perfection of democratic society have little understanding of either ants or men. If they would turn away from their idealistic fictions and look at the ants themselves, they would see a community of blind and deaf automatons motivated by instinctive drives over which any individual member of the community has very little control. The colony survives, but the values won by the individual ants are far from utopian by human standards. T. H. Huxley in 1894 commented upon this fundamental difference between insect and human societies, and many other authorities before and since that time have noted it.

The integration of the ant colony is assured by the nature of its intrinsic organization, that is, by the interplay of the constituent castes in an equilibrated system, with no dominant overlord in control. It is an efficient way to assure survival of the colonies and the species and their adaptation to a wide range of conditions, but this efficiency is at a low level as measured by human standards. So the systematists rank insects as a class lower than mammals despite the former's larger numbers and more extreme specialization. In the course of evolution the insects appeared many millions of years before the earliest mammals, their specialization was in a direction different from that of mammals, and from the Carboniferous period until now they have spread horizontally on the original low plane of biological differentiation. The mammals have lived on earth for a much shorter time, and they have progressed at a constantly accelerated rate up to man, who has succeeded in bringing a large part of the rest of creation under his control, although it must be admitted his warfare against the insect world has been marked by many failures.

In the animal world there is another type of totalitarian social organization which is seen in those communities that are dominated by the strongest or more resourceful member who then becomes the leader and master of the group. We see this in the pecking rank of barnyard fowls, in the harems of the fur seal rookeries, and in unlimited monarchial and fascist human governments. In this type of social structure aggressive ability of an individual or an oligarchy succeeds by force in getting control of a population composed not of robots but of members equipped with a larger measure of modifiability, initiative, and intelligence than any insects possess. The integrative agency here resides in a head or central power. This too is efficient if the leadership is powerful, aggressive, and competent.

In animal communities Allee finds that where leadership arises spontaneously within the group because by common consent some individual shows greater capacity for it the organization is more flexible than it is where the group is held together by force, whether that of dominance and subordination or of defense of territorial rights. The same is true in human societies, and flexibility of organization and administration is indispensable in the present confusion of human affairs. The rigid totalitarian type of social structure is efficient and stable at the insect's level of intelligence, but in human cultures it is intrinsically unstable, for it inevitably disintegrates by internal corrosion or rebellion.

In contrast to the totalitarian social structure of insects and seals, social organization in the vertebrate phylum as a whole, and especially in its higher members, is more *individualistic*. Each organism has a larger measure and a wider range of capacity for independently motivated conduct and improvement of performance by experience and practice. The contrast between human and insect societies is relative, not absolute, but it is nonetheless evident and significant. In the lower ranks of vertebrates (fishes, amphibians, reptiles) the individualistic traits are only incipient, but such as they are they are not suppressed or masked by any elaborated totalitarian organization. Birds are more richly endowed with individual capacities, which are, however, limited and subordinated, not to a totalitarian social organization like that of insects, but to inherited patterns of stereotyped instinctive behavior in diverse forms, each of which is characteristic of the species as a whole.

The mammalian line was characterized from its inception by enlargement and specialization of the cerebral cortex, with corresponding increase in learning ability and general intelligence. This development went on with extraordinary rapidity, as evolutionary time is measured, and at the transition from ape to man the change was even more accelerated. This speeding up of the evolutionary process and rapid transition from a physiological level of integration to the psychological level is unique, and the acceleration is still in process. The transition from brute to man began with the acquisition of the erect posture. Long after the first man appeared (probably more than a half-million years ago) he learned to speak, to invent tools, and to acquire skill in their use (Allee *et al.*, '49; Greenman, '48; Haskins, '39, '51; Howells, '54; La Barre, '54; Pannekoek, '53; Yakovlev, '48). The development of the unique human pattern of social organization began early, developed slowly, and has been accelerated at an increasing rate during the few thousand years of recorded human history.

This more plastic individually modifiable behavior culminates in a social pattern which in human culture we call democracy. Here as in insects the social groups are so highly organized that the welfare and often even the survival of the persons depend on the stability and efficiency of the group. But these groups, unlike those of insects and totalitarian tyrannies, are voluntary associations in which the persons freely give up some advantages in the interest of general welfare and are so organized that the individuals retain the largest possible measure of personal freedom and social responsibility. Provision is thus made for the survival of the group *and* all persons concerned and for progressive enlargement and diversification of the scope of all activities, with more varied needs and satisfactions. These changes involve also increase in the self-sufficiency of the person and ability to adapt to a wider range of external conditions, with more efficient control of these conditions. The social unit is organized for the benefit of its members and it is their servant, not their master.

The totalitarian and the individualistic types of adaptation are not mutually exclusive, for all animals, from the lowest to the highest, show some capacity for self-improvement and at least a rudimentary kind of learning ability. And, again, in all ranks of life there is some measure of group adaptation, group integration, and group control. The significant thing in this context is that in the most specialized members of the several phyla of animals one or the other of the two directive trends is generally predominant, so that we recognize these rather sharply contrasted types of progressive differentiation of both individual and social organization.

Innate and acquired factors

The significance of the two types of social organization just mentioned for problems of practical adjustment in human affairs cannot be fully understood without clear recognition of the distinction between homology and analogy to which reference is made in Chapter 9. Factors of behavior which are hereditary and therefore common to all members of a species or group are products of biological mechanisms that are radically different from the mechanisms of those factors which are individually learned. The former are predetermined in the genes and are transmitted with only minor variation from generation to generation. The latter are individually acquired and what they are depends very largely upon surrounding conditions, that is, upon the opportunities available for development of the genetic potentialities.

The first type is represented in the individual animal by inherited reflexes and instincts. The social organizations of most animals, and conspicuously of insects and birds, are of this sort, with predominance of inherited ways of behaving that are common to all members of the species or race. In cases where the evolution of any particular personal or social pattern of behavior can be followed from its simple origin in lower species to its elaboration at higher levels of organization, the complicated final pattern is said to be homologous with the simpler patterns of its predecessors.

The social patterns of insects, birds, and mammals have few such genetic relationships with one another. Each pattern has evolved independently and is, therefore, not homologous but analogous. Notwithstanding this, the course of the evolutionary development has been governed in accordance with some biological principles that are manifest in all of them, although the common principles are often masked and hard to recognize. The analogies when adequately analyzed and interpreted are very instructive, but if they are uncritically regarded as homologies only confusion and mischievous misapplication results.

Individually learned patterns of behavior do not directly affect the genes and hence cannot be passed on to succeeding generations by protoplasmic heredity. In human society this learned behavior plays a larger role than in any other animal society, and progressively so as cultural processes advance. Yet even here the inherited patterns of behavior are everywhere strong and often dominant. In addition some acquired social patterns are transmitted from generation to generation by methods which are highly elaborated in all human communities, and some of these learned patterns of personal and social behavior may be so firmly stabilized in habit as to be with difficulty distinguished from inherited instincts. Here we find established codes of behavior transmitted by "social heredity," that is, by example, oral tradition, taboo, family and tribal organization, educational institutions, written documents, legal enactments, and so forth. None of these personally acquired patterns of behavior and cultural accomplishment are heritable. They must be learned by each individual of each succeeding generation, starting from no knowledge of them whatever.

Nevertheless, in an advanced human culture, social heredity plays the dominant role and the efficiency of the social unit depends on the diverse competencies of the individuals composing it. This competence can be assured only by good home training, supplemented by a well-conceived and well-administered system of public education and by all the other appurtenances of good living. The traditions and physical property of every social group are distinctive for that group, and some of these are very stable. This stability gives to many patterns of culture a perdurability that may last for centuries with little change. So it comes about that the patterns transmitted by social heredity may be so firmly implanted in the cultural structure that they are dominant over the strongest instincts, even the instinct of self-preservation. A patriot may choose death rather than dishonor.

In this survey our primary concern is with the homologous patterns of social structure, because we are searching for the evolutionary factors and the laws of their development. From some other standpoints of sociobiology the analogies are of equal interest and importance, as clearly shown in some of the recent works cited in this text.

Human social structure

The importance of the difference between the patterns of human social organization and those of all other animals is enormous. Because men can communicate with one another by speech and other symbols of ideas as well as by example, a learned skill may be immediately shared with all members of the group. This binds the members of the group together more firmly and at the same time tends to diversify the groups and to separate them into rival clans. A far more important advantage of man's command of language and greater learning capacity lies in his ability to transmit all skills and accumulated knowledge and the products made by the group to his offspring by tradition, written records, and other vehicles of communication. In this way each community develops its own specific highly organized superindividual culture with a relatively stable pattern which is handed down from generation to generation. The capacity to develop such cultural units grows out of man's uniquely superior learning capacity.

In current usage the terms "totalitarian" and "individualistic" have become political clichés, but in the preceding discussion they are defined biologically and illustrated by examples in various subhuman cultures. In human societies the two patterns are inextricably blended, but the difference between them is radical and operationally very important. This distinction is not definable in terms of any political or other administrative machinery, but rather by the way the available organizations are actually used to get the desired results. It is the end sought, not the means employed, that is significant.

An absolute monarchy or a monopolistic corporation may administer its affairs so as to promote the welfare and advancement of all the people concerned. This is not democracy as politically defined, though it is individualistic rather than totalitarian in practice. In a true democracy there must be some administrative control, but this control is subject to the will of the people, not to that of an autocrat.

The human patterns of flexible social structure did not arise as sudden mutations. Their precursors and germinal stages have been clearly described by students of comparative psychology. The closest relatives of man among the primates live in loosely organized communities, individualistic rather than totalitarian, and they are characterized by a capacity for mutual aid in co-operative enterprises and in some species for friendliness rather than aggressive rivalry. The organization of the groups is flexible, with ample scope for personal initiative and enterprise. Yerkes ('43, p. 123) writes: "Once more I would stress the observed fact that what we recognize as social status in chimpanzee life is rather a matter of brains than of brawn, for temperament and intelligence, apart from sex discrepancies, may overbalance size and physical strength." Leadership and dominance gradients are maintained in some of the groups more by exercise of skill, resourcefulness, and social amenities than by tyrannical power. The species differ in their patterns of social organization and social control, but the agencies of social integration in all the higher primates are strikingly different from those of the higher insects. In these primates we have a clear exhibition of an early and imperfect manifestation of those personal and social characteristics which form the cohesive agencies of human society—group pressure, intelligently guided co-operation of free persons, and some of the voluntary subordination of personal interests to general welfare which is altruism. Antecedent to this consciously motivated altruism there is a biologically motivated "primitive altruism" which is the behavioral expression of a social appetence manifest in some degree in animals of all kinds.

Some degree of internal rivalry and conflict of patterns of growth and differentiation is inherent in the vital processes everywhere. If the local activities are for any reason released from central integrative control, there may be excessive overgrowth, as in some pathological monstrosities and in cancer. A large proportion of human mental and social disorders arise from conflicts between innate instinctive traits—heritages from our brutish ancestry such as impulses of self-preservation and sexual gratification—and those social conventions and taboos that derive from our social relations and responsibilities. Successful resolution of these conflicts is essential for sanity and contentment. In our local and international relations with other people similar conflicts arise as group rivalries which split a social unit into antagonistic factions and as uninhibited nationalism (which is a malignant cancerous disease) with its inevitable cultural, economic, and belligerent contentions.

Internal conflicts and competitive social enterprises cannot be avoided. They are inherent in the nature of the vital process. In ordinary human relations social tensions are not abnormal—they are, in fact, the efficient agencies of social progress. "Without some tension, social energy cannot be put to the service of man" (Quincy Wright, '48). The practical problem here is to direct the social energies into constructive rather than destructive channels. "Tension, like the voltage in an electrodynamic system, would permit energy to flow in useful channels without dangerous resistances which might destroy the structure." Successful treatment of all social disorders requires stronger integrative machinery than we now possess, and experience has shown that the only workable mechanism that will ensure social stability is an enlightened public sentiment that demands it in a form that is essentially democratic. It cannot be implemented by forcible regimentation.

This emphasis upon the importance in social evolution of innate and acquired individual differences and capacities seems to be in sharp contrast with the basic postulates, methods, and objectives of the late Trigant Burrow ('53) and his colleagues at the Lifwynn Laboratory. This program of research in phylobiology is directed explicitly toward a search for those components of behavior which are common to man as a species and for objective criteria which distinguish the natural biological norms of racial experience and conduct from those secondary accretions and distortions that result from social conditioning by "affect" or prejudice and from arbitrary and often irrational codes of social convention, legal enactment, and moral standards.

The experiments are designed to bring out the contrast between what is biologically normal, or adaptive, and what is artificially and often mistakenly regarded as the "normal" or "right" behavior under the social conditions prevailing at the time and place. The socially imposed secondary norms are inconstant and as various as are the cultural patterns that fashion them. The individual thus acquires a false scale of values based on a system of beliefs and conventions imposed by tradition and other forms of social pressure—a factitious system quite out of harmony with the actual situations to which he must adjust. Merely superficial mores and moralities have replaced the natural biological balance which is our hereditary endowment. This dissociation results in personal distress and, too often, in mental disease. A much more serious result is widespread social disorder which Burrow diagnoses as racial psychoneurosis.

The pathology of this biosocial disease does not differ in principle from that of a psychoneurotic sheep or man. "In human societies no less than in the single experimental animal the essential conflict is somatic or physiological." In both cases the treatment must necessarily be applied individually to particular persons. "Undoubtedly, individuals and social communities are in need of a basic alteration in behavior-adaptation, but they will find this needed alteration only through specific physiological adjustments internal to themselves."

It follows that Burrow's emphasis upon the racial or phylic nature of man's social disorder is not really inconsistent with the emphasis which I place in this book upon the individual members of the race. These are two aspects of the same medical problem, a problem which Burrow approaches by way of phylic or racial constants and which I approach by way of the development of biologically normal (adaptive) behavior as this is manifested in both innate (phylic) and acquired (learned) patterns.

We agree that the most promising approach to the acute problems of successful social evolution and the cure of both personal and social maladjustments is, first to learn what the native capacities of individual persons are and the biological norms of adaptive behavior for each of these patterns, and then so to train the persons that their thinking and the resulting behavior will be biologically normal rather than perverted by pernicious ideologies that lead inevitably to inappropriate conduct and often to personal and social disease (cf. the comments of Muller, '43, p. 126).

It is instructive to compare Burrow's analysis of the "ditensional" conflicts between man's biological or phyletically determined nature and the unnatural and pernicious figments of his cultural codes with Whyte's account ('48, '48a) of the history of the actual development of a destructive ideological dualism in Europe. During a period of more than three thousand years there was a tendency to split the world of human experience into two independent and irreconcilable domains of matter and spirit, with conflict of ideologies and the ensuing conduct. As a result of this personality dissociation, leadership passed into the hands of distorted men and general approval of the distortion became a compulsive neurosis. The turmoil so engendered continues to our day. But during the last three centuries the wounds caused by this split have begun to heal, and now it is possible to see clearly how to reintegrate our personalities and our social structures in accordance with the unitary principles of our common biological heritage.

From time immemorial false ideologies have motivated individuals and great masses of people to conduct that is pathological. These codes are false because they are fantasies in conflict with the natural laws of successful adjustment in human social organizations, and the conduct is pathological for the same reason, with injurious results. The logical mechanisms of these perversions of the life of reason are analyzed by Rapoport ('50, '53).

Democracy

The events of human history, among which are included creation and change of social structures, have been motivated by various blends of two basically different types of behavior—first, the innate instinctive and intuitive drives, and, second, ideologies of a distinctively human sort acquired individually and propagated socially. In some movements the second type predominates. In others, like Hitler's campaigns of conquest, we see a recrudescence of innate bestiality at its lowest level. In all of them these two components of behavior are inextricably intertwined.

Some social structures are rigidly totalitarian and powerful; some are radically individualistic and weak; between these extremes there are various blends of centralized administration and decentralized local autonomy. The experience of millenniums of human history gives evidence that neither completely totalitarian control nor unrestrained individualism can yield a stable and satisfying social organization. A workable balance must be struck between central control and individual freedom, and for this no general formula can be written. The problem must be solved by each cultural unit in its own way in accordance with its own previous history, mores, and natural resources.

That the solution of the problem has been to some extent satisfactory in various patterns of tribal organization from the dawn of human cultural evolution is evident, for otherwise no tribe could survive. The records of cultural anthropology furnish illustrations of these experiments in endless variety. The procedures of social control may be imposed in detail and enforced by the ruling power, as in the ancient empires and in Russia today, or they may be equally inflexible but enforced only by custom and taboo. Two instructive examples of the latter type of social organization among contemporary people may be mentioned.

This pattern of tribal organization is present in typical form among the naked blackfellows of central Australia. These nomads have a stone-age culture which is probably as primitive and as little affected by outside influence as any that now survives. The social code is elaborate and rigidly enforced by tradition and taboo, with no formal tribal organization whatever, and yet this aboriginal law is so ingeniously administered that no hunter, even the most successful, can derive personal advantage from his skill. Only one of the elders, and usually a different one each day, is allowed to cook the catch or apportion it to the others. The food brought in by the hunter is not his; it belongs to the tribe, and his only reward is the joy of the chase and the approbation of his fellows (Mountford, '51, p. 122).

A less extreme example is illustrated in Margaret Mead's *Coming of Age in Samoa* ('28), which describes a social organization that is essentially communal and in which most of the activities of the individuals are regulated by a social convention subordinating every personal interest to the concern of the village as a whole. The well-ordered community life is thus totalitarian in effect, though the regimentation is by common consent, with a minimum of legal or other enforcement. The result is a peaceful and conservative social structure in which individual initiative is discouraged and improvement is not desired.

In some of the larger and more progressive cultural organizations, with further specialization of functional groups, where dominance by a dictator or oligarchy is rejected, the Samoan pattern is radically modified. The difference lies in putting the emphasis on individual rights and opportunities rather than on traditional convention and taboo. If this individualism is regulated by an efficiently organized and wisely administered provision of law and police which the people themselves control, such a system preserves the largest possible measure of individual freedom of action, stimulates effort for improvement of the persons and their groups, and assures stability of the social structure. This is the only kind of social organization that merits the name *democracy*.

We have conspicuous examples of socialistic pseudodemocracies that are in effect tyrannically totalitarian. A socialistic bureaucracy may in actual operation be as tyrannical as an all-powerful dictator. We also have evidence that the necessary central control can be administered democratically regardless of the formal pattern of the government—whether a monarchy, a republic, or a loose confederation of autonomous states—as has long been true in Switzerland and several north European monarchies. For successful democracy what is needed is not more centralized control but the least possible governmental interference with local affairs that is compatible with efficient administration in the public interest. This central control requires some sacrifice of "rugged individualism" and an efficient suppression of local gangsterism and also regulation of monopolistic enterprises, whether these are departments of government, incorporated businesses, or labor unions.

The democratic way of life does not mean equality of the fit and unfit, the industrious and the lazy. The world owes no one a living, but society owes to everyone the opportunity to make a living and as good a living as possible with due regard to the obligations involved in accepting the opportunities. These obligations include provision for the incompetents, the children, the aged, the sick, and the defectives in body or mind.

Until relatively recent times most of the great empires of the world have been absolute monarchies or dictatorships, but none of these have long endured. They have been either enfeebled by the internal corrosion of corrupt administration or else, if not transformed by democratic process, they have been destroyed by rebellion or conquest.

To avoid the disasters that inevitably follow ruthless exploitation of the masses by intrenched industrial, political, or military tyranny, many public-spirited idealists have attempted to organize communities on an equalitarian basis. These utopian projects have always failed and they probably always will, because the fundamental conception of the uniformity and equality of all members of the community is biologically unsound. Such futile enterprises usually disintegrate from internal friction and die of autointoxication, or else they are captured by a dictator or an oligarchy and so are transformed into totalitarian organizations, as has happened in Russia.

The individualism of democracy must not be equated with decentralization. An efficient social unit (of government or any other kind) must have a head or dominant center, with power to control those movements that affect the general welfare. The central power of a democracy differs from that of a tyranny in that it is power granted by free act of the people governed and accepted by them. It is power that is limited by legal enactment and that can be revoked by the people themselves. Democracy is not a political pattern. It is a pattern of togetherness controlled by personal attitudes of people toward one another, and it may take a different political form in every cultural unit.

In democratic theory the government is the servant of the people. The details of the political machinery by which this policy is administered must be adjusted to the mores of the people and local conditions. What is good democratic administration in North America may be inappropriate in India and quite impracticable in central Africa. The avowed intention of the teachers we send to the Eskimos is to educate them so they will think and act "like us." This is exactly the wrong way to go about it, and, in actual result, the policy turns them into pauperized mendicants. The best contribution to the welfare of these sturdy people that we can make is to train them to be more skillful and proficient Eskimos.

The democratic ideal has never been fully realized. The peoples of the earth have tragically failed to find a satisfactory answer to the basic problem of how to live together harmoniously and productively. At the present moment progress is obstructed by a recrudescence of nationalistic ideologies and lust for personal and group supremacy by methods that are essentially bestial rather than human. The most powerful of these methods are not reversions to bestiality, for they use refinements of cruelty of which no beast is capable. Successful democracy in a highly organized community requires a judicious blending of socialistic central administration and regulation of some of the major public utilities (military, police, sanitation, communication, etc.), with the largest possible encouragement of individual and corporate independence, initiative and freedom from restraint.

The patterns of human social organization—the best of them as well as the worst of them—are deeply rooted in the biological origins of human nature. The primordial "primitive altruism" has no ethical implications whatever. Our most urgent task now is to preserve this biological heritage and to refine and strengthen it with moral sanctions. For this is the most effective way to resist the dis-integrating enmities that threaten to destroy all that we have won through millenniums of struggle for better social cohesion and se-curity now that all social groups, from families to nations, are forced to recognize their world-wide interrelationships and interdepend-encies.

The moral standards of fitness to which reference is made above comprise the cement that holds a free society together. Enlightened self-interest may be a sufficiently strong bond to unify a group, but such a group cannot be called truly democratic unless that enlighten-ment recognizes that integrity, honor, and mutual trustworthiness are in the long run more profitable than lust for power, greed, and deceit. Wherever the cohesive moral strength of a community is weakened, this is an opening for attack by propaganda and other skillfully directed disintegrative processes that prepare the people for acceptance of totalitarian ideology. This has happened and it is going on today. Some forcible defense measures are necessary, but force can be only a temporary palliative. The only way for the democracies to get lasting security is to practice what they profess and so develop immunity to subversive internal parasites and strength to resist external aggression.

The fundamental issues here are not those of power politics. They are essentially moral. The moral issues evidently have biological sig-nificance as such and so they can be evaluated and implemented scientifically. Under existing conditions moral values are survival values and we ignore them at our peril.

Summary

In the evolutionary series we recognize two principal branches which lead up to the insects and to mankind, and these phyla differ in their social behavior in ways that are here characterized respec-tively as totalitarian and individualistic. These types of social organi-zation culminate in the ant colony and in human democracy. Both are biologically successful, the former in number of individuals and of species that survive in the struggle for existence, the latter in the wealth of experience and the satisfactions derived from it in the individuals themselves.

These types of social organization are not mutually exclusive, and both are represented in all human cultures. This results in rivalry and conflict between the persons and between the groups to which they belong. The strength and efficiency of totalitarian social structures derive from their use of primitive animalistic impulses of aggrandizement of one's own group at the expense of other groups and the inevitable subordination of the welfare of the individuals to that of the group. This structure is rigid and inherently unstable at the present stage of human cultural development. The individualistic (democratic) social structures are more satisfying and enduring because the patterns of organization and the administrative methods are determined by the voluntary choice of the people concerned. This gives a more flexible organization, greater opportunity for each person to reach the highest level of competence, productiveness, and contentment of which he is capable, and so it has unlimited potentialities for further cultural progress.

CHAPTER FIFTEEN

The Social Sciences

Sociobiology

The principles laid down in the preceding chapter are basic for understanding human social organization. The evolutionary history is instructive, but it took a long time for the social scientists to profit by it. The earlier attempts so uncritically transferred analogies from brute to man that they are now generally ignored.

That era is ended. Recent work, some of which is cited in the preceding chapter, is developing a comparative sociology comparable with the older sciences of comparative anatomy, physiology, and psychology. Because in current literature of the sciences of man "comparative sociology" is generally given a more restricted meaning, namely, the comparison of human societies which are culturally different, we may avoid confusion by adopting the term "sociobiology" for the field here under consideration, the primary concern of which is the search for the biological origins and nature of human patterns of social organization.

The conclusions which I express in this and the preceding chapters are based largely on the works (some of which are cited in the appended bibliography) of the following authors and their colleagues: Allee, Bagehot, Burrow, Cantril, Carmichael, Carpenter, Dewey, Emerson, Frank, Gerard, Gesell, Haring, Hartung, Haskins, Holmes, Howells, the Huxleys, Jennings, Keith, Köhler, Kroeber, La Barre, Sargent, Schneirla, Tinbergen, Warden, Wheeler, Yerkes, and Zuckerman. The symposium edited by Scott ('50) is a useful introduction to the methodology of sociobiology, with special reference to studies of behavior under natural conditions. Attention is directed also to Kurt Lewin's *Field Theory in Social Science* ('51). Rashevsky's *Mathematical Biology of Social Behavior* ('51) points the way to quantitative treatment of some factors of social analysis.

A half-century ago my brother (C. L. Herrick, '04) published a short article in which he wrote: "When we speak of the social self we mean the social reflected in the individual or else we mean an abstraction of common elements in the individual selves constituting the society, which common factors we may thereafter use, like an algebraic expression, as though it had an independent existence." The term "social consciousness" can legitimately be used only for the former concept. To this he added: "It is customary to say that the social self is ejective, i.e., that we project our feelings and experience into others and act in view of them. Another and in some respects a truer way of expressing it is that the self is constantly enlarging to embrace new elements." The biological origins of this empathy and the part it plays in the evolution of morality in mankind were sketched.

In the two books by Haskins previously cited it is clearly shown that, although neither natural selection nor any other known biological principles can fully explain human history, yet natural selection is still operative throughout the course of human evolution. Here it takes unique forms, for the criteria of survival and progress in efficiency are plasticity of behavior, educability, and individual freedom joined with social responsibility.

Sociobiology and particularly social ecology are now under active investigation in a variety of experimental and statistical studies with excellent results. A comprehensive and critical survey of the field has been published by Allee *et al.* ('49). The short survey by Haring ('50) and Alfred E. Emerson's recent papers also are noteworthy. It is significant that the reorganization of the Rockefeller Foundation in 1951 was guided by the conviction that current and future activities should be planned on the broad basis of human ecology. The sociological relations of science in general and of the sciences of man in particular are critically examined by Barber ('52), and a good picture of the present status of the social sciences, their current defects and achievements, is drawn by Muller ('43).

The economist Boulding claims ('49) that the concept of an ecological system is an interpretative principle of the utmost value in the social sciences. This is not merely wishful thinking; such a system has been tried and it works wonders. A carefully planned and skillfully executed study of the Hopi Indians from the ecological standpoint, as outlined by Laura Thompson ('50), has brought to light hitherto neglected principles of social organization that have great practical significance for the solution of world-wide problems of political, economic, social, religious, and psychological import. Another valuable practical demonstration has been given by Darling's ('51) West Highland Survey in Scotland.

During the course of human evolution the two patterns of social organization which we have contrasted have been elaborated in a great variety of forms, so that the five thousand years of which we have historical record provide ample evidence of their relative worth. The available data show with unmistakable clarity that the totalitarian pattern is very efficient on the brutish level of conquest and exploitation, but that it is unprofitable, in the long run, even for the dominant group. At the present level of human cultural development totalitarianism does not work. The rights, privileges, and obligations of the individuals are paramount, and all social organizations must be so structured as to recognize and enhance the dignity and efficiency of individuals and to secure the voluntary co-operation and self-sacrifice which are the only efficient integrating agencies in an individualistic society.

It is no longer possible to question the truth of this generalization. Our problem is to get people to understand this plain teaching of history and to plan their lives accordingly. In ordinary affairs, as in science, the way to find out whether some project is practicable and useful is to try it. It is more difficult to devise and carry out large-scale experiments of long duration on human populations than on rats and monkeys, but we have before us the record of both millions of years of nature's own experiments and thousands of years of human trial and error in groping for workable social and political programs. Throughout the range from primitive tribal organizations to the most powerful nations of today it is clear that an organization that is in practice democratic, whatever political form it may take, assures greater stability and a larger measure of satisfaction of human needs, cravings, and aspirations than any totalitarian form of government can provide.

Democratic organization is incompatible with both totalitarian regimentation and unrestrained individualism. What we want is order, not anarchy, an order voluntarily assumed without compulsion. This cannot be achieved by the blind operation of those biological agencies that work successfully at the lower level of anthill and wolf pack economy. The law of survival of the fit is not abrogated, but its formulation must be recast in conformity with different patterns of behavior and different criteria of survival value and fitness. The dinosaurs were not fit to survive in competition with mammals, and today no nation is fit to survive that cannot adjust its internal and external affairs to a code of decency, honor, and social comity regardless of the form of government in vogue.

Personal factors

As human society is now organized the law of the jungle is outmoded and the sooner we find this out the better it will be for us. We have entered a richer field which England's distinguished jurist Lord Moulton ('24) called "the domain of manners." Here the law of the jungle is supplanted by a higher law which recognizes the largest measure of individual freedom which is compatible with personal and national responsibility for the general welfare. In so far as we succeed in adjusting our affairs to the laws of this domain of manners no police power is needed, because conformity to the code of good manners is the natural expression of that humanitarianism which is our birthright as men and which separates us from the brutes. The eminent English legal expert defined true democracy as "the domain of obedience to the unenforceable, which covers all cases of right doing where there is no one to make you do it but yourself."

This can only mean that national survival, and hence in the end personal survival also, is up to us as individuals. We cannot pass the buck to the state or to any abstractions postulated as inviolable laws of nature. The laws of human nature are not inexorably imposed upon us in the social domain. In the "domain of manners" our manners are what we choose to make them. This choice is the crux of the problem. What kind of people do we want to be? This is not an easy choice to make.

Here we need guidance. The mass of the people cannot be expected to see the big issues in proper perspective. We are all too deeply concerned with the insistent problems of earning a living and adjusting conduct to the petty problems of daily life. How to get concerted action is the big problem in an individualistic society. No mass movement in peace or war can go far or last long unless in some way the objective sought is sold to the people as individuals.

Every politician knows this. Mass education of any kind for any purpose must be based on the education of the separate individuals; and mass psychology is personally motivated. The mass, it is true, is a unit of different kind from that of the person and does things that the individual cannot or would not do, yet the integrating mechanism of the mass after all resides in the separate people who compose it and each person is different from all others. The cohesion of the mass lasts only as long as some common motive can be drawn out of this heterogenous assembly and directed toward a goal which is considered desirable by each of them.

Though the primate ancestors of mankind were individualists with potentialities of social evolution which were superior to those of other animals, their human descendants made slow progress in the actual realization of these potentialities. For thousands of years tribal and national independence and power have been won by brutish methods of war, conquest, and plunder. For these methods totalitarian social organization is efficient. Such cultural progress as has been made within each of these competing factions has been due to the inventiveness and enterprise of superior individuals (the "creative minorities" of Toynbee) who have succeeded in organizing their fellows into co-operative groups held together either by force or by mutual agreement. Since it is only the latter method that yields a stable and satisfying social structure, the crucial problem of the social sciences is to discover the essential properties of true democracy and to explain to the people how they must conduct themselves in order to get it.

Our present society is very sick and the social scientists have found few remedies because they have not looked for them in the right place. A correct diagnosis and a good prescription have been written by Lawrence K. Frank ('48), who points out that culture is man's own creation, and that our traditional culture is disintegrating. The resulting tensions must be resolved, and the way out is to make the true social values emotionally acceptable to the people. People work for what they want, and they must want what is good for them before they will do anything about attaining the good. This calls for an educational program which should be guided by enlightened social science. In a later work ('51) Frank strikes a hopeful note, for sociology is now developing an ecological approach to man's place in nature. "Through transactions with nature, man has developed what is essentially human, but which historically has been regarded as superhuman and supernatural."

The advice attributed to King Solomon, "Go to the ant, thou sluggard," still holds good for sluggards, but to look in the anthill or the rathole for guidance in our present social turmoil is a blunder with tragic consequences that now threaten the foundations of civilization. For millenniums people have muddled along, exploring with simian inquisitiveness the resources of their world and of their own native capacities. In this slow process of learning by trial and error the errors up till now have too often overbalanced the successes and we seem fatuously unwilling to learn from our own mistakes. Why? We have better brains than ants and monkeys, but we still must learn how to use them for our own good.

The social scientists seem to an outside observer to have been inept in reading the lessons of both phylogenetic and human history. A chemical engineer (Robert R. Williams, '48) has seen the light more clearly. He says: "We need nothing physical half as much as we need better understanding of men and of human affairs. . . . Only science can lead civilization out of its present morass." His reading of the history of evolution leads him to conclusions identical with my own formulation in the preceding chapter, although that chapter was written long before his paper appeared. Trenchant pleas for more intensive study of the individual as such and of individual differences have been published by Dr. Williams' brother (Roger J. Williams, '46, '53, '55), also a chemist. A comprehensive summary of the recorded facts regarding the biological basis of individual differences is available in a big book by Leo Loeb ('45). Snyder ('49), a geneticist, outlines a different approach to the subject, and Cantril ('47) examines the place of personality in social psychology.

The social sciences, like all the others, have been devoted for the most part to the search for generalizations, with the result that the differences among the particulars are neglected. Vast accumulations of statistics have been gathered in the quest for the average man, the economic man, the typical child, the normal diet, and so on. Of course, we do not actually deal with such things. These are normative abstractions. The man-in-the-abstract does not exist. What we have to adjust to in medicine, business, politics, and war is people, individually or in groups, and the character of the group is determined by the qualities of the several people who compose it. "All insight into the organization of human beings must rest upon a knowledge of the individual units involved" (Roger J. Williams).

Cultural factors

In current discussions of basic theory of the social sciences there is active controversy between those who defend a conception of human society which is essentially totalitarian (as this term is defined in the preceding chapter) and those who put the emphasis on the individual persons who compose the society. The traditions of positivism (Mill, Comte, Sumner, *et al.*) are characterized by Hartung ('45) as in their actual application essentially fascist, because individual initiative is suppressed by subordination to greater powers over which there is no possibility of control. Human nature is equated with animal nature, "with the nature of the ways of other animals" (Sumner); custom (folkways) and not reason is the guide to life. As Walter Bagehot ('73) convincingly argued, this was in large measure true in the earlier stages of cultural evolution, but, as he emphasized, times have changed. I grant that the animal ways are still with us, but have we no better ones? If not, then man is a helpless cog in a blind machine, and he is equally helpless whether the machine is driven by cosmic forces beyond his control, by a human dictator, or by his own enslavement to irrational taboo and social pressure.

So when a cultural anthropologist (White, '48) who is also a cultural determinist declares that "man is wholly at the mercy of external forces, astronomic and geologic" and that "human beings are merely the instruments through which cultures express themselves," one wonders how this impersonal culture actually operates and why anybody should take the trouble to find out. If, as Professor White says, "it is possible for man to exert more control over the weather than over culture" and if "he exerts no control whatever over his culture, and theoretically there is no possibility of his ever doing so," then why in the world does man teach cultural anthropology or anything else?

Education is the most potent instrument of cultural change, and

it is the individuals who are educated, not the culture. Social movements are motivated by the needs and wants of individual people.
The society changes only as its individual members change in concerted ways. These changes are transmitted from generation to generation little, if at all, by genetic heredity; but the mechanisms of
social heredity (of which education is the dominant member) act
efficiently and far more rapidly, so that a culture may be more
radically changed in this way in a single generation than it could be
through genetic heredity during millenniums of struggle for survival at lower biological levels.

The overemphasis which these social positivists place upon environmental and impersonal cultural factors leads to a social entropy
which tends to reduce all social movements to the low level of
inorganic mechanics. The logical outcome is Haeckel's evaluation
of man—"Our human nature sinks (under scientific scrutiny) to the
level of a placental mammal, which has no more value for the universe at large than an ant or the fly of a summer's day." Human
society is actually moving in the opposite direction, by reversal of
entropy, toward constructive integration at a higher level; and the
operative agencies are individual people endowed with capacity for
creative work. Professor White's contention that the individual is
irrelevant to an explanation of the cultural process leads to a nihilism
that would paralyze all man's effort to improve his condition, and
this is not what science is for.

This reification of the culture as an autonomous and self-sufficient
entity leads to a dismal fatalism and is a confession of defeat. Opposed to it is the counterclaim that the concept of culture as an
independent entity is an abstraction which has no scientific utility or
justification.

Haring ('47) takes the position that the real social unit is the person,
not the "culture." "Cultural behavior is observable and scientifically definable; 'culture' is not. . . . The objective unit of observation is a human
being behaving. . . . The important facts are specific persons, ideas, beliefs,
and goals of action."

Professor White cites an impressive list of authorities who claim that
the individual lies at the foundation of all social and cultural phenomena,
and he interprets this to mean that *the* individual to which reference is

made is the mythical "average typical human organism," which "may be regarded as a constant and hence irrelevant to an explanation of the culture process." To this I object that it is the *diversities* found among human individuals that are significant here, not the racial constants.

At the Yale Clinic of Child Development, Arnold Gesell has found that normal children tend to follow a general sequence of growth which is characteristic of the human species and of a cultural group. But in the process of acculturation no two children follow this sequence in the same way. The actual growth of the children is by no means an irrelevant racial constant. It is patterned differently in each child in accordance with his own intrinsic individuality, and these differences must not be ignored in the study of culture.

Intermediate to the extreme opinions about the status of "culture" as a social unit which have just been mentioned is the present trend toward a position which recognizes a "culture-personality" interaction in which the individuals, their social organizations and cultural patterns are definable but not independent factors in the adjustment of human affairs. The persons, the social structures, and the cultural patterns represent different levels of organization, each of which has its own distinctive characteristics and principles of operation. The activities at these levels are inseparably related, yet at each level the patterns are recognizably different. A book by Sargent ('50) is addressed to the task of "integrating the individual and group approaches."

In two important papers by Kroeber ('48, '49a), which have been cited in another connection, it is pointed out that for successful pursuit of the study of culture we must find out as much as we can about the persons involved, about their social relations, and about those cultural patterns which can be identified and critically evaluated apart from the individual personalities who embody them. Examples of the last group are familiar—such as language, mythologies, conventional folkways, and formal codes of manners, morals, and law.

If the social scientist is studying the culture as such, he will naturally attend *primarily* to the data and principles which are germane to this level, without ignoring the data and principles which are characteristic of the other levels. The "culture" as this term is used by the anthropologists is a distinctive and unique human type or pattern of performance at a higher level of organization than the social and organic processes.

The student of behavior surveys a wider field, for all animals behave. His *primary* interest is in the behaving individuals, their motivation, their conduct and its consequences. Human behavior is conditioned by social and cultural factors; but, as Kroeber makes clear, the causes—"efficient causes"—of human conduct, including all cultural phenomena, are found within the persons of the people who behave—"psychosomatic individual human beings."

The impersonal cultural patterns to which reference has just been made—language, mythology, and so on—are not separate entities detachable from the people who exhibit them. An organism is not an isolated body but a body in transactional relation with its environment, and it can be understood only in this transactional relationship. So a "culture" is not something detachable from the human population which manifests it; apart from the people who speak the language and cherish the mythologies, the idea of a "culture" is an abstraction, for these cultural factors do not exist except as they are embodied in life-in-process, that is, in the lives of individual people. All of the factors are people-in-action or they are nothing at all.

The social positivism to which the preceding criticisms are directed is, in my opinion, a perversion of the true significance of positivism as a general principle. If positivism is defined as the rule that we should never impute to a concept more properties than its operational definition allows, it follows obviously that we should never neglect any factors which do have operational efficiency. I claim, accordingly, that it is a violation of the rule of positivism to claim that the individual person's needs, desires, and ideals have no operational significance. I go further and insist that operational efficiency does not tell the whole story. Herbert Muller ('43, p. 89) reminds us that "throughout the history of science, very broad and speculative hypotheses—hypotheses at the time incapable of verification and never verified in their original form—have altered operational meanings and produced new ones."

Cultural values

There is no place for values in most current sociological positivism. In many fields of sociological and anthropological investigation, values are of no immediate concern. Such studies yield an indispensable store of factual data, of "accumulative knowledge," but for an adequate understanding of human conduct at all levels of performance we need more than this. We cannot neglect the motivating influence of the values that people prize and work for. This is recognized by increasing numbers of sociologists.

An economist (Boulding, '49) gives a clear and incisive demonstration of this movement. He writes: "Nowhere is the positivistic fiction of a dispassionate, objective observer wholly removed from the field of his observation more absurd than in the social sciences. The difference between the social and the other sciences, however, is merely one of degree."

George A. Lundberg ('47) also has published an urgent demand for reform, a plea for a unified method of attack upon social problems which "must be that of modern natural science applied fully to human society, including man's thoughts, feelings, and 'spiritual' characteristics." The values which motivate all human effort, including all sociological research, must of necessity be included here, for, to quote Ginzberg ('48), "the most 'objective' work in the social sciences will be stillborn unless it can be related to the values that men have and the values which they seek." In discussing economics, Boulding makes the same point: "It is an inevitable logic that has turned the study of prices into a theory of value."

In the work cited, and even more clearly in a subsequent article, Professor Lundberg ('50) demonstrates that the generally accepted standards of scientific method can be employed (and have been) in the domain of human behavior and culture with no essential changes or limitations. It is merely a question of learning how to adjust the details of the procedure to the material under investigation. The behavior of human beings is more labile and unpredictable than that of the planets in their orbits, but in no case does science ever reach ultimates or absolutes of knowledge or predictability. The probability of the truth of a verifiable law or principle is one of the things to be determined.

The biological sciences are pre-eminently "functional" (p. 26); they are not bodies of static truth. In a function there is always an end to be achieved and the function is meaningless apart from the effect toward which it is directed. Means, accordingly, cannot be dissociated from ends in any function of an organism or a social group. Behavior as a total pattern must be viewed in its entirety. The distinction between means and ends is a logical artifact—a useful one as a tool of inquiry—but in the actual situation every end achieved is a means to another end and the two are inseparable.

Failure to recognize that means and ends are inextricably integrated in every causal situation has led to much unseemly controversy. I protest Lundberg's accusation that "those scientists who contend that they can scientifically determine not only the means but the ends of social policy should be exposed as scientific fakers as well as would-be dictators." A scientific program that is concerned only with means, not ends, is only half of science, and not the better half. It can furnish tools for productive work, but it cannot tell us what we are working for or why we work at all. It can accumulate facts, but it cannot tell us which facts are significant or what the facts mean. And these are things we want to know.

At the end of his plea for restricting science to means, not ends, in discussing the United Nations, Lundberg makes a concession that nullifies his argument. "What is to be gained," he asks, "by organization unless administrators *know what to do,* including how to secure international support for action which can be shown to be adapted to the ends sought?" How are the ends sought to be selected, and how can it best be shown what means are best adapted to reach them? Is there any more successful way to find these things out than the time-tested scientific method of discovering the relevant facts and drawing conclusions from this factual knowledge rather than from traditional dogmas and wishful thinking?

When we are told that "no science tells us *what to do* with the knowledge that constitutes the science," my counterclaim is that to tell us *what* to do is exactly what science is for—not telling us what we ought to do in terms of unscientific dogma or telling us what we must do, but showing us what it is good for us to do and how best to do it with the resources available. What we mean by "goodness" in biology and sociology is explained elsewhere (p. 147). Here we need only emphasize that it is a legitimate function of science, and more than that an unavoidable duty, to point out those ends that are most valuable for us; that is, what is most worth while for us to work for, and why.

The bogey of scientific dictatorship is factitious and irrelevant here. It is true that science may be abused by pressure groups and dictators—just as art and religion may be—and social science is no less vulnerable than atomic science. The social scientists have a tremendous responsibility here which they must not shirk. One of America's most competent atomic scientists, in a paper which should have the widest possible circulation (Condon, '48), says: "The only way to security in international relations lies in a devotion to study of the social problems confronting mankind as a whole. This calls for an undreamed of development of all the social sciences and their application to social problems in a spirit of high responsibility."

What we are after in science is control of natural processes, or if that is impossible, sufficient knowledge about them so that we can adjust our own behavior to them. That is why we invent machines, compute tide tables, and establish weather bureaus. The social sciences deal with human nature in the same ways, and so we make forecasts of probable political and financial movements, organize chambers of commerce, and demand efficiency in government. Some social movements have not been brought under control, but it helps to be able to predict them. Intentional control may be exercised either by imposing police power that compels people to behave as directed by government, or by informing people what it is profitable for them to do and showing them how to do it. Under present conditions a democracy must employ both methods but the democratic ideal is more closely approached the more the second method supplants the first. How to accomplish the approach to the ideal is a scientific problem which resolves into this: How can we persuade people to want what is good for them? There is no better way than to explain to them what is good, what is bad, and why; for democracy and freedom can be won only by winning the minds of men, not by decree or by either economic or military pressure applied against the resistance of their own desires. For "democracy is anchored deeply in man's physical nature—his individuality" (Sinnott, '45).

The democratic method of social control is well illustrated by the history of the public health program in this country. This program has been left so far as possible to private initiative and local management, but some features of it must be implemented by the government. So we have legislation involving large expenditures for quarantine, community sanitation, food and drug inspection, and many other safeguards. These measures of preventive medicine are efficiently administered to the advantage of every citizen. But the most acute of our medical problems, the preservation of the mental health of our people, is not so far advanced.

Our provision of hospitals for custodial care and treatment of mental disorder is inadequate, and there is still more urgent demand for the instruction of all the people in the elements of mental hygiene. Prevention of mental disorder is far more important than any curative treatment that can be applied. Howard E. Jensen ('53) in an eloquent plea for practical application of this truism emphasizes that "good mental health is largely a product of good human relations." Genuine education, he says, consists in motivating people to want accurate knowledge and to make rational use of it. Only as he knows what people want and how they get it can the mental health educator motivate them to want something better and tell them how to get it more efficiently. Not content with these generalities, Jensen tells in detail how education of everybody in the essentials of mental hygiene can be immediately carried out in every community with available resources.

More and more of our expert students of the sciences of man are now convinced that the attitudes of masses of people can be changed and that it is the province of the social sciences to point out those directions of change which will resolve personal and social tensions and to show how to go about effecting these changes. This conviction has motivated the organization of the "Tensions Project" of the Social Science Department of UNESCO, the purpose of which is to stimulate research on methods of changing attitudes and to study the influences which predispose toward international understanding (Cantril, '49a).

There is general agreement that it is not the province of scientists, as scientists, to legislate, to tell people what they *must* do. But it is the duty of legislators, because in general they are not expert in science, to consult qualified authorities in every special field of legislation. This is the domain in which the social sciences can make their largest contribution to general welfare if given the opportunity and if the sociologists themselves can rise to the opportunity. The scientist's obligations as a scientist and as a citizen are inseparable. Our obligations to apply scientific knowledge and methods to social problems are clearly defined by Chisholm ('49), and he tells us what each one of us can do about it.

An experienced social worker (Meyer, '55) shows keen insight in her description of the futility of much of the unco-ordinated effort in this program and of the steps which can be taken to remedy it. These steps take their departure from this impregnable position: "The artificial division that now exists between the natural and the humane sciences, and between the scientists and the humanists, is a survival of an outmoded dualism between things of matter and things of the mind. What we need today is a humanism that is scientific, and a science that is truly humane."

The critical social issues are problems of human relations. Whether we are dealing with small local affairs or with the big problems of international policy, no program for relief of social tensions can succeed unless it has the active support of the individual people concerned. Social science has already developed scientifically acceptable ways to find out by extensive inquiry and experiment what policies are desirable and how to get people to accept them.

From the beginning of the record until now, large-scale experiments with various kinds of social organization have been made by all kinds of people in all sorts of environments. Some of these have developed unwittingly as spontaneous expressions of adaptation to local conditions. Others have been deliberately planned—for instance the constitution written by the founding fathers of our own republic and the policies adopted for the administration of Cuba, the Philippines, and Puerto Rico. Such plans are always mixtures of good and poor judgment, and should therefore be subject to change in the light of experience. Such a mixed plan may work out well if the revisions are skillfully adjusted to changing conditions. It will work out badly if, as in Russia, it is conceived as infallible dogma, enforced by arbitrary decree. And it will destory itself if, as in Hitler's Germany, it is altogether bad. How any plan does actually work is determined, in the long run, primarily by what the people learn to want. If they prefer docile submission to tyranny, they will have slavery. If they prefer independence, they may have to fight for it.

Summary

    In mankind personal behavior and mass movements are motivated by various blends of instinctive drives and ideologies individually learned and socially propagated. The personal factors and the cultural factors of human social organizations are analyzed and their mutual interplay is emphasized.

    Both biological values and consciously cherished rational values as motivating influences are vital factors of human conduct. These values have no behavioristic significance except as objectives that people work for. They work for what they want. They want what they think is good for them, and it is the proper task of the social sciences first to show which of their desirables are really good for them and then to devise ways of inducing them to prefer these values rather than others of less worth. It is not the province of science to legislate, to tell people what they *must* do, but science can tell people what is good for them to do. Since this is what they want, the prime function of education is to teach people what values are most satisfying and how to get them.

CHAPTER SIXTEEN

The Self

The biological self

It has been emphasized from the beginning that the interest of the behaviorist centers in the behaving individual. In the course of development of behavior the *primary* factors which determine patterns of performance are inside the organism, not in the environment. The sociologist and the social psychologist may regard this as an over-emphasis upon the individual self, and we will grant them their standpoint in this regard. Attention is naturally and properly directed primarily to group relations and cultural structure if one is investigating the influence of such factors on human conduct. And from any standpoint these factors must not be neglected in a general survey of behavior. But human social structures differ from those of all other animals because individual men have abilities that make these structures possible. In all programs of study of social forces and advancement of human welfare the motivation and conduct of individual people are the key factors.

From the biologist's standpoint every organism may be regarded as a self. As such it differs from all other natural objects by virtue of its intrinsic capacity for living in a pattern which is unique and to some extent self-made. Of course, it is not an independent autonomous entity. It can exist only by maintaining active reciprocal relations with the environment from which its materials and its energies are derived and to which it delivers the products of its own activity.

It is a growing thing which can reproduce itself and so repeat the cycle of growth indefinitely, with some change of the pattern in each generation. In this flux of change the cycle from ovum to disintegration at death is the biological individual, the self as here defined.

This definition, like all others, is a logical artifact, for life is continuous from generation to generation, and the self as a unit is part of a larger whole from which it cannot be detached or sharply circumscribed. The determination of the exact date which marks the beginning of the life of the person has interested students of human behavior from the earliest times, for the question has been regarded as important in its legal, theological, and philosophical contexts. The moment when the ovum is fertilized by the sperm is the most appropriate point of reference for recording the "true age" of the individual. The beginning of behavior as conventionally defined is marked by the first appearance of overt movement of the fetus or its members, the "quickening."

Neither of these dates can be determined accurately and the "true age" at both quickening and birth varies within wide limits. Furthermore, both of these ages, even if determined accurately, must be regarded as merely convenient landmarks, useful for description and analysis, but arbitrary; for life does not begin at conception and the qualities of the person depend in large measure on the racial experience of uncounted previous generations.

If we insist that the individual is self-made, not passively molded by hereditary and environmental influences, then we must enlarge our definition of the self to include the living body and everything else with which it has and has had transactional relations. This is the only possible answer to the question asked by the Persian philosopher of the *Rubáiyát*, "Who is the Potter, pray, and who the pot?"

In an over-all view of the animal world we recognize many different kinds of units of various degrees of complexity, each of which has a significant place in the structure of science. In this hierarchy of biological units the one that is of paramount importance for both theory and practice of behavior is the individual organism, the person who behaves. In other contexts smaller or larger units within the body or groups of bodies may occupy more strategic positions, and these other units are significant for behavior; but behavior is a total pattern of an individual body, and the integrity of this body is the essential prerequisite for successful adjustment.

Whatever philosophers and psychologists may say about the nature of the self, for the biologist the concept has a simple operational meaning. I experience myself in action as immediately as I experience things with which I act and things acted upon. It is true that "I am a part of all that I have met" and, as William James taught ('90, chap. 10) and G. H. Mead ('34) emphasized, that the self can be understood only in terms of its relations within the total frame of experience—my body, my property, my neighbors, and all the rest—yet the empirical self is polarized as the *me* against the *mine*, the *knower* against the *known*. The knower cannot merge with the known without losing his own identity. This clear-cut conscious polarization of subject and object arises rather late in human psychogenesis. The infant begins to use personal pronouns ("me," etc.) at about two years of age, implying the acquisition of the idea of the self as a separate entity. The origin of this idea is to be sought in the use that he makes of his extraspective and introspective experience.

In this social setting the relationships of the self are widened and the self must become a socius. The difficulties encountered in any attempt to analyze the innate and the socially conditioned components of the personality are discussed by Conklin ('30, '43), Cantril ('47), and Stern ('49).

This conception of the self is usually elaborated in psychological terms, that is, in terms of one's awareness of these relationships. But this awareness rests on relationships of much more general nature, as is frequently illustrated in ordinary conversation. If I say, "The dog himself was tired," or "The machine itself is worn out," the implication is that the object designated as a self is set apart with an individuality of its own. If, then, we accept the psychologist's definition of the self as "the subject of the individual's consciousness or self-consciousness," we must recognize that such a self has biological antecedents in the domain of the unconscious and that the biological qualities of the self must not be neglected in psychology and sociology.

An animal's attitudes toward things sensed are determined by values (implicitly or explicitly), that is, by the significance of the things in relation to his own interests or welfare. In human social attitudes there is the additional factor of recognition of the attitudes of the others toward the self, with corresponding complication of the value-judgments involved and increase in the hazard of conflict. Since these judgments are for the most part determined by the social code or cultural pattern to which the individuals have been acclimated, social contacts of diverse cultures almost inevitably result in antagonism and conflict unless the education of the people is liberal enough to efface the prevailing barriers of racial and provincial attitudes. So far our educational systems have not succeeded very well in this respect, and such conflicts will not be resolved until much more serious and skillful attention is given to the problem in all homes and schools.

The worth of the person

From the standpoint of cosmic evolution the individual unit may appear to be an insignificant cog geared into a stupendous mechanism and passively pushed by forces over which it has no control. What is our Earth but a minor planet revolving around one of the smaller suns among millions of other suns in a cluster of stars that is one of millions of other galaxies? And what is a man but a rattlebrained bipedal primate imperfectly adjusted to his erect posture and endowed with an overgrown cerebral cortex that he has not learned how to use well enough to protect himself from his own stupidity?

But is so happens that this is our planet and we have to live in it whether we like it or don't; and, if I am the man in question, it is a matter of supreme importance to me as a cog in the cosmic machine that I fit into my appropriate niche without undue friction. It is also true that, if there are things in my world that I don't like, I can sometimes change them to fit my needs and, if there are inimical things that I cannot change, I can adjust myself and my conduct to them and so survive and prosper. The cosmic machine of which I am part regulates itself, and I have a significant part to play in this regulation.

This ability to control things and events and to exercise self-control is not an exclusively human prerogative. All animals possess it in some measure or they would perish. Intrinsic control is characteristic of all inorganic mechanisms also; indeed, this is what machines are for (page 56). The earth is not passively driven through its orbit. It is an active participant in the process by gravitational and other forms of interaction between earth and sun and all other heavenly bodies. And I am not passively pushed about by cosmic forces over which I have no control. I can do some pushing on my own initiative and in my own way.

It took people a long time to find out that our earth is not the center of the universe, and many people seem not yet to have discovered that the world does not revolve around their own needs, desires, and whimseys. But when all is said it remains true that a man's own life is his chief concern, and properly so. If he does not look out for himself, nobody else will—not to his satisfaction. Inevitably *his* world does center in himself, and he is the most important thing in it—for *him*. This is one illustration of the basic principle of relativity.

Men cannot control the earth's movements; but they can control to some extent their own adjustments to the resulting cycles of day and night, summer and winter, and so on. This control is real. It is not our business to run the universe, but it is our concern to accept it, to understand it, and to regulate our conduct in accordance with the laws of nature and our own nature in particular. It behooves each one of us to take himself seriously, to make the most of himself, and to devote himself aggressively to the serious business of living. All that I do I do in the quest for satisfaction—my own and other people's—and this satisfaction is a personal matter with each of us. A laissez-faire policy is biologically interdicted. The record of thousands of years of human history demonstrates that the individual man has not been a negligible factor in determining the course of this history.

This is as true of scientific investigation as of any other human enterprise, and so I contend that, though the facts of science are impersonal, science as a social structure cannot be impersonal. It necessarily carries the impress of the people who make it. All scientific endeavor is directive effort, the objective being a larger measure of satisfaction for the people who make it and for the people who profit by it; and these satisfactions reside in the persons concerned, not in science nor in the culture which it fosters.

It is true that throughout evolutionary history the wastage of individual organisms has been enormous, a wastage that continues now even in the most "enlightened" human communities. In these struggles for survival the individuals seem to be of little account. Those who deviate far from the established pattern of the species or group are generally eliminated, and so nature is regarded as conservative of the species and neglectful of the persons:

> So careful of the type she seems,
> So careless of the single life.

This is a true picture of the totalitarian animal communities, but it is not a fair expression of nature's method in the over-all view. Nature is very careful indeed of the single lives that are fit to adjust to conditions as they are; and this is a positive selection of the fit and a positive improvement of their fitness, not a mere rejection of the unfit.

It is a fortunate circumstance, too, that natural selection does not eliminate all atypical individuals. Some of the aberrant members who do not conform to the type of their species or group survive. All evolutionary changes and all social movements away from established cultural patterns depend upon the appearance and ultimate dominance of these exceptional persons.

It is granted that at subhuman levels the units of evolutionary movements are populations rather than individuals. The individual has little influence unless he is the bearer of one or more mutant genes which are beneficial to the species or group. It is probable, however, that a far more important source of heritable variations is the recombination of the patterns of paternal and maternal genes in each generation at the time of fertilization of the ovum by the sperm cell (page 115).

New heritable traits produced by either of the ways just mentioned can influence the direction of evolution only if they reappear during many generations and are slowly incorporated within the genetic stock of the group. In human social evolution, on the contrary, a gifted individual may sell his invention or his idea to the whole community, so that it may be incorporated within the mores in a single generation. Here the individual may play a far more significant part than in any program of eugenics, however skillfully and drastically carried out.

These precious individuals have a better chance of survival in human society than at subhuman levels. Their expectancy is better because human social organization is integrated by ideas, and these can be propagated more rapidly than the genes. So life becomes more secure for the pioneers and the adventurous. Or it would be so except for human stupidity. So long as any nations continue the slaughter of their most vigorous and competent youth in aggressive warfare they are acting unbiologically, and they thereby show that they are not fit for survival as nature's most favored children. And, so long as we tolerate slums that breed incompetents and criminals and too often allow genius to starve, there is the possibility of loss of the precious achievements of creative talent.

The self as a free agent

The human self is traditionally regarded as a free moral agent, and this belief is generally held to be incompatible with any radically mechanistic conception of the personality. But a better understanding of the essential properties of mechanism and of mechanistic determinism shows that the order of nature is wide enough and flexible enough to embrace both determinism and freedom, both causal relationships and moral responsibility.

First, it must be recognized that in a mechanical system there is no uncaused action; every movement is determined in a lawful way. But this determinism does not necessarily imply *pre*determinism. In directive behavior, as in every other causal system, the determination of the pattern of action is intrinsic to the system, and changing patterns are determined anew from moment to moment as the internal conditions change (page 53).

In any causal situation as we now see it, temporal sequence is not an essential factor (page 71), and in conceptual processes as experienced subjectively both time and space as we know them perceptually may play no part whatever. In this domain the causal situation must be conceived relativistically and freed from any restrictions such as are imposed by the traditional conception of causal necessity which ties events together in a linear sequence. Instead of a sequence which is rigidly predetermined from the beginning of time, what we actually find is a fluid situation within which readjustments may generate novel patterns of performance which are not framed in time or space.

The individual machine or person, by virtue of its own internal organization, has some measure of autonomy and initiative (the "immanent causality" of Sellars) and so is properly described as a free agent within the limits set by its structural pattern and the operative restrictions imposed by surrounding conditions. In human behavior the scope of this natural freedom is enlarged, because the cortical mechanism can act rationally and so foresee the probable consequences of choices made.

This intelligently directed freedom of choice is the most characteristic feature of the highest level of biological integration that we mortals know anything about. The operations at this level are not uncaused; but the psychological laws of "immanent causality" in this domain cannot be formulated in terms of a linear temporal sequence, every step of which is inexorably predetermined by the preceding steps, such as is implicit in the laws of causal necessity in the codes of conventional inorganic mechanics. The choice is determined at the moment of its exercise in accordance with psychological laws of a different order.

This relativistic way of looking at human nature is incompatible with the positivism of our conventional systems of biomechanics, as is now recognized by increasing numbers of competent workers. A few examples will next be cited.

Conklin ('30, p. 460) long ago drew the distinction between the rigid predeterminism of conventional mechanics and the freedom allowed by recognition of the fluid character of natural processes, processes which are determined as they go along by causes which are intrinsic to the formative process itself. There is nothing fatalistic about this, and in the domain of human purposive action the purpose itself is a causative factor which is not incompatible with a certain amount of freedom and responsibility. In my comments on this theme ('49, p. 224), several other authorities are cited in support of this distinction between freedom and predeterminism.

It has been mentioned by Cameron ('48) in a stimulating address that when the creative feature of causality is recognized and the lock step of traditional causal sequence in which every event is clamped to the preceding and succeeding event with rigid unalterability is broken, the perspectives of science are immeasurably widened. This is most clearly seen when the living body is viewed as a continually evolving system which never reacts identically to repeated exposure to apparently identical conditions. The act of response alters subsequent responsiveness. This alteration is neither random nor lawless. Creativity, as has been emphasized repeatedly, is exhibited in some measure by every mechanism. It is manifested at successive levels of integration throughout both inorganic and organic realms, and it culminates in human purposive behavior, constructive reasoning, and inventiveness.

Natural freedom has been characterized in this way: To be determined by one's own nature is to be free. This freedom consists in action which is in accordance with the nature of the acting mechanism, and it will be exhibited in different measure at every level of organization. It is lawfully determined at all levels, and it is far greater at the higher levels.

This is the principle upon which I based my essay on determinism and freedom ('26a) and the little book that followed it ('26b), in which I made the claim that moral freedom grows naturally out of our capacity for making intelligent choices in view of probable future consequences of the choices made. As soon as social privileges and obligations are recognized, this so-called freedom of the will becomes moral freedom, and this justifies the further claim ('41b) that a naturalistic ethic has valid scientific standing.

Any freedom in a mechanistic universe is, of course, limited. The operations of every mechanism are conditioned and restricted not only by its internal organization but also by the field with which it has transactional relations. This is as true of a psychobiological mechanism as of any other. A "free choice" has obvious limitations. An unlimited and absolute freedom is biologically impossible and would be practically suicidal, for an organism can survive and develop only through lawfully ordered transactions with surrounding things and events. The intentional suicide accomplishes his purpose by flouting these laws.

Thomas Huxley's famous Romanes Lecture, "Evolution and Ethics," delivered in 1893 served for half a century as point of departure for a searching examination of the scientific status of current ethical standards and moral codes of conduct. This lecture immediately came to my attention and, though I was at that time only a callow junior instructor in a small college, I had the temerity to publish ('94) a protest against the distinguished lecturer's thesis that "social progress means a checking of the

cosmic progress at every step and the substitution for it of another which
may be called the ethical progress." The gist of my argument was repeated thirty years later ('24, p. 7), when I charged that Huxley's antith-
esis between the cosmic process and ethical progress betrays the cause
of human evolution.

This severe indictment should be qualified, for in the light of the subsequently published "Prolegomena" and of Huxley's letters of that time it
is evident that he failed to make his own position clear. The lecture, which
Irvine ('55, p. 346) characterizes as "the culmination of Huxley's pes-
simism," seems to show a lapse from the normal rigor of his mental processes. Some of its obscurity and inconsistency may be due to the fact that
he was very ill when it was written and delivered.

My adolescent essay on the evolution of Huxley might well be followed now by another on the evolution of two Huxleys, for the grandson
and devoted disciple of the Master had the unique privilege of delivering
a Romanes Lecture on the same subject and from the same rostrum exactly fifty years later. Julian Huxley has published these two lectures, with
illuminating annotations (Huxley and Huxley, '47), and it is significant
that he chose as his title, not "Evolution and Ethics," but "Evolutionary
Ethics"; for here the junior Huxley has succeeded in closing the gap
which baffled his illustrious predecessor. He was able to show that "our
ethics evolve because they are themselves part of the evolutionary process."

At about the time when Julian Huxley delivered his Romanes Lecture,
S. J. Holmes ('44) issued a critique of the elder Huxley's essay. This and
the same author's more comprehensive work ('48b) should be required
reading for all those students of nature, of philosophy, and of morals
who are puzzled about the place of altruism in a world where the struggle
for existence and the survival of the fit are the rule. Huxley was right in
asserting that the infrahuman cosmic process has "no sort of relation to
moral ends," for only man is a moral agent. But man is part of nature
and, as Holmes makes clear, man is "organically moral" because he alone
among the animals has the capacity to create an ideal of goodness, that is,
of fitness, in terms of social relations and obligations. This ideal is at war
with the ape-and-tiger technique of survival, but altruism has not been
added to human nature by miraculous intervention—its roots are readily
found in certain amoral components of the family and social life of many
infrahuman species. And just as in these primitive societies such components
have utility in the preservation and enrichment of life, so also in mankind
under our social organization some moral standards of social comity have
actual survival value.

An important scientific contribution to the natural history of ethics was
made by E. G. Conklin in a series of essays and in two books ('30, '43).
Simpson's more recent discussion of naturalistic ethics ('49, chap. 18) is

recommended as an antidote to much current wishful thinking. The biological foundations of ethics and social progress are explained and interpreted in the comprehensive work by Allee *et al.* ('49). Emerson ('54) has given us a valuable survey in concise form of the general principles of social and ethical evolution. He puts the emphasis on Walter Cannon's principle of homeostasis, i.e., the regulation of all bodily activities so as to maintain a relatively stable equilibrium. This is not a static balance, but a constantly shifting readjustment of the innumerable diverse vital processes. Two classes of functions are involved: first, the regulation of the internal operations of the person so as to keep him in good bodily and mental health; and, second, regulation of all his transactions with the physical and social environment. Sociobiology is concerned primarily with the second of these classes, and this again includes two groups of factors, those which are given in the genetic organization and those which are personally acquired.

In comparing human patterns of behavior with those of other animals the distinction between homology and analogy (page 106) must be sharply drawn. The most distinctive factors of human social behavior (language and other symbolisms, esthetic and moral values, and many others) have no homologues among the subhuman animals, although there are some instructive analogies. Emerson, accordingly, gives particular attention to these analogies. Our interest here is in the evolutionary history of the uniquely human factors, and we find that all of them—symbolism, altruism, and all the rest—are deeply rooted in the prehuman ancestry of mankind. There is, then, no inconsistency between Emerson's analysis and ours, although the emphasis is different, and the two supplement each other.

One of Professor Conklin's disciples, Chauncey D. Leake, has given us a brilliantly clear exposition of "Ethicogenesis" and the place of naturalistic ethics in the cultural development of mankind. Several of his papers, accompanied by those of a distinguished philosopher, have been assembled together with some new matter in a small book entitled *Can We Agree?* (Leake and Romanell, '50). This friendly controversy brings out in sharp relief the contrast between the naturalistic and the normative methods of approach to problems of human adjustment. There is gratifying agreement on many important questions, but there is disagreement on the essential nature of scientific method, of ethics, and of value. It is my opinion that the disagreement stems from the fact that Professor Romanell does not understand either the method or the objective of natural science.

The issues involved here are not clarified by the dialectic of Romanell's more recent essay, "Does Biology Afford a Sufficient Basis for Ethics?" ('55). His polemic is directed specifically to the paper by Emerson ('54) cited above. A few of his many failures to understand the biological principles of valid sociobiology need emphasis in our present context.

He draws a sharp contrast between ethics as a "normative science" and biology characterized as a "descriptive science," and he defines the normative disciplines too narrowly as concerned only with what things "ought to be" and what men "ought to do" (a definition which I have criticized on page 29). His application of this principle sets "proper ethics" apart from our world as actually experienced in a way that is essentially dualistic.

Again, the charge that Emerson's recognition of the principle of homeostasis as a factor in ethicogenesis involves a *reduction* of ethical ideals to the mechanical order of lower-level physiological processes is not true. On the contrary, evolutionary ethics involves a succession of progressive changes from lower to higher levels of organization, a series which culminates in human ethical ideals and judgments. Ethical values, I repeat, do not arise miraculously. As I have elsewhere shown, there is an evolution of values, and all human idealistic values have their roots in biological values which are recognizable and definable. Having reached the level of human standards of moral behavior they are still biological values regardless of any other qualities they may have. Homeostasis at the level of human social adjustment must not be equated with that of the chemistry of body fluids.

Finally, I would emphasize that naturalistic ethics is not a "descriptive science." It is granted that here we are searching for "social facts," and we insist that "social ideals" are also facts of experience. But we do not rest with description of the facts. What all science is after is the *meaning of the facts for human betterment.* Some of the facts and theories of ethics have biological meanings which are instructive, but those of us who attempt a scientific approach to ethics do not claim that this is the only way to study ethics or that this inquiry can tell us all we need to know about ethical ideals and practice.

To the myopic cynic the world seems to be a mad disorder. It is true that some natural events do not conform with human standards of orderly procedure—an order measured by human comfort and complacency. Hurricanes and pestilences are disturbing, but they are not disorderly. They are law-abiding processes, though the laws are not those of human convenience. Nature as a whole is unmoral according to human codes of ethics, but it is not immoral. Only a man can be immoral, and what he regards as immoral varies with his culture. In some communities the murder of incompetent seniles is a moral duty, and in "civilized" communities of today genocide involving the ruthless extermination of millions of innocent and competent people has been defended as morally acceptable by large numbers of people who boast of a superior "Kultur."

The world is not mad. It is only some of the people in it who are mad. The world is orderly, and even human madness is lawfully ordered, having causes and consequences which can be discovered and ameliorated. The ability to be irrational and immoral seems to be the price that must be paid for the ability to think rationally and to live a reasonable and moral life, with its accompanying satisfactions.

When the process of organic evolution advanced from the physiological to the psychological level of integration, when man acquired the ability to choose his own course of action with intellgient foresight of probable consequences, then he won the freedom to go to perdition in his own way if he chose unwisely. This is the price we must pay for freedom. Freedom is worth the price, and there are enough people in the world who choose their values wisely and pursue them rationally to save humanity from suicidal folly.

Summary

Throughout this discussion emphasis has been placed upon the individual animal as the biological unit that is of crucial significance for behavior in both theory and practice. The contrast between the self and the not-self is manifested operationally at all lower and higher integrative levels, and at the higher levels it is apprehended in consciousness as the distinction between the knower and the things known. The conscious recognition of this contrast begins in perception with the distinction between the perceiving subject and the things perceived.

A man's behavior is controlled primarily in the interest of his own survival and welfare, and his attitude toward other things and people is necessarily self-centered. But in a social situation this attitude is influenced also by the attitudes of other people toward himself. The self is socialized, and the recognition that his own welfare is bound up with that of his group conditions his behavior at a higher level of integration.

Human freedom of choice is not uncaused action. The cause is intrinsic to the situation. The action is not predetermined by an extrinsic causal agent. It is determined at the moment of its exercise.

Every mechanism has a measure of natural freedom to operate in accordance with its own structural organization. In a man this freedom to act purposefully with intelligent forecast of probable consequences becomes moral freedom when the social consequences of the act are recognized and taken into account. Only a man can be moral, and morality is never impersonal.

The basic causes of social disorder lie in people, not in their governments, institutions, or cultural styles. Not until people learn how to live together in peaceful co-operation, with mutual adjustments of personal, national, and cultural interests to the common welfare, can there be any hope of cultural progress or even of survival of the culture already achieved.

CHAPTER SEVENTEEN

The Outlook

The critical question

The present disordered state of human affairs shows that there is something radically wrong with the management. Who, then, manages our affairs and what can we do to put them in order?

The human population of the world is an integral part of a cosmic order with which we must maintain smoothly running transactional relations if we are to survive and prosper. We have succeeded fairly well in learning the rules of these transactions and conforming our conduct with them so as to make workable adjustments to the rigors of climate, the ravages of disease, and all the other conditions imposed by the physical nature of our world. We have done even more: by harnessing the forces of nature with ingenious inventions, we have made these forces in part the servants of man. This control of the resources of nature has improved our health and comfort and enormously enlarged the range of the satisfactions enjoyed. The quality of these satisfactions has been stepped up from the level of physical comfort and luxurious living (for the "successful" members of a community) to an appreciation of higher values in the domains of literature, art, science, philosophy, and morals.

These remarkable achievements of humanity at its best are convincing proof that human nature is basically sound and healthy, in other words, that it is biologically fit not only for survival but for further evolutionary development of efficiency in directions and to an extent not now predictable. But if this progressive movement is to continue, it must be recognized that the standards of fitness—of *biological* fitness even for survival—have radically changed during the last few millenniums of human history. When feral man became a domesticated animal, as he did when the social unit was expanded from the family to the tribe and nation, then also the protective and co-operative care seen in many animal communities became highly elaborated so that it was the key factor in that social regulation of conduct which is essential for survival and prosperity under modern conditions.

At the transition from brute to man the chief motivating factors of behavior were stepped up from the physiological to the psychological level. Social units of diverse patterns were slowly elaborated and held together by emotionally and intelligently directed concerted action. During the early stages of this process of socialization of behavior the survival of the individual came to depend more and more upon the survival of his group. The law of the jungle still prevailed, but the standards of fitness were in large measure transferred from the individual to the group. The stronger and more resourceful tribes overpowered and subjugated or destroyed the weaker. The ravages of aggressive warfare as well as the more subtle methods of subjugation by commercial exploitation and ingeniously deceptive propaganda continue to our day and now threaten the total destruction of all the values that we cherish and even life itself.

Why? What is the matter with us?

The answer

The threatened collapse of the imposing social structure which is the framework of modern civilization is not due to any physical or mental deterioration of the human race. On the contrary, we have within the last few centuries increased our productive capacity more than a thousandfold by the use of tools of great power and precision. Some of these instruments are mechanical laborsaving devices and others, of far greater value, are more efficient mental techniques for widening the range of experience and rational interpretation of it. We have at our command all the physical and mental resources that are needed for further advance in this direction if only we do not squander them in senseless and suicidal rivalry and conflict.

The trouble is that too many of us are blind to the fact that the course of human evolution has now reached a stage which is even more revolutionary in method and consequences than the initial revolution through which humanity emerged from apedom. We have won intellectual supremacy over the brutes, but that is not enough. We have not won control over our own brutish impulses for self-gratification at the expense of our neighbors. We have not learned that the voluntary renunciation of some personal and national advantages is the only possible way to keep the peace and win security and opportunity for cultural progress.

The current revolution began not very long ago, as evolutionary time is measured. It began when men realized that the law of the jungle is outmoded in human cultures, that a stable human social structure cannot be made according to the social standards of the anthill or the wolf pack. Not until the man became a socius could the manhood of humanity come to full fruition. This means that the individual man—not his overlord or his government or any power of impersonal "culture" acting as a coercive entity—that the person as his own master takes the management of himself and of his group relationships into his own hands. It means also that this aggrandizement of his individuality shall be not at the expense of his fellows but with their co-operation, that mutual aid, not antagonism, is the price that must be paid for workable social relations.

The practical application of these principles is democracy—self-government—and the democratic unit cannot function or long survive unless the individual selves first learn to govern themselves and to sacrifice some personal profits and preferences for the welfare of the group. This is altruism. Quite apart from any ethical considerations and in terms of strictly biological survival value, altruistic behavior marks the highest level of cultural evolution. It is a key factor, and the only one that can relieve the tensions that now endanger all the cultures of the world. This is not a speculative vagary or a fantasy of wishful thinking. It is validated by the whole history of human evolution and especially clearly by current events.

The rapid mechanization of our present social organization has tended, as mentioned on page 73, to gear the man to his machinery, to mechanize the man himself, at the expense of his own initiative and social obligations. As Julian Huxley ('44) has pointed out, this increasing dependence upon mechanical devices has come with explosive violence so that we are now living in a period of revolution that is far more radical and exciting than any other since the industrial revolution began about two centuries ago. The most significant thing about the present revolution is a reversal of the trend toward mechanization of the workers and emphasis upon the humanizing of the mechanism in industry, politics, and international policies so as to restore to each individual and social unit that dignity, autonomy, and productive efficiency which is our human birthright. This trend meets great resistance from vested interests and our only hope of its eventual success lies in a renaissance of that basic morality which again is the most precious fund of our human heritage.

Altruistic conduct is the basis of a practical morality that can be defined in behavioristic terms. It is motivated by the conviction that the advantages arising from social organization carry with them the obligation to protect and strengthen that organization intelligently at the cost of personal sacrifice. This is a moral judgment. As such it is a unique human achievement, but its biological origins are seen in those patterns of protohuman behavior which show parental care, family cohesion, and co-operative enterprise. Although only a man can be moral or immoral, the roots of his morality are found in his brutish ancestry and he is intrinsically, that is, biologically, a moral agent. And this is necessarily a personal morality. No social organization, no government, no "culture" can be moral, for these are merely the vehicles of expression of the personal morals of the constituent members.

If it is not recognized that this natural personal morality is an essential component of every stable social structure and that it must come to expression in a workable code of moral conduct, then social disorder and disintegration inevitably result. It follows that the discovery of what is good for us, that is, what is "right" conduct, is a scientific problem which can be solved only on factual evidence.

This evidence has long been available. Five hundred years before

Christ, Confucius laid down this rule: "Do not do unto others what you would not have others do unto you." This, as he said, is a fundamental principle of all other good rules of conduct. The closer we follow this golden rule the more stable and efficient is our culture, a fact confirmed by abundant historical evidence.

The causes of our most acute personal and social distress lie in ourselves, not in our surroundings or in what we have or have not. They arise from what we are and what kind of people we want to be. I grant that a population that is living in utter destitution, lacking the essential necessities of life, is apt to resort to violent methods to provide for mere subsistence, for survival value is the primordial motivation of all behavior. But if the essential necessities of life are available, what use is made of them is determined by other considerations. That this is so is shown by the fact that some of the most destitute people on earth are the most contented and well behaved and by the disquieting observation that the most devastating scourges of aggressive war and inhuman cruelty have been perpetrated by highly organized, productive, and prosperous nations.

What kind of a person a child wants to grow up to be is determined in part by the capacities and limitations which he inherits from his forebears, and in larger part by the social environment in which he is placed. The control of environment—physical, mental, and moral—is, accordingly, the strategic field within which the social sciences reap their largest reward.

Education for democracy

It follows from these considerations that the most critical problems of social control are educational rather than economic or political, however important the latter may be. Democracy is not a panacea for all human ills, but as above defined it is the best prescription we have for the cure of social diseases. And this democracy cannot be imposed by sumptuary legislation. The people must be taught to want it, they must know what it means and what it costs, and they must be willing to pay the price. This we have not succeeded in doing in this or any other country. It can be done; but only if we devote more serious and intelligent attention to it than we are now doing.

The more advanced cultures of the world must not shirk their responsibilities to provide basic educational facilities for their less fortunate neighbors. The Voice of America carrying the message of the meaning of democracy and its advantages can pass the iron curtain, the bamboo curtain, and every other obstruction; but before this message can carry conviction we must put our own house in order. Our own democracy is falling apart, and the most serious danger which threatens it is not aggression from the outside but internal decay.

Our political administration of local and national affairs is usually notoriously inefficient and too often flagrantly corrupt. The natural partnership of labor and capital is disrupted by open or covert warfare. In our international relations enlightened statesmanship is not infrequently sabotaged by powerful selfish special interests. And what do we do about it? Less than half of the qualified voters in three recent national elections took the trouble to vote, and in many places it is the wrong half that casts the ballots. Those who do vote show the most amazing indifference to the qualifications of the candidates selected. Our people are getting better government than they deserve; but what they are getting is not good enough to save the life of the nation if present trends continue.

We are not educated for democracy and we are doing little to improve the situation. We have the most elaborate and expensive educational machinery in the world, as we should. But an appraisal of the returns from the investment shows that there is something wrong with it. Here are a few items. The national census shows that there are nearly three million adults in the United States who cannot read and write. The U. S. Department of Commerce reported that the national income in 1947 was $200,000,000,000. The expenditures from this income included about $15,000,000,000 for gambling, $10,000,000,000 for alcoholic beverages, $4,000,000,000 for tobacco, and $2,000,000,000 for cosmetics. These total about 15 per cent of the national income, which is six times as much as the total expenditure for education, public and private. Our people spend twice as much for amusement as they do for education. In more than half of our cities the average teacher earns less than the average truck driver.

These are typical examples of the esteem which our voters have for education. In many communities the taxpayers approve extravagant expenditures for ostentatious public works, highways, and promotion of business interests while at the same time school buildings which decades ago were condemned as firetraps are falling apart from age and neglect. If this is the attitude of parents toward their civic responsibilities, can anything better be expected of the children?

The progressive educational movement puts the emphasis, as it should, on self-determination. But it is too often overlooked that the sound basis of self-determination is self-control, and this we are not teaching successfully. Unrestrained personal freedom can lead only to anarchy, and that is what we are getting. Self-centered isolationism under the guise of self-expression, family and local pride, or patriotism can lead only to self-destruction, and yet some of the strongest nations of the world today (not excepting a considerable fraction of our own nation) seem to be committed to this suicidal policy in their local and international relations. This is further evidence that we are not successfully educating our people for democracy. This we are beginning to recognize, for the literature of protest in popular and technical publications is already every extensive. This is too complicated and controversial a subject for treatment here. For clear formulation of the problems and explanation of principles and practices recommended by qualified authorities the reader is referred to the literature issued by the Foundation for Integrated Education (with headquarters at 246 East 46th St., New York, 17) and by the Educational Policies Commission of the National Education Association (as described by David B. Dreiman, '55).

A discerning social scientist (Eby, '51) gives this definition of an educated man: one who can see the consequences of his acts in the sum total of their relationships. The relationships that are most significant for human conduct are those with other people, and in the present state of world-wide communication this means all the people there are. The isolationist (in family, church, or state) is not an educated man, however learned he may be. We are members of the world, whether we like it or not, and the history of our world teaches that our survival depends upon keeping on friendly terms with this world in relationships that are honorable and hence mutually advantageous. The author quoted, who calls himself a "stubborn Dutchman," warns that we must face history, not back into it.

The survival of civilization is dependent far more upon our ability to understand the biological requirements of successful living in security and productiveness than upon any military or other power that can be forcibly applied to an unwilling people, however necessary this may be in emergencies. How to get people to recognize and use efficiently the resources they already have, the forces of reason, justice, and altruism—this is the most urgent problem now before us. We have the wit to do this, to make wise judgments about what kind of conduct is good for us, about how to get along with ourselves as well as we do with the rest of our natural surroundings. The necessary knowledge is available. Have we enough intelligence and fortitude to pattern our behavior in accordance with it?

The key to progress

So we end as we began, with a plea for more general and more radical application of scientific method to the management of human affairs. Now, just what can we expect of science in this program?

Can science save us?

No! We must save ourselves. Science is not a body of dogma. Like art and religion, it is a way of life, a vital, growing expression of human creative ability. Its product is organized knowledge—organized for a purpose, that is, for the enrichment and refinement of human satisfactions. But science as knowledge is inert. It cannot give us the will to live and to live more abundantly. Fortunately we have this surge of vitality by nature. What science can do is to show us what is most worth living for, which of the values that we crave are genuine and which are spurious; and when we have made our selection, science can guide our quest for the values chosen.

The record of thousands of years of history and observation of current events give convincing evidence that man himself is the cause of his cultural developments and also of his most serious disasters. He manages to survive in spite of his own blundering, and we have enough knowledge of the causes of his failures to show us where to look for the remedies. Some of these causes are bad management of our external affairs, but our most flagrant social disorders are due to bad management of ourselves, to faulty standards of what constitutes good living, with resulting behavior which is misdirected, unsatisfying, and often dangerous. Most people of all races of mankind have wit enough to understand the essential requirements of bodily health and community welfare if only the facts can be presented to them in ways that they will accept.

Humanity is basically decent, sturdy, and resourceful; but we are pitifully ignorant. This is bad for us because we cannot rely on our inherited instincts and impulses to take care of us. We have greater capacity for learning by experience than any of our brutish ancestors, and if we do not succeed in developing this capacity so as to conform intelligently with biologically acceptable moral standards of fitness we perish.

Scientific research has pointed the way to more comfortable living with gratifying efficiency in the domain of mechanical engineering. But we have failed disastrously to make corresponding progress in human engineering, in the conduct of our personal and social affairs. We know that these problems can be solved satisfactorily because many individual people and some communities have so solved things. Those rules of conduct that yield healthy bodies, security, productivity, and contentment in the case of the individual man are equally applicable to groups of men in their communal and international relations, and the results are equally good. The golden rule has been shown to be as good for corporations, labor unions, and governments as it is for churches and for you and me.

An over-all view of all living things gives us a biological criterion of goodness. It is good to be alive, and it is better to live as richly and productively as possible. No simple general formula for betterment can be written, for what is good for one individual or for one sort of situation may be evil for or in another. A way of life that is good for a fish would be fatal for a frog. A little fire in my fireplace is good for me. A similar fire in my waste basket is not. There are some general criteria of goodness, but the application of these standards to particular instances must be adjusted to the facts as they are, not to any arbitrary codes devised by men.

No biologist whose view of life is wide enough to encompass the hundreds of millions of years of progressive evolution and the dramatic history of the hundreds of thousands of years of man's gradual metamorphosis from a simian biped to the modern engineer, statesman, poet, or philosopher can be a pessimist, however disquieted he may be about the futilities and frustrations of his own generation. The history of animal evolution is marked by recurrent periods of stress and conflict. Humanity is now experiencing a revolutionary change of explosive turbulence. Some countries have been devastated by irrational mass murder of competent and useful citizens and by military action which destroyed the machinery of production, priceless treasures of art, and a large proportion of their most efficient citizens. We are now threatened with even worse disasters. But humanity is not yet defeated and, judging by the past, we have reason to hope that out of the ruins of an outmoded social structure a more refined and constructive humanism will emerge, a new code of social and international relations that will yield security and healthy growth.

Notwithstanding the fumbling ineptitudes of our social machinery which have been mentioned, we citizens of the U.S.A. are making real and indeed very rapid progress in some directions that give promise of a more stable cultural organization with provision for further refinement of our highest humanistic values. A statistician (Turck, '52) calls our attention to some trends in American expenditures during the preceding decade which may serve as indexes of what our people want and are getting. In this short period a new pattern of tangible and intangible values has come to expression with unprecedented rapidity. A few examples are selected from the article cited.

For the first time in our history there were more consumers (54 per cent) who owned their homes than paid rent. In 1951 Americans were spending 104 per cent more (in constant dollars adjusted for change in purchasing value) for education than in 1940. This increase is far greater than that of the population in the period. In this decade the amount of literature purchased also increased, and much of it was of high quality. In 1950 we spent 96 per cent more constant dollars for books than in 1940.

Another significant index of changing attitudes is seen in American philanthropy. In 1944 about 40 per cent of all government expenditures in this country was for welfare work, in a broad definition of that term. The total expenditures for public and private philanthropy in the aggregate in this country are now exceeded only by those for insurance, manufacturing, agriculture, and trade. Our enormous expenditures for public welfare have spread so far in foreign lands that "many people, in many corners of the world, hold that American charity is the heartbeat of American greatness" (*Time*, Nov. 8, 1954).

People now have more money to spend than they had ten years ago. The average American's real purchasing power was 53 per cent greater in 1950 than in 1940 after adjustment for the rise in living costs. But more money to spend does not explain these trends toward increased expenditures for culturally more desirable things.

We have faith in ourselves and in our ability to live at progressively higher levels of production and harmonious adjustment of differences. We have faith that this achievement will yield the satisfactions that we crave. This faith is not a figment of wishful thinking. It is based on scientifically validated knowledge. Yet it is a faith, not a fact—a saving faith that may guide our steps into ways of peace and contentment. We live by faith—blind "animal faith" in the uniformities of nature and a matured intelligent faith in ourselves. Let us, then, be true to ourselves and so not false to any trust that our humanity imposes upon us.

Man's capacity for intelligently directed self-development confers upon him the ability to determine the pattern of his culture and so to shape the course of human evolution in directions of his own choice. This ability, which no other animals have, is man's most distinctive characteristic, and it is perhaps the most significant fact known to science.

In the final paragraph of Sir Arthur Keith's book on human evolution ('49) we find this sentence: "The evolution of mankind is not something which happened long ago and far away but it is happening here and now under our eyes." The human evolution now going on under our eyes is not something that is happening *to us*. It is something that is happening *by us*, and in so far as we know what we are doing and what we are doing it for we can set the direction of the further course of our evolution. But first we must decide where we want to go.

In what kind of a world do we want to live? We can get what we want within certain limitations if enough of us join our forces. We can exploit other people in our local communities and in the community of nations and acquire wealth and power at the cost of continued disorder and sooner or later of war. Or we can co-operate in competitive enterprises in lawfully ordered ways and win peace and prosperity.

PART II
The Evolution of Brains
Neurological Factors of Psychobiology

CHAPTER EIGHTEEN

The Spiritual Life of a Mechanist

Occasionally I have been honored by invitations to lecture before academic and other assemblies. The announced subject of one of these lectures, delivered before a scientific audience at the Ohio State University, has been chosen as the title of this chapter, introductory to Part II. At the beginning of the lecture I said, "Under such a title you will expect a sermon, and I shall not disappoint you." Accordingly, I introduced the address with this scriptural text:

> That was not first which is spiritual,
> but that which is natural; and
> afterward that which is spiritual.
> I Cor. 15:46

I take it that the Apostle Paul was here speaking as a naturalist rather than as a metaphysician, and in this sermon I undertook an exegesis of the naturalistic implications of his doctrine. Our program in this book is an amplification and documentation of these implications.

Examination of the relations between the "spiritual" components of human experience and the "natural" components is the province of psychobiology, a field of inquiry that began to acquire scientific status only about a hundred years ago. This science is still in its infancy, for it has not yet matured any considerable body of basic principles about which there is general agreement among competent authorities. Almost every proposition that has been stated about the relations between mind and body has been questioned or contradicted by learned men.

When people nowadays talk about the spiritual life, the reference generally is to man's conscious experiences, that is, to mental processes that are known only subjectively and are therefore not open to public inspection. These private mental acts evidently are radically different in kind from the events of the physical world which can be examined objectively by all competent observers. The former are commonly described as "spiritual" and the latter as "natural."

At about the time when the sermon to which reference has just been made was delivered I published ('28) in a religious magazine the substance of that discourse. I emphasized the necessity of cultivating our spiritual values intelligently so as to avoid pledging allegiance to spurious values, for our success in life depends very largely upon the skill with which we adjust all our rational and emotional mental processes to the actualities of the physical world in which we live and of which our bodies are parts. Psychobiology, accordingly, is not an esoteric cult. It deals with the most practical problems with which we are confronted in the daily task of making a living.

If we do not keep our thoughts and feelings in harmonious adjustment with what is going on around us, we are in serious trouble. Our business goes bankrupt, we lose our friends, and life is ruined. Radical failure to make these practical adjustments of the spiritual life to things as they are is a disastrous disorder; those people who are subject to such disorder we call insane and put in mental hospitals for medical treatment. These problems have always been with us and have been given serious attention by thoughtful people from prehistoric times.

Primitive man early recognized this twofold quality of his experience. He conceived his body as part of the natural world and as a house which could be occupied by immaterial spirits who controlled its movements arbitrarily. Magical agents and instruments thus came to play an increasingly important part in all his personal and social enterprises. This appeal to the supernatural was a compensation for lack of knowledge, as it still is in all modern cultures today.

With the advancement of practical and scientific knowledge through the centuries the primitive demonolatries have been generally (although by no means universally) abandoned in the domain of inorganic nature. The primitive spiritistic tradition lingers, however, under various disguises in many reputable scientific circles, and in the vast domain of human affairs probably the majority of men today believe as one of their most cherished articles of faith that the human personality comprises a physical body which is "natural" and a spirit which is unnatural and in some inscrutable way may control the movements of the natural body.

If it is true that human nature is a blend of the natural and the unnatural, then natural science is baffled—and the basic problem of psychobiology is scientifically insoluble and must be turned over to the metaphysicians. This is the opinion of many philosophers and a considerable number of biologists. Some of the latter try to evade the issue by exclusion of everything "mentalistic" from their science. That, of course, is a feckless subterfuge, for this opinion, like every other, was conceived mentally and has no existence apart from this mental act. It does no good to declare that consciousness is a negligible epiphenomenon in the face of the fact that the most significant things people do are consciously motivated and consciously directed. One does not solve a problem by leaving out the troublesome factors.

The current revolt against "animism" in science is a defense reaction, an attempt to protect science from contamination by the mysticism of the transcendentalists. But this is a confession of defeat for psychobiology. Defeatism is an unhealthy scientific attitude; it is, in fact, radically unscientific, for science has a legitimate interest in everything of which we have veridical experience. We have ample scientific evidence that a man's mental processes—his thoughts and emotions—are tied in with his physical behavior in lawfully ordered ways. If we do not know just how this is done, the thing to do is to try to find out by skillfully designed experiments. The answer will never be found if the plain facts of common experience are ignored and the mental factors of behavior are left out of consideration.

In scientific circles the consensus now is that all known events are operations of natural mechanisms and that it is the function of natural science to describe these mechanisms and to discover the laws of their operation. The naturalist, then, must of necessity be a mechanist. To get the full significance of this statement we must inquire into the essential and distinctive properties of mechanism as such. In Chapter 5, I discussed the misconceptions about what a machine is and how it works and that argument need not be repeated here.

All our objective experience is of mechanisms in action. Subjective experience has been regarded in our tradition as nonmechanistic, that is, as action without mechanism. If this is granted, then mystical agencies must be invoked and we are as far from a satisfactory scientific explanation of the known facts as were the magicians of our primitive ancestors. The modern psychobiologist is not content to let the matter rest here. Let us start with the working hypothesis that mentation is the operation of a natural mechanism in just the same sense that muscular movement is the operation of a different kind of mechanism.

The evidence so far found indicates that in the development of every human child the "natural" life, that is, the physiological process of living, reaches a rather advanced stage of organization before the "spiritual" life can begin. This seems to be true also in the longer span of cosmic evolution. There is good evidence that in both series of events the emergence of conscious experience takes place naturally in accordance with biological principles that can be discovered—some of them, in fact, have been discovered. It follows, then, that the spiritual life too is natural life and that human nature is an integrated biological unit, not a house divided against itself into natural and unnatural incompatibles. It is as natural for the brain to think as it is for the heart to beat.

In the present state of knowledge the tasks of the psychobiologists may be grouped in three classes of technical studies. Highly trained specialists must carry on these studies, and in the past the three groups have worked for the most part independently and sometimes at cross purposes. That era is passing and now the co-operative efforts of these experts in diverse fields give promise of fruitful results.

The first task is to discover by objective inquiry the properties of the living mechanisms that execute all animal behavior, including that which is motivated intelligently and emotionally. This gives us the physiological factors of behavior and the laws of their operation.

The second group of studies must be concerned with the investigation of all kinds of mental processes by scientifically controlled introspection. This is possible because the strictly personal mental experiences can be described verbally and otherwise, and thus an objective record of them is available for scientific study. Introspective pyschology gives us scientific knowledge of the spiritual life and the psychological factors of behavior.

The laws of the physiological factors and those of the psychological factors are not directly comparable, for no common units of measurement for them have yet been found. The third task of psychobiology, then, is to define as exactly as possible the relations existing between the physiological processes and the colligated mental processes. This is the province of physiological psychology. When these relationships are adequately known we shall be able to formulate the principles of the mechanics of mental processes. This goal has not yet been reached, but we have reason to believe that it is not unattainable.

The rest of this book, accordingly, is devoted to the nervous system, the evolution of its structure, the general principles of nervous action, and the known relations of these physiological functions to the colligated mental processes. Only a sketchy outline of this vast body of knowledge can be presented here. The topics selected for consideration are treated more fully in other and more technical works, some of which are cited.

A short untechnical paper by Sperry ('52) approaches the mind-body problem from a different standpoint. Our two studies were carried on quite independently with material and methods that have little in common. We differ from each other about some things, and yet our major conclusions are so similar that Sperry's paper might be used as a condensed summary of my own program. The same may be said about a six-page essay, "The Most Important Thing," by Frederic Andrews Gibbs ('51), in which this experienced neurologist tells in simple and graphic language what our brains are for and how stupidly we neglect to make efficient use of these little mechanisms that make products that are (for us) the most important things in the world.

The nervous tissues have many peculiar and distinctive physiological properties, and these are all derived as specializations of more general properties of all protoplasm. The nervous factors of behavior, accordingly, can be understood only if set in the broader frame of reference of the nonnervous biological factors. In the first part of this book I have discussed the evolution of behavior from this general biological standpoint. The principles which are stated there and defended with some documentation comprise the foundation of theory upon which the following analysis of the neurological factors of behavior is developed.

CHAPTER NINETEEN

The Origin and General Properties of the Nervous System

Neurosensory and neuromotor relations

All plants and the most primitive animals get along well enough—for them—without nervous systems, for the distinctive nervous functions, viz., irritability, conductivity, and integration, are essential properties of all protoplasm, although at a low level of organization. Some nonnervous animals, e.g., the sponges, may grow to large size, but they are sessile and their local movements are slow, restricted, and incompletely integrated; in short, their behavior is essentially plantlike. A freely moving animal of large size needs a much more complicated body, with division of labor and specialized parts adapted for registering a wider variety of things and events in the surroundings, for responding to them by rapid locomotor and other movements, and for maintenance of the bodily apparatus itself and the integration of all its activities.

To meet this need the nervous and muscular tissues were gradually differentiated, at an early stage of animal evolution, from more generalized structures. In this early stage of differentiation of tissues the motor apparatus took the lead; muscles appeared before nerves (Parker, '19; for some critical comments on these observations see pp. 85-87 of my book published five years later, '24). In Parker's account of the behavior of sponges it is shown that in these large multicellular animals co-ordinated motor activity is possible without nervous control. The tissue elements which execute these movements are neuromotor cells which perform both muscular and nervous functions, but the motor apparatus is far more highly elaborated. In this prodromal stage of the evolution of the nervous system motility is the key factor. In the embryological development of higher animals this phylogenetic history is recapitulated, for muscles generally mature to functional efficiency before they have any nervous connections. The earliest movements of the embryo are generally myogenic, not neurogenic, and all muscles retain in adult life some capacity for intrinsically generated contractility.

The reason for the precocious development of the muscular tissues is that motility in its most elementary form is the cradle of all behavior, and the higher patterns of behavior are possible only through acquisition of more efficient apparatus of expression. Motility is also the cradle of mind, for mentation arises within behavior and primarily for advancement of its efficiency.

With increase in the size and complexity of animal bodies there is demand for conductors adapted for speedy communication from part to part. The flow of blood with its contained chemical messengers meets some of these requirements. Ordinary protoplasm is a conductor of physical, chemical, and electrical energies, though the transmission is slow and diffuse. Slender strands of protoplasm are spun out as nerve fibers to secure more rapid conduction without decrement for long distances by insulated pathways. These nerves keep all parts of the body in communication with one another, and in the most primitive nervous systems known this is their primary function. In the simpler polyps there is no brain to act as a dominant center of control. A diffuse network of nerves is spread almost uniformly through the entire body. Integration of the local activities is effected simply by the mutual interplay of part with part through a system of conductors, the whole thus comprising a dynamically integrated body.

The nervous systems of higher animals with larger and more complicated bodies all have more or less elaborate centers of control—ganglia and brains. These are organized on many different plans, and in all of them integration in the interest of the body as a whole is the most important nervous function. These nervous systems show progressive increase in size and complexity of structure and each of the large divisions of the animal kingdom has its own characteristic structural plan of nervous organization. The two major branches of the phylogenetic tree leading respectively to insects and mammals have nervous systems composed of similar elements—nerve cells and fibers—but these elements are combined according to radically different structural plans, so that the nervous systems of insects and men have no homologous parts. This is correlated with the fundamental difference in their patterns of behavior (Chapter 14).

The diffuse nervous network seen in polyps and jellyfish is incapable of making the refined analysis of sensory and motor experience of stimulus-response type that is essential for the more complicated patterns of behavior. In the higher animals, accordingly, the analytic apparatus necessary for sorting out the various kinds of sensory excitations and motor responses is progressively specialized and refined. This complication requires a central adjusting apparatus to canalize the different kinds of incoming messages and to direct them into the appropriate outgoing pathways. The central nervous system performs these local analytic and co-ordinating functions in addition to the general integration of all bodily activities. The importance of this distinction between the analytic and the integrative factors of behavior is explained in Chapters 7, 8, and 9.

This central control and synthesis increases progressively from lower to higher animals as the problems of behavior become more complicated, and so there is corresponding enlargement of the brain. This is true in both insect and vertebrate phyla; but in the latter the process of cephalization goes much further, reaching its culmination in the differentiation of the cortex of the cerebellum and cerebral hemispheres, which are integrators par excellence.

In the series of backboned animals from fish to man the fundamental plan of the brain is similar throughout, but the modifications of this plan in adaptation to various modes of life are amazingly great and diversified. Among the factors which determine the directions taken in these divergent lines of specialization the most important for the behaviorist is the distinction between, and the relative parts played by, the innate components of the action system and those that are acquired. This distinction we meet at every turn of our inquiry.

A second factor is the relative importance of the several senses in the economy of different species of animals depending on habitat and customary ways of making their living. For example, in most birds vision is the dominant sense and the senses of taste and smell are used but little. In dogs the sense of smell is highly developed and vision is poor. The internal structure of the brain shows corresponding differences.

A third consideration arises in connection with the various types of motor adjustment. Specialization for running, digging, climbing, flying, and swimming requires in each case a readjustment of the nervous mechanisms involved. The most striking illustration of this is seen at the transition from fishes to terrestrial animals. The simple paired fins of fishes act chiefly as rudders, not propellers. When the mudfishes emerged from the water to become amphibians these fins were transformed into legs, and quadrupedal locomotion requires much more complicated machinery than fishlike swimming. The movements at each joint of each leg must be co-ordinated and synchronized with the movements at other joints and with all movements of each of the other legs. Similarly all the other activities of land animals must be adjusted to much more diversified environmental conditions than prevail in the water.

This radical change in mode of life—from water to land and air—which began in the Devonian period about 300,000,000 years ago, marks a critical turning point in the evolution of behavior. A bigger and better brain was essential for survival and successful exploitation of the resources of the wider and more heterogeneous environment. Swimming as a total pattern requires far less refinement of central control than does walking, with its multitude of partial patterns. This change in the neuromotor apparatus is begun in the lungfishes, is carried further in the amphibians, and is completed in reptiles and all higher classes (Herrick, '48, p. 14).

I think it may safely be claimed that throughout the whole course of vertebrate evolution the motor systems—the apparatus of expression—have played the leading part in setting the directions taken in the various lines of divergent specialization. This is so because every animal's success in life depends on his behavior, and this in turn must be adjusted to the motor equipment he has to work with. A larger measure of success, a richer life, may be won through improvement of the efficiency of the motor organs by the slow process of natural selection or by the acquisition of more skill in the use of the organs so provided.

Mechanisms of analysis and integration

The contrast between innate and acquired components of behavior appears in both the analytic and the integrative patterns and in the apparatus employed. The mechanism of integration in the higher vertebrates, where learned behavior plays the dominant role, is different from that found in lower animals, where most of the behavior is reflex and instinctive. So also the analytic apparatus of the stereotyped sensorimotor reactions of lower animals is inadequate to resolve the problems of behavior presented in conduct which is intelligently directed and so more individually variable. The primitive analyzers of the brain as we find them in fishes are, accordingly, in higher animals supplemented by additional nervous adjustors at a higher level of structural organization in the thalamus and cerebral hemispheres.

The analytic organs of the stereotyped inherited patterns of behavior are fixed systems of nerve cells and connecting fibers which are relatively stable and similar in all members of a race or species. The pattern of this arrangement differs from species to species in conformity with their diverse modes of life, and these arrangements have been described in great detail. The apparatus of the integrative functions and of all learned behavior, on the contrary, in the more primitive species is dispersed and hard to identify, and even in higher animals, where it is massively developed, its essential structure and method of operation are inadequately understood.

Because sensorimotor experience is concerned primarily with the adjustments of the body and its movements with reference to external things which are oriented in space and time, the organs concerned are also precisely localized in the brain. These functions are relatively uniform and predictable under standardized conditions and the temporal relations of these activities are accurately measurable. None of these statements apply with equal precision to the integrative apparatus.

Although most acquired behavior and all higher mental processes are essentially integrative, they must operate for the most part through the mediation of the analytic systems, for the data of sensory and motor experience are all they have to work with. Analysis and synthesis of experience go on hand in hand and simultaneously. It is therefore not surprising to find that the sensorimotor and the integrative tissues of the brain are closely related and intricately interwoven. Nevertheless these tissues in most regions can be distinguished when the details of structure are adequately known.

In the brains of all vertebrates it is much easier to see and describe the relatively well-defined structures which control the stereotyped reflex behavior and to test the functions performed by experiment than it is to make a similar analysis of the apparatus of integration. Because the evolution of the sensorimotor components of the nervous system has been more completely described, these components will next be examined and then the evolution of the integrative apparatus will be surveyed.

The analytic apparatus

When I first began to be interested in comparative neurology I turned to the fishes and amphibians, because I anticipated that their simple stereotyped patterns of behavior would be correlated with correspondingly simple and schematic patterns of nervous structure, so that in these simple brains it would be possible to map the courses of the several reflex circuits much more clearly than can be done in the more complicated fabric of mammals. Nothing of the sort happened. To my surprise I found that the closer we approach the primitive generalized ancestral species the less well-defined and sharply localized are central pathways and nervous centers which form the analytic apparatus.

In my description of the generalized brain of a salamander ('48, chaps. 6 and 11) it is shown that although the sense organs and their peripheral nerves are highly specialized, the muscular system is at a relatively low level of differentiation. In terms of behavior this means that the salamander is well equipped for the analysis of sensory experience, but the motor responses are, for the most part, mass movements of total pattern type. The repertoire of local reflexes is less than in higher quadrupeds, and these local movements are more closely bound to the mass movements. This is especially so in the legless larvae which swim in the water; but even the locomotion of the adults when they walk on land is fish-like, for all movements of the limbs are co-ordinated with rhythmic contractions of the body musculature. In short, the sensory analyzers are much more elaborately developed than are the motor analyzers.

These features of the salamander's behavior explain the peculiar structure of the central adjusting apparatus in this brain. Because most of the activity is relatively simple mass movement, the central apparatus of motor adjustment is correspondingly simplified. The nervous impulses received from the complicated sensory analyzers have only a few motor outlets and these lead to a motor apparatus with a limited variety of possible movements.

The general plan of the primitive vertebrate brain is most clearly seen in the salamanders. The brains of two of these species I have described in detail—the mudpuppy, Necturus ('33b), and the tiger salamander, Amblystoma ('48).

Figure 1 is an enlarged drawing of an amphibian brain dissected so as to open the cavities (ventricles) of the cerebral hemispheres, thalamus, and medulla oblongata. Here the cerebral hemispheres, which comprise the largest part of the human brain, are very small and the medulla oblongata is relatively very large. In this brain the medulla oblongata is the central receptive station for most sensory nerve fibers except those of smell and vision (as is true also in the human brain). The end-organs and nerves of the several senses—touch, taste, vestibular control of posture, etc.—are well developed and separately localized, but within the brain these various systems of nerve fibers converge to only two great pools, each of which extends throughout the entire length of the medulla oblongata. Precise localization of function stops at this place where the peripheral nerve fibers make contact with the central nerve cells in a dense feltwork of interlaced fibers, termed neuropil (page

249). One of these pools—the visceral sensory neuropil associated with the fasciculus solitarius—receives all fibers of gustatory and general visceral sensibility and discharges into the visceral motor mechanisms. The other pool—the somatic sensory neuropil—receives fibers of all types of cutaneous and deep sensibility that are concerned with adjustment to the external environment, i.e., the exteroceptive and proprioceptive systems of Sherrington's analysis ('48). This neuropil discharges into somatic motor apparatus that controls the movements of the skeletal muscles.

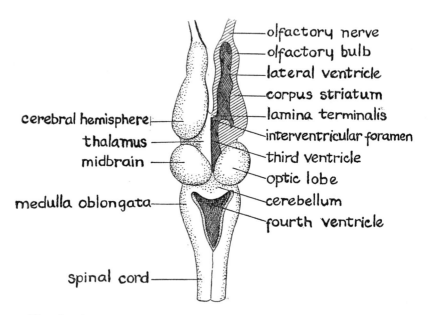

Fig. 1.—Dorsal view of an amphibian brain. The roof of the cerebral hemisphere and thalamus has been removed on the right side to open the lateral and third ventricles. After Herrick ('24).

This segregation of all sensory nerve fibers, except those of vision and olfaction, into only two receptive centers is the only well-defined localization of sensory functions present in the medulla oblongata. It corresponds with the fundamental difference in behavior between internal visceral activities and somatic sensorimotor activities that have an external reference. The visceral movements are for the

most part of total pattern type. This is as true in men as in salamanders. Accordingly, there is little more specialization or separate
localization of function in the fasciculus solitarius neuropil of men
than of salamanders.

The evolutionary history of the somatic sensory neuropil is different. In salamanders most of the activity of the skeletal musculature is mass movement of total pattern type. No matter which sense
organ excites it to activity, there are only a few things the animal
can do about it. From a single pool of receptive neuropil which may
be activated from any one or all of several kinds of sense organs,
motor impulses go out to a limited number of motor systems, each
of which is so organized as to activate the appropriate mass movement as an integrated unit. Since there are few autonomous local
reflexes available, no sharply segregated and well-insulated pathways for localized reflex arcs are needed. And this is just what is
found. In these generalized brains there are few clearly defined
tracts for the service of local reflexes.

A man, on the contrary, has reflex and voluntary control of his
separate fingers and innumerable other local movements. These
separately individuated partial patterns of behavior need and have
an elaborate provision of segregated cellular masses ("nuclei") connected by well-insulated tracts of fibers. The primitive diffuse receptive center seen in the somatic sensory neuropil of the salamander
is here separated into many cellular areas, or nuclei, each of which
receives sensory fibers of a specific modality, e.g., touch, hearing, etc.
Each sensory nucleus may discharge nervous impulses by short circuits to specific motor nuclei or by longer paths (the lemniscus
systems) to higher centers of correlation. In the salamander the
specific localization in space of the several modalities of sense is
carried only so far as the terminals of their peripheral fibers in the
medulla oblongata. In the man this specificity of the analytic apparatus is carried forward as far as the thalamus and the sensory
projection areas of the cerebral cortex.

It should be mentioned that the preceding description of the medulla oblongata of the salamander is somewhat oversimplified. The
somatic sensory pool of neuropil is not strictly equipotential. There
is an incipient localization of function of the different modalities of

sense, but this is not advanced to the grade where separate reflex arcs are recognizable. From this pool of neuropil there are several outgoing pathways. These are lines of preferential discharge. Which of them will be activated in any particular situation depends on the internal physiological state of the neuropil at that time. There is nothing here that can be compared with the switchboard of an automatic telephone system with its perfectly insulated separate circuits. Just what is the mechanism by which different kinds of sensory excitation are analyzed and canalized into the appropriate neuromotor organs of response is now under active investigation.

The most primitive vertebrates now living (lampreys and their allies) have brains that are relatively smaller and less differentiated than are those of salamanders, but the general plan of internal organization is the same and so is that of the primitive ganoid fishes, like the sturgeon. The brain of the salamander is a convenient type form or standard of reference for study of the evolution of the brain because it retains many of the structural peculiarities of the most primitive brains and yet its internal differentiation has advanced sufficiently to enable us to see recognizable germinal stages of the main features of all higher brains.

The evolutionary history of the transformation of these primitive brains into the vastly more complicated human thinking machine has been so intensively studied by many people in many lands that it is now possible to record its broad outlines. These details cannot be reviewed here. They have been summarized concisely by Ariëns Kappers ('29), Schepers ('48), and others, and much more fully in an encyclopedic work by Ariëns Kappers, Huber, and Crosby ('36).

The integrative apparatus

Turning now to the history of the differentiation of the integrative apparatus of the brain, we find a series of structural changes of radically different kind. In the most primitive fishes and amphibians the internal texture of the brain is more nearly homogeneous than in the more specialized fishes and all higher animals.

For the reasons just mentioned, the localization of function is more clear-cut on the sensory side than on the motor side, because most of the muscular activity of the unspecialized animals is mass movement. The nervous elements concerned with the analytic functions are generally recognizable and among these nerve cells and fibers there are others that are integrative in function. The latter form a very closely woven fabric of interlaced thin naked fibers, the neuropil. The bodies of all nerve cells and their widely spread dendritic branches are embedded within this fibrous mat and closely enveloped by it. Every contact of these fibers with the cell is a synaptic junction (page 262), and a single cell may have a hundred or more of these contacts with fibers from near and remote parts of the brain (Figure 2). This web of neuropil permeates the entire brain and acts as a non-specific conducting system which puts every part of the brain into physiological connection with every other part. It is the primary integrating mechanism, but it is much more than this. It is germinative tissue with potentialities for further differentiation in an endless variety of ways. During subsequent stages of cerebral evolution its derivatives form the largest and most complicated structures in the brain. The details of the structure and properties of the amphibian

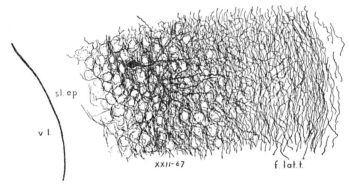

Fig. 2.—Detail of the neuropil in the anterior part of the corpus striatum of the frog, from a Golgi preparation. Magnified × 142. The lateral ventricle is marked v. l.; the ependymal layer is marked st. ep.; the lateral forebrain bundle, which is the precursor of the human extra-pyramidal system of fibers, is marked f. lat. t. This tissue is a dense entanglement of very thin nerve fibers within which are embedded the cell bodies of the neurons. Only one of these neurons is stained. The clear circles mark the positions of other unstained cell bodies of the gray substance. Compare Figures 12 and 13, pp. 392, 393. After Herrick ('34).

neuropil are described more fully elsewhere ('48, pp. 29-39, 80, 88).

In the adult amphibian brain the web of neuropil binds the parts together and so does for the central nervous system what the diffuse nervous network of jellyfish does for the whole body; but it is not the first nervous tissue to reach functional maturity in vertebrate embryos. In the early development of these more complicated bodies it is essential that certain movements that have adaptive value should develop precociously, so that the newly hatched or born animal can fend for itself as soon as possible. The moment after a salamander emerges from the egg it can swim; a newborn horse can stand and walk. To make this possible there is first laid down in the brain a system of direct nervous connections which make provision for a limited number of mass movements and local reflexes. The latter usually mature later than the former. Then there follows an out-growth of an increasing number of collateral branches of these pio-neer fibers and the central linkage of the several sensory and motor pathways by more and more complicated interconnections.

During this process some nerve cells are set apart for integrative functions only. Their fibrous processes take longer or shorter courses, branching freely, and so they form a major component of the neuro-pil. These nervous elements are not at any time concerned with specific reflexes, but with the co-ordination and integration of all movements. Some of the longer and thicker of these fibers may be fasciculated to form definite tracts which are tied in with one or another of the neuromotor systems for higher control of their ac-tion. In this way all the sensorimotor systems are interconnected. There are well-defined pathways of preferential discharge which activate the standardized patterns of reflex and instinctive behavior, but which ones of these will be activated in any particular situation depend on numberless factors of peripheral stimulation and central excitatory state, such as fatigue, temporary condition of the vascular and endocrine systems, etc.

The nerve cells that are concerned primarily with internal cor-relation and synthesis of behavior may be mingled with those which serve for analysis of sensorimotor reactions, but during the course of evolution the apparatus of each of these two classes of function becomes more and more specialized and the nerve cells set apart for integration are segregated and clustered in local nests, or nuclei, each of which serves some particular phase of the integrative process. In the human brain there are very many of these, such as the habenulae, interpeduncular and pontile nuclei, the thalamic nuclei, and the inferior olives. The three largest of these integrative centers are the cerebellum, the corpus striatum, and the cerebral cortex. These regulate all bodily movements and in addition they have vast reserves of potential nervous energy which may be discharged on occasion to reinforce, inhibit, or otherwise modify the routine activities of the brain stem and spinal cord. These nuclei must not be regarded as specific organs of the functions ascribed to them. On the contrary, they are merely critical nodal points in systems of communication of wide extent and the functions in question are performed by the system as a whole.

The undifferentiated neuropil of lower vertebrates is by no means homogeneous in texture or equipotential in function. It is under constant activation from the periphery and the physiological quality of this activity differs from region to region and from moment to moment. The same is true in those highly specialized derivatives of this neuropil that are seen in the human brain, the most complicated of which is the intricate system of thalamo-cortical connections.

There is localization of function in both the analytic and the integrative apparatus, but the principles of localization are radically different, as explained in Chapter 32.

It was long ago recognized by the pioneer explorers of the human brain (Meynert, Hughlings Jackson, and others) that a succession of levels of structural and functional complexity can be seen, the series extending from the peripheral end-organs through the spinal cord and brain stem to the cerebral cortex. This series is a rough register in the adult of the successive steps which were taken during the course of evolution of the integrating apparatus. This analysis, though obviously somewhat arbitrary, corresponds to levels of physiological integration. In the light of present knowledge I would list these levels as follows:

1. A low level of integration is seen at the periphery in the sensory and motor end-organs. In some of these organs, notably the eye and ear, the apparatus of both analysis and integration is elaborate.

2. A second level of integration is represented in the spinal cord and brain stem by the primary sensory and motor centers (i.e., centers directly

connected with the periphery) and the systems of fibers that connect them with one another so as to provide reflex circuits for the simpler components of standardized behavior.

3. A third level is represented in the diffuse neuropil and its more specialized derivatives, such as the thalamus and the stem part of the cerebral hemispheres. This structural level serves two quite distinct sorts of physiological integration: first, the more elaborately organized instinctive complexes, including the accompanying emotional drives; and, second, conditioning of reflexes and some other kinds of individually learned behavior. The corpus striatum of reptiles and birds is the largest and most complicated structure of this level. In man this body is reduced in relative size and its action is, for the most part, ancillary to that of the cerebral cortex.

4. Historically considered, a fourth level may be recognized, characterized by the appearance of simple cerebral cortex of reptilian type. Precursors of this are found in amphibians and some fishes. Some vestiges of it remain in the human brain at the margins of the cortical field.

5. The fifth level is characterized by the mammalian type of cortex, concerned primarily with learning and the organization of learned behavior. This learned behavior is founded upon reflex and instinctive behaviors and it supplements them.

6. Finally, the human type of associational cortex carries behavior to an integrative level capable of devising and using tools and symbols and of semantic processes of reasoning.

The activities characteristic of the fifth and sixth levels are not confined to the cerebral cortex. For the most part they are circular in pattern, with the thalamus and the cortex working in reciprocal interrelationship, as clearly explained by Dusser de Barenne ('34).

The levels just mentioned are concerned primarily with adjustments to the surroundings and their integration. The internal affairs of the body are analyzed and integrated by complex systems of visceral and proprioceptive nervous organs which also may be arranged in levels of successively higher order. The cerebellum is the highest member of the proprioceptive system, as Sherrington pointed out in 1906 and I have recently ('47) again emphasized with some revision of former conceptions of its functions.

I have distinguished ('25) six levels of visceral functions: (1) Some measure of intrinsic nonnervous tonicity and automaticity is characteristic of all living substance and is especially pronounced in human muscles and viscera. (2) The visceral functions are especially susceptible to chemical control by endocrines distributed in the body fluids. (3) There is local regulation of the viscera by intrinsic autonomous sympathetic ganglionated plexuses. (4) There is central regulation of these plexuses through sympathetic nervous circuits in the cranial and spinal nerves, the efferent path

going by way of preganglionic and postganglionic neurons. (5) Superposed upon these circuits there is a series of cerebral visceral centers in the
brain stem, the most important of which are in the hypothalamus. (6)
Finally, all of these lower levels are under some measure of control by
the cerebral cortex.

Investigation of the biochemical properties of the various parts of the
central nervous system reveals a metabolic gradient from cortex to spinal
cord which is analyzed by Himwich ('52 and works there cited) into five
functional levels. He points out that in the course of vertebrate phylogeny
there has been a progressive shift of physiological dominance of several
critical vital functions from the lowest level in the medulla oblongata in
fishes to the cortex in man.

This analysis of the nervous system into levels, however defined, is of
course artificial; it is very important to recognize that all levels of integration interpenetrate and one never operates independently of the others.
Each higher level is derived from the lower and can work only with the
instrumentation provided by the lower levels. Nonetheless each level has
its own distinctive qualities and the laws of its operation are peculiar to it.

Reflexology

Because the structural arrangements of cells and fibers of the analytic apparatus are most clearly revealed by the staining methods
commonly used by microscopists and the experimental methods of
the physiologists, attention has been directed chiefly to stimulus-
response types of behavior. Much research has been devoted to
mapping the courses of the reflex circuits involved in all standardized
forms of behavior. This has been so successful that during the past
half-century an ambitious program of reflexology was elaborated,
notably by Pavlov and the American school of behaviorism. The
avowed objective was to reduce all animal and human behavior to
systems of interlocking reflexes of various grades of complexity.
The conditioning of these reflexes by personal experience was invoked as the mechanism of learning. The simple reflex was regarded
as the unit of behavior, and all other kinds of behavior were conceived as brought about by the linkage of these units in successively
more complicated patterns.

The simplicity of this scheme is attractive but illusory. In the
first place, the simple reflex is a pure abstraction. There is no such
thing in any living body. A more serious defect is that all the information we have about the embryology and phylogenetic develop-

ment of behavior shows clearly that local reflexes are not the primary units of behavior. They are secondary acquisitions. As is clear from the researches of Coghill and many others, the actual behavior as manifested in reflexes and instincts is not developed by an additive accretion of separate reflexes; but these local partial patterns are secondarily individuated within the primordial total pattern, they are integral parts of it, and they are never completely emancipated from some measure of control by the integrative apparatus in the interest of the welfare of the body as a whole.

In current doctrines of reflexology conditioning of reflexes (learning) plays a major role. Conditioning is an observed physiological fact, but how it is done remains obscure. McCulloch (Frank *et al.*, '48, p. 266) has suggested an ingenious hypothesis to explain some features of the mechanics of conditioning; but until this subject is further clarified there is a fatal gap in the Pavlovian system of reflexology. This much is clear: learned behavior (whether unconscious or intentionally directed) and all higher mental capacities are total patterns. Reflexes as partial patterns are used instrumentally in learning, but they do not initiate it or direct it. Learning and thinking are not analytic; they are synthetic processes; and the apparatus employed is to be sought in the integrative tissues of the brain, not in the reflex arcs.

That the local reflexes are integral and subordinate parts of the total pattern was most clearly shown by Coghill's discussion ('30; cf. also Herrick, '48, pp. 73-81) of the part played by inhibition in reflex action. He called attention to the familiar fact that for the execution of a local reflex it is essential that all antagonistic or conflicting acts must be inhibited and that in early stages of the development of salamanders it can easily be seen that the total patterns are completely inhibited before a local reflex appears. It is often equally evident that this is true also in the adult animal. He concludes, "It is then in a field of total inhibition that the local reflex emerges." We may now accept Coghill's definition: "The reflex may, therefore, be regarded as a total behavior pattern which consists of two components, one overt or excitatory, the other covert or inhibitory."

Summary

All protoplasm has the properties of irritability, conductivity, and integration. The nervous tissues were first specialized for the refinement and further differentiation of these functions. The most primitive nervous systems (as seen in polyps) have nerve cells with very long fibrous extensions distributed everywhere throughout the body. These cells and fibers form a network that serves to keep all parts of the body in communication and so facilitates orderly coordination of the bodily movements. In higher animals with more complicated structure and behavior special collections of nerve cells are set apart to provide more efficient coordination and integration. These ganglia and brains take a great variety of forms in different animals depending on the patterns of behavior manifested.

Among the general properties of the nervous system one of the most significant for behavior is the contrast between the apparatus of the stable innate components of behavior and that of the more labile individually acquired components. The mechanisms of these two kinds differ in origin, evolutionary and embryological development, and significance for problems of practical control of conduct.

The innate structural plan of the nervous system is given. The animal must accept it as it is. The larger part of this inherited structure is the sensorimotor equipment for the performance of reflex and instinctive behavior. These analytic functions are the necessary tools for the cultivation of the intrinsic values of life, the satisfactions that accrue to the organism. Satisfaction is a total pattern and the integrative apparatus is amplified and specialized as the range of needs and desires is enlarged.

The early stages in the differentiation of the nervous system have been briefly outlined, with emphasis on its primary function as integrating apparatus. The sensorimotor analytic systems are differentiated within the primary totalizing appartus and always remain subject to control by it. The history of the progressive differentiation of the analyzers is contrasted with the quite different evolutionary development of the nervous mechanisms of integration.

Localization of function is more precise and easily demonstrated in the analytic components of the system. For this reason the reflex was long regarded as the elementary unit of behavior, but the history of both embryologic and phylogenetic development shows that it is not. Accordingly, some current doctrines of reflexology need radical revision.

CHAPTER TWENTY

The Nervous Functions

The expanding horizons of psychobiology

Solution of the basic problems of psychobiology has been sought in many fields of inquiry and most often by philosophical reasoning from metaphysical postulates for which there is little factual support. Thousands of years of this sort of speculation have yielded only futile controversy and the clear demonstration that these problems will not be solved by dialectic until more facts are available. It is evident that at this stage of the inquiry the critical facts are neurological. We must learn more about the nervous system and how it works before we can hope to clarify the mind-brain relationship.

In the present generation knowledge about the distinctive peculiarities of the nervous tissues has advanced more than during all the preceding years. These spectacular achievements were possible because radically new methods of study were devised. The invention of instruments which enable the observer to see and record with remarkable precision what is going on in living nervous tissue under ordinary and experimental conditions has revolutionized our conceptions of the physiology of the nervous system and opened hitherto unexplored fields of inquiry, the full fruition of which we are not yet able to predict.

These recent improvements in the instruments of research and technical skill in their use have been accompanied by a still more important change in the attitudes of the workers toward their problems. Many traditional conceptions which were purely speculative and were not supported by good evidence were questioned or discarded. Minds having been liberated from bondage to intrenched dogmas, the search has been extended in directions which formerly were regarded as inaccessible or unprofitable. The details of these researches are very technical, and we shall touch very lightly here upon only a few of the general principles.

Nervous conduction

Any complicated mechanism, inorganic or organic, can operate efficiently only if all parts are so connected by channels of communication that their operations are co-ordinated and synchronized in proper sequence. Some military planes now in production carry more than 1,000 pounds of electronic equipment with about thirty miles of electrical wirework to provide the communications needed for their intricate operations. The Empire State Building in New York has within its own walls 3,200 miles of telegraph and telephone wires. The human body is the most complicated mechanism in the world and the structure of its apparatus of communication is far more intricate than any other that we know. A great variety of devices are employed and two of these are of paramount importance—the body fluids with their contained hormones which serve as chemical messengers, and the nervous system. The latter is the dominant member of this complex, and it exerts more or less regulatory control over all the other members. If the telegraph, telephone, radio, and radar apparatus in the world could be compressed into a half-gallon cup, it would be less intricate than the three pints of brain that fills your skull or mine.

This apparatus has a twofold function. The first and primary function is communication. The second is integration, and this depends upon the first, because the manifold diverse actions of the parts cannot be carried out in proper order unless they are in communication with one another and with a central station that regulates their action.

All nervous functions derive from the basic properties of protoplasmic irritability and conductivity. In the nervous tissues these are refined and locally differentiated. The nerve fibers differ from other strands of protoplasm in their ability to transmit nervous impulses for long distances without decrement. As in a powder fuse, the energy required for transmission of the impulse is supplied locally within the fiber itself. And, unlike the fuse, the fiber has remarkable capacity for self-repair. When a pulse of transmission has passed, the fiber quickly recovers and after a latent or "refractory" period of about a thousandth of a second it is ready to transmit another pulse.

All fibers are outgrowth of nerve cells, and the cell body controls this growth and supplies the essential substance required for growth of the fiber and for its functional efficiency (Weiss and Hiscoe, '48). The fiber, however, is not a passive conductor, for nervous transmission involves active and very rapid participation of the fiber itself.

In the human body some large nerve cells, such as those in the ventral horns of the spinal cord and the motor area of the cerebral cortex, have fibrous processes more than two feet long. The total mass of such a fiber may be a thousand times greater than that of the cell body from which it has grown. In a huge animal like a whale these fibers are more than ten times as long as any human nerve fibers. What goes on in these fibers during nervous conduction has been learned in great detail.

Because the peripheral nerve fibers are most accessible to observation and experiment, our knowledge of the properties of these fibers is most exact and comprehensive. The process of conduction is fundamentally the same in all nerve fibers: a vital process of metabolism involving respiration (oxygen consumption with liberation of heat), other chemical processes, alteration of the permeability of membranes, and changes in electrical potential. The electrical and chemical activities involved are inseparable, for they are different manifestations of the same processes. The electrical changes can be measured and recorded with high precision, so that these are the most useful indicators of nervous activity. The electric properties of nervous tissue are clearly and concisely described, with references to the technical literature, by Brazier ('51); for other summaries see Eccles ('53), Katz ('52), Nachmansohn ('51), and Hoagland ('49).

The transmission of nervous impulses is rhythmical. The successive waves are marked by measurable changes in electrical potential. The rate of transmission is correlated with the thickness of the nerve fibers, varying in man from 160 meters per second for large fibers to less than 2 meters per second for very small fibers. There is only one kind of nervous impulse, but the velocity of transmission varies in different types of fibers.

There has been much speculation about the reasons for the great variation in the size of nerve fibers in different animals and in the various systems of fibers in the same animal, but no consensus has been reached. However, from this extensive literature one indisputable fact emerges: the thickness of fibers and their sheaths is correlated with speed of conduction. It is also evident that the demand for fast conduction arises in a great variety of situations and that we can write no simple general formula other than that thick fibers are developed wherever a quick response is required. For instance, most visceral fibers are thin and visceral movements are usually slow; on the contrary, motor fibers for skeletal muscles are thick and here speed of response is often vitally important.

If conduction is excited in any nerve fiber, it delivers its maximum discharge (the all-or-nothing law). The velocity of conduction and magnitude of the discharge are independent of the intensity of the stimulus. An increase in the strength of the stimulus results in a more rapid series of impulses and it may prolong the duration of repetitive discharges. Intensity of stimulation is registered by means of temporal and spatial summation of impulses.

There are no differences in the electrical properties of impulses of fibers of the various sensory systems that can be regarded as characteristic of the several modalities of sense. These qualities result in part from central analysis of the incoming nervous impulses in terms of speed and rhythm of transmission and the relations in space of the conducting fibers. There are specific chemical and physical properties of the nerve cells and fibers of the several functional systems, but there is no clear evidence that this specificity affects in any way the quality of nervous conduction. The current opinion is that "nerve impulses are essentially homogeneous in quality and are transmitted as 'common currency' throughout the nervous system" (Sperry, '52).

Peripheral and central relations

The reciprocal relations between temporal and spatial factors in all complicated nervous processes must be well understood before the mechanics of perception and higher mental processes can be discovered. Some illustrations of these reciprocal relations are cited in the chapters on sensation and perception, and they are conspicuous features of all cortical functions. Each of the various systems of peripheral sensory fibers (optic, auditory, tactile, etc.) discharges its nervous impulses into one or more specific receptive centers, or nuclei. All of these centers are so interconnected by nerve fibers that they form an equilibrated dynamic system. Any disturbance of the system by a single sensory stimulus or by simultaneous excitation of sense organs of several different modalities results in a central readjustment which registers the quality, intensity, and location of the sensory stimuli and so determines the nature of the response.

The mechanisms employed in these central adjustments are not well understood. It is not clear how the different modalities of sense and the "local signs" are discriminated. The modalities of cutaneous sensibility and the mechanisms employed in their discrimination have been experimentally analyzed by Bishop ('48).

Correlated with the precise localization in space of the different functional systems there are differences in the histological structure, chemical constitution, and electrical properties of the several centers and in the temporal rhythms of their connecting nerve fibers. During growth the nerve fibers somehow are so guided as to establish appropriate patterns of nervous connections, and during normal function these systems are selectively activated so as to give appropriate responses. Many factors are involved in the selective patterns of growth, regeneration, and functional specificity. In addition to those just mentioned many others have been suggested—the physical properties (molar, molecular, and submolecular) of the substrate (Weiss), "neurotropism" (Cajal), "neurobiotaxis" (Ariëns Kappers), various kinds of "tissue affinity" (Holtfreter), to cite a few examples. Differences in the modalities of sense and in the various "local signs" and the differential affinities of various systems of motor fibers for particular muscles are correlated with differences in the chemical properties of the nerve cells and fibers themselves (Sperry, '50). There is good evidence that some of these differences are impressed upon the nervous elements by a retrograde "modulation," that is, by influence of the end-organs upon the nerves with which they are in functional connection. These developmental problems are critically reviewed in recent publications by Weiss and others ('50) and Sperry ('51, '51a).

The properties of the nerve fibers are essentially the same in the central and peripheral nervous systems, but the nerve centers contain other components (cell bodies with processes polarized as dendrites and axons, synaptic junctions, neuroglia, etc.) which complicate the picture and introduce variable factors in countless number. A few of these have been isolated experimentally so that the mechanical principles involved can be discovered. Some of these principles conform with those of conventional chemistry and physics, some with those of quantum mechanics, and others are refractory in that they are *sui generis* without obvious relationship with any of the laws now accepted in other domains of science. The group last mentioned includes all subjective experience.

The neuron and the synapse

As explained in the preceding chapter, the most primitive nervous systems as seen in jellyfishes are composed of nerve cells with branching fibrous processes which are joined to form a continuous protoplasmic network. This nerve-net may conduct nervous impulses freely in all directions. In these animals and the allied polyps some of the cells are more specialized so that each of them is separated from the others by structural barriers (termed synapses) which permit nervous conduction in only one direction. Such a cell is called a neuron. For illustrations see Figure 11 (page 391). In the higher animals practically all nervous elements are neurons.

The typical neuron is anatomically and physiologically polarized because the cell body and some of its branches (the dendrites) can be activated by other nervous elements with which they are in contact, while another branch (and usually only one, the axon) transmits nervous impulses from this neuron to other nervous elements in contact with it. Axons and dendrites can conduct in either direction, but the direction of conduction across the synaptic junction is not reversible, so that each neuron is a polarized nervous element, normally transmitting in only one direction, from the receptive dendrites or cell body to the emissive axon. Conduction in the reverse direction is usually impossible because every synaptic junction acts like a valve, allowing nervous transmission through it in only one direction, toward the cell body in the dendrites and away from the cell body in the axon. There are exceptions, but this is the rule.

Polarized fields

The "polarization" of the nerve cell to which reference has just been made relates to the *pattern* of structure and nervous transmission of the element in question. The word is used with quite different meaning when we speak of a physical polarization field. In the latter case a charge, electric or magnetic, sets up a pattern of lines of force, and the molecules of the surrounding medium, if they have polar structure, orient themselves with their axes along the lines of force. In such a polarized field the center is distinguished from the field by action that may be measurable and expressed in units of energy. All nerve cells are polarized electrically in this second meaning of the word, and if a cell or any part of it is depolarized there is a measurable release of energy.

The word "field" has a wide variety of meanings, some static and some dynamic. In common usage and in this text it may refer to an area with definable boundaries, to a specific topic of discourse, or to some sort of pattern of action, such as the field of a magnet or of an electric charge. Field theories of the third class are now receiving a great deal of attention in mechanics, biology, psychology, and sociology.

Margenau ('50, p. 198) says that "the method of science reaches its fullest development in the theory of the electromagnetic field." Here we must not look exclusively upon the hard and rigid particles of mechanics, as has been done so often in the past. In another passage (p. 36) he draws an interesting analogy between "the picture of a spectator (perhaps a mind) embedded in an objective universe" and the Coulomb field of classical electrodynamics. The "classical field" interacts with material objects (e.g., electrical charges) which may be present. The object at a fixed point is regarded as having a stable mass with properties quite different from those of the field. This classical theory as developed by Einstein in relativistic terms gives a satisfactory explanation of large-scale physical phenomena, but it breaks down in the domain of subatomic physics. Electrons and other elementary particles do not behave according to the classical rules. To explain the observed facts, the new theory of quantum mechanics was developed. The "classical field" was supplemented and perhaps replaced by the "quantum field" in which objects are not hard and rigid and are not regarded as separate entities in fixed positions that react with the field. While still called elementary particles, their properties are identical with those of quanta of energy and the particles are loci or patterns of energy. The field can be defined only by its dynamic properties. The particle and its field are inseparably one, and the polarization of the fields must be expressed in complicated and rather abstract terms. The dominant center of the polarized field is not a fixed point, and no mechanical model of such a field can be constructed in terms of Newtonian mechanics.

This contrast between two ways of looking at the electromagnetic field is one illustration of a difference of wider scope between the general theories of particle physics and theories of field physics. The former direct attention primarily to the stable objects concerned, the latter to the system as a whole as exhibited "in the form of the relations of the motion of the parts" (Maxwell). Different individual particles may be engaged from time to time, but the pattern persists.

The history of this shift in physical theory from atomistic or particulate analysis to relativistic and quantum analysis is written by Margenau and more concisely in an essay by Burr and Northrop ('35; cf. also Burr, '47, and Dyson, '53). The conflict between these two ways of looking at nature has been with us since the time of the early Greek philosophers. Greek science at its best discarded the particulate theories of the earlier atomists and put the emphasis on the eternal stability and constancy of formal structure in a unitary system with relations that are best expressed in the abstractions of mathematics. The gods did not make the world as a man makes a machine and then meddle with it occasionally. The gods were immanent within the world and regulated it from the inside. This monistic conception was in sharp contrast with the dualistic Jewish and Christian philosophies whose God was transcendent to the natural world and acted upon it by arbitrary interference with natural processes.

Modern science puts the emphasis on the variability and the evolution of forms, with a tendency in both Newtonian and quantum mechanics to revert to the earliest systems of atomistic philosophy in modified forms. This particulate analysis led to concepts of discontinuity of natural processes, random behavior, and a dualistic or pluralistic natural philosophy.

Attempts to reconcile these contrasted views of nature were rather futile until atomic physics was supplemented by field physics with emphasis on the unitary nature of the field rather than on the individuality of the contained particles. To quote from the 1935 Burr and Northrop essay cited: "The particle both conditions and is conditioned by its field. . . . In short, any local system in part constitutes and is in part constituted in its behavior by nature as a whole. . . . and the physical field in which it is embedded. . . . The reciprocal causal relation between field and particle amounts to a union of both viewpoints." The unity of nature is a causal factor in every situation, but it is not the sole cause. The particulars also play a part which differs in each situation.

The inseparable relations between physical particles and their fields are discussed from a different point of view by Whyte ('49, pp. 45–53). The same author ('54, chap. 4) has written an interesting history of the controversy between atomism and holism and the reconciliation which is now in process.

The electromagnetic field as now conceived, like all physical fields, gives direction to the movements of the charges and so is potentially capable of establishing changing patterns of arrangement of the charges and the associated particles. It is this property of the dynamic fields of living tissues which gives direction to vital processes and so makes possible the orderly growth, evolution, and normal function of organisms. The fields with which we are concerned in cerebral physiology, psychology, and sociology must not be defined in terms of particulate mechanics, but rather in terms of the total pattern of performance as a dynamic unit without artificial detachment of focus and field by experimental analysis or logical dialectic.

The organizers of Spemann and the embryonic fields of biomechanics are defined in terms of the patterns of their action. The materials employed may be of diverse kinds at different places and times, but the pattern persists. So also if mentation is a vital process carried on in a field of metabolic activity, then the mind must not be regarded as an entity separable from its field of operation, a being which somehow pulls the strings that move a mechanical robot. The mind and the field are inseparably one. And the pattern of any particular mental act is not dependent upon the configuration of any stable structure. This pattern may come to expression wherever and whenever a suitable occasion arises, and it may operate by means of a different setup of nervous connections on each occasion. The field in question is not a structure; it is a pattern of process. But such a pattern may occur only in some particular region of the brain with the requisite structural organization, and this region, which has more or less definite boundaries, may be called the field of this particular type of process, that is, a field defined in terms of its relations in space to other parts of the brain. The context will usually show which of these various meanings of the word "field" is meant. See the further discussion in Chapters 32 and 33.

In the application of field theory to current problems of psychobiology another fundamental principle of relativity must be taken into account. The spectator of our analogy previously quoted does not occupy a fixed position. He is in transactional relations with his field of observation, and the act of observation itself influences his field. This is another factor of the situation that is not explicable in terms of Newtonian mechanics.

Heisenberg's principle of indeterminism is based on the fact that the observation necessarily modifies the thing observed. This is true not only of electrons but of everything else in our cosmos *as this is known to man*. Margenau ('50, p. 38) asserts that not only in subatomic physics but also in every other domain of human experience "the act of observation has an important effect upon the observed;

indeed the act of knowing has an important effect upon the known."
And in a subsequent passage (p. 387): "Uncertainty arises from a
fundamental shift in the meaning of physical reality. . . . it represents in fact a basic departure from the customary approach to
reality."

The last point is elaborated by Bentley ('50), who insists that we
must abandon "root, branch, and fruit, the conventional severance
of detachable knowers from detachable knowns." The inseparable
transactional relationship between knower and known I agree is an
observed fact, not a philosophical speculation. Nonetheless we must
recognize that the knower cannot be indistinguishably merged with
the known without losing his identity.

None of the field theories now current in physics or in psychology
are adequate to explain the exact nature or the mechanical principles
of psychoneural operations. Current discussions suggest to my mind
that space and space-time treated relativistically may have properties
far different from any that have so far been recognized in either
Newtonian or quantum mechanics. In this I follow Einstein in his
search for a unified field theory which will give a coherent picture of
the universe as a whole (Leonard Engel, '55, has outlined Einstein's
ideal in simple language without reference to the technical details).
These dynamic properties of space as a field of radiant energy may
when adequately explored open a new approach to the mysteries of
the mechanics of the body-mind relationships and perhaps also of
the unexplained "psi phenomena" recorded in the literature of telepathy and clairvoyance (page 270). Such speculations, of course, can
have only heuristic value (if any) as suggestions for possibly fruitful
lines of further research.

The type of field here under consideration is structurally a fabric
of interwoven nerve cells and fibers, and the nervous impulses to
which reference is made above reside within these nervous elements.
These elements are embedded in a nonspecific matrix. This intercellular substance is regarded by the Gestalt school of psychologists as
a secondary electrical field. Massive field forces spread through this
substrate and the nervous elements enveloped by it in patterns which
are supposed to give rise to conscious experience. There is also good

evidence that humoral mechanisms acting via the blood stream have significant effects upon nervous transmission at the synaptic junctions.

The nervous and nonnervous components of the brain evidently are functionally related in ways not yet adequately known. We know a great deal about the structure and physiology of the nervous elements, but we do not know how sensory patterns of nervous conduction are translated into the motor patterns which activate the muscles so as to give the appropriate response. It may safely be predicted that the answers to such questions will be found in some form of combination of known physiology of nerve cells and fibers with the field properties of the nonnervous matrix regarded as a volume conductor. For further discussion of these problems see Sperry ('52), Marrazzi ('53), and Köhler ('51).

In higher animals the nervous system is not merely a random network. It is composed exclusively (or nearly so) of neurons which are polarized in both senses mentioned above. Each neuron is separated from other nervous elements by one-way synaptic junctions so that traffic moves in only one direction. This directive polarization is of the utmost importance for understanding the mechanics of all nervous activity. It is one of the distinctive peculiarities of nervous tissue. Another is the organization of the nervous tissue in dynamic fields of the type just under consideration. The unique properties of this synaptic tissue provide the indispensable mechanism for all central adjustments that result in behavior, and this includes also those cerebral processes that eventuate in conscious experience and conscious control of behavior.

The synaptic junctions are the critical points in the determination of the patterns of all central nervous processes. All nervous transmission is delayed at these junctions, and whether any particular nervous impulse may or may not cross this barrier is determined by variable factors of general central excitatory state and the physiological conditions then prevailing at the synapse in question. The excitatory state is influenced by general nutrition, oxygen supply, and various endocrine and other chemicals carried by the body fluids, also by previous activities such as established habits, temporary fatigue, etc. Whether a particular neuron can be activated by the nervous impulses which reach its synapses depends on variable factors, such as the chemical and electrical properties of the local junctional tissue and the influences exerted upon that tissue by all the nervous impulses that reach it.

All nervous functions are significant for behavior. Some of these are mentioned here in various contexts; those concerned with mentation are discussed in more detail in the chapters to follow. The interplay of analytic and synthetic processes, as we shall see, plays a very important part in the development of those higher nervous functions that precede and accompany perception and all other mental processes. Many other well-known properties of the nervous tissues might be mentioned, but such information is readily available elsewhere and these details can be omitted here.

Summary

The distinctive nervous functions have been derived by specialization of the irritability and conductivity possessed by all protoplasm. Nerve fibers can transmit nervous impulses for long distances without decrement, and their structure and physiological properties have been described in great detail, with quantitative measurements. Nervous activity always involves a chemical process and an associated change in electrical potential. The electrical changes are the most useful indicators of what is going on in both the peripheral and the central nervous systems, because they can be recorded with great accuracy from the living body under normal and experimental conditions.

The most characteristic properties of the nervous tissues arise from two types of structural and physiological polarization of the nervous elements. The first type is *structurally* determined by the fact that each neuron is physiologically separated from all others with which it is in contact by barriers—synapses—which nervous impulses can pass in only one direction. Nerve fibers, accordingly, usually transmit nervous impulses as one-way traffic. The second type of polarization arises from an organization of the nervous tissues such that *electrodynamic fields* may be activated in relatively stable patterns that are not inflexibly bound to any particular arrangement of the nervous elements.

CHAPTER TWENTY-ONE
Psychophysics

Three revolutions in mechanics

Current research in psychobiology, in full recognition of the difficulties arising from the differences between the laws of mentation and those of the objective world, is now attacking these problems from surprisingly different directions of approach. A few illustrative examples are cited in this and the following chapters.

Repeated attempts to systematize and quantify the relations between subjective experience and the correlated objective data have yielded results of uncertain significance. The Weber-Fechner formula for the relation between stimulus and sensation is the most familiar of the psychophysical principles so far investigated. It can be simply stated: The intensity of the sensation is approximately proportional to the logarithm of the strength of the stimulus. This looks exact, but it does not fit the facts. Our conscious experiences are too labile to submit to so crude and rigid a formulation. Although this law has been discredited as an exact mathematical formulation, Wiener ('48, p. 29) shows that it has significance physiologically and mathematically as a first approximation.

The failure to go further in this or any other direction suggests the need for revision of some current principles of mechanics. Suggestions for such a revision are given by the physicist E. T. Whittaker ('43), who summarizes the history of two great scientific revolutions—from Aristotelian to Newtonian conceptions and from Newtonian mechanics to relativity and quantum mechanics. To this he adds some comments on a third revolution now in process. A similar demand for reorientation in psychology has been expressed by Bentley ('41). "The established attitude of the psychologist came to be that his facts were 'in' the Newtonian universe but not technically 'of' it." The psychologist's efforts were futile because "whenever any brash adventurer attempted to force psychological fact into mechanistic forms, a lifeless residue was all he obtained." In this article Bentley indicates the direction to be taken from a fresh start. "Psychology," he says, "has always concerned itself with facts which do not tolerate technical description in technical Newtonian space and time. . . . Psychology is now at last free to describe them as it finds and observes them. Such observation and description became practicable within the frame of a full naturalism for organic and environmental facts. . . . If the organism enters naturally, it should be *kept* natural. . . . Search for a specifically behavioral space-time is legitimate within the present framework of science. . . . The behaviors are present events converging pasts into futures."

One might draw from current literature a large number of additional statements from scientific workers in the top ranks who demand a reorientation of both science and philosophy toward man's place in nature and the mechanics of the processes by which he acquires his knowledge of nature.

This third revolution may be very radical and far-reaching in its effects. Our knowledge of the organic substrate of the mental life is now increasing at an unprecedented rate. The revolution of neurophysiology, as mentioned at the beginning of the preceding chapter, has been accelerated by the application of new methods and new instruments in electrophysiology. These advances have gone hand in hand with equally spectacular achievements in electrical engineering in other fields and with improvements in neurological, neurosurgical, clinical, psychological, and mathematical techniques.

The most important advances, I repeat, are due to a change in attitude toward the problems and a better understanding of the range and variety of factors that may be involved. When experts in anatomy, physiology, biochemistry, biophysics, biomathematics, neurosurgery, psychiatry, and philosophy converge their technical skills upon a problem—its formulation, operational procedures, and interpretation—results are achieved that could never be won by the same investigators working in isolation from one another.

Space, time, and space-time

Some fundamental principles of psychophysics are implicit in the preceding discussions. Because some of these principles cannot be expressed numerically with mathematical precision, it does not follow that they are nonmechanistic. That results expressed in quantitative form supply indispensable instruments of psychobiological research has been abundantly demonstrated during the whole history of experimental psychology (Boring, '50, and Stevens, '51, give a convenient documentation). The continuous intensive search for mental measurements has yielded much of great value in the field of applied psychology and some important general principles. But these are measurements of performance rather than of mentation as such, and they shed little light upon the fundamental problems of psychophysics. The intelligence quotient (IQ) and factor analysis of intelligence are discussed in Chapter 28.

Mental operations evidently cannot be described and quantified in the numerical units employed in conventional mechanics. The disparity between private subjective experiences and those which we objectify has already been illustrated in the domain of values (Chapter 12). If, however, we find mechanisms the operations of which have awareness as one of their properties, then the other properties of these distinctive mechanisms can be measured numerically and these measurements are amenable to mathematical treatment.

In Coghill's search for those objectively observable properties of the living body that are demonstrably in organic relation with conscious experience, he found that the most instructive of these properties were those concerned with the spatial and temporal relations of things. Everything in our objective world is set in a frame of perceptual space and time, but all conceptual processes are more or less independent of this frame of reference. All thinking is now and here; but in this present act of thinking, memories of things past in time and remote in space and predictions of the future are tied into the mental process, so that in thought the perceptual data of time and space lose some of their specific qualities and limitations. When symbolized in the mental processes they may merge, lose their sharply defined boundaries, and reappear in a radically different setup of relationships. In some of these processes the temporo-spatial factors seem to disappear entirely. Some of our abstract ideas may be totally devoid of any temporal or spatial quality.

These timeless mental acts are, of course, performed by a body which as perceptually known is acting here and now. This difference between perceptual knowledge (which must be oriented in time and space) and all higher mental processes suggested to Coghill that this contrast gives a cue which points the way to a fruitful analysis of those vital processes which go on at lower levels of integration and are the precursors of the conscious processes. He did not elaborate this idea in sufficient detail to be very convincing.

As I interpret Coghill's fragmentary references, his "organismic" functions are analytic and his "nonorganismic" processes (or "mentation" as he defines the term) are integrative. From this it follows that the analytic functions, which are primarily concerned with adjustments of the organism to its environment, must of necessity be oriented in space and time with the body of the organism as a fixed point of reference. The integrative processes, on the contrary, are wholly internal to the body and some of the laws of their action are relativistic rather than inflexibly bound to dimensions that can be measured in absolute units of space and time. The analysis of sensory and motor processes must be made (consciously or unconsciously) in terms of spatial and temporal relations that can be numerically expressed. Integration combines the products of this analysis in a constructive process in which space and time may not be separately individuated but retain a primordial unity as space-time defined relativistically and in parameters different from those of Newtonian mechanics.

Our ideas of space and time, measurable in arbitrarily chosen absolute units (such as inches and seconds), are constructions of the human mind, and these constructs are patterned in accordance with the limitations of our apparatus of perception (page 295). Einstein showed that this dichotomy is not inherent in the nature of things and that relativistic space-time is a more fundamental conception.

Ideas of individuated "space" and "time" are necessary for the human kind of perception, but they are not required for description of some factors of behavior. Coghill illustrated this by pointing out that in all animals muscular movements are not made in space *and* time but in integrated space-time. Accordingly, he took space-time as an appropriate starting point for the study of primordial animal behavior. His published references to this subject are few and tantalizingly brief. I have assembled ('49, chap. 23) these and others from his unpublished papers, and the following sentences are quoted from the most important of these references (Coghill, '38).

"The living organism has three essential and constituent elements: structure, function, mentation. It may be called a psycho-organismal individual. . . . Mentation, it was observed, does not conform to space and time. . . . Mentation, like structure and function, began where and when the individual began, and, like them, undergoes development by expansion and individuation. . . . Motility precedes sensitivity in embryonic development. . . . It is legitimate, therefore, to think of the motor system as having mentation and of this mentation as being in terms of movement. But movement occurs neither in space alone nor in time alone. It represents both space and time, and, to the psycho-organismal individual, it *is* space-time. In the course of development space-time undergoes individuation into space and time insofar as the capacity of the individual permits; but that individuation is never absolute, as the confusion of language concerning these modalities proves. Space-time is, then, a total pattern of mentation; and space and time are partial patterns arising within it. . . . [Space-time] is the matrix of all subconscious and conscious mentation." In another context he said "action itself is psycho-organismic space-time."

Here it is made clear that all action involves both spatial and temporal components and that primitively these acts are performed in integrated space-time. The separate recognition of space and time comes later in perceptual experience, but their organic relationship is still implicitly, if not explicitly, expressed in common practice, as when we speak of "a short length of time." Space and time are similarly integrated in all inorganic activities.

The distinctions drawn by Coghill between partial patterns and total patterns and between organismic and nonorganismic vital processes are recognized and formulated in a great variety of ways in the current literature of biomechanics. One of these discussions merits comment here. Moulyn ('50) contrasts what he calls "mechanistic" and "holistic" principles. The former resemble Coghill's "organismic" and the latter his "nonorganismic" or "mentation" processes. The characteristic features of these contrasted vital patterns are clearly stated, although I think the terminology adopted is unfortunate. The "holistic" processes are said to be nonmechanistic because they are not juxtaposed in perceptual space and time. To this I object, for the holistic, or "nonorganismic" patterns of action are as truly mechanistic as are the partial patterns, although the mechanisms are of different order and the laws of their operation are different.

This argument is developed clearly and simply by Schrödinger ('44), showing why "present-day physics and chemistry could not possibly account for what happens in space and time within a living organism" (p. 2). To this he adds (p. 81): "We must therefore not be discouraged by the difficulty of interpreting life by the ordinary laws of physics. . . . We must be prepared to find a new type of physical law prevailing in it. . . . The new principle that is involved is a genuinely physical one: it is, in my opinion, nothing else than the principle of quantum theory over again."

The term "mentation," or minding, as defined by Coghill is applied to all activities in which space and time are not separately individuated, whether these are performed consciously or unconsciously. As I have repeatedly stated, in my opinion it is preferable, in the present state of knowledge, to restrict the use of the words "mind" and "mentation" to conscious processes. Coghill, in common with many others, did not accept this limitation; but certainly there was no confusion in his mind between unconscious and conscious "mentation." In view of this difference in our definitions of the word, all references here to Coghillian "mentation" are distinguished by quotation marks.

Coghillian "mentation" is coextensive with life, and its most characteristic index is that component of behavior which exhibits integrated space-time. This comes to expression in behavior first as muscular movement. We see, then, that the concept of space-time is not a mere mathematical abstraction. It can be identified behavioristically in all motility. Having found it here, Coghill used this concept as a tool for further study of the relations between the analytic and integrative components of behavior in general.

The dimensions of integration

It is now clear that the analytic description of the individual in terms of space and time is incomplete. It must be supplemented by further description of the activities that are oriented in space-time or some other kind of parameters. Our adult ideas of separately individuated space and time have been acquired from behavioral experience of external things and events. The newborn babe has no such ideas. He lives in a world of space-time, just as the ameba does. Space and time, however, are individuated so early in his psychogenic experience of the surrounding world that in later life these ideas are regarded as intuitions, that is, as simple primary elements of experience—and this they certainly are not. Ideas of space and time are not innate.

Since all perceptual knowledge is given in terms of three-dimensional space and linear-dimensional time, it is impossible at the perceptual level to construct an idea of integrated space-time. Moreover, we do not need this idea in the ordinary affairs of life. The abstract idea of space-time was constructed at a higher conceptual level of integration, and here it has great utility, as illustrated in Einstein's principles of relativity, where absolute units of perceptual space and time are dispensed with. In relativistic theory time and space are not left out of account, but they are set in a frame of reference different from that of Newtonian mechanics. Having acquired the relativistic conception of space-time, Coghill proceeded to use it in his analysis of the embryogenesis of behavior, and here he observed that integrated space-time is manifest in behavior long before space and time are separately individuated in conscious experience.

In both phylogenetic and embryological development, unconscious action in four-dimensional space-time precedes our perceptual individuation of three-dimensional space and linear-dimensional time. Let us see if we can find out why this is so.

In perception the three dimensions of space are integrated in immediate experience because they can be measured in the same units of length, say in meters. Duration of time, however, cannot be measured in meters, and so the units employed—years or days—cannot be perceptually integrated with the three dimensions of space. In naïve experience, accordingly, space and time are separately apprehended as disparate elements of experience and a fourth dimension cannot be directly sensed. What cannot be done perceptually has been accomplished conceptually, and we now have the idea of integrated four-dimensional space-time. This concept is mathematically useful, and in order to rationalize it search was made for a unit of measurement that is applicable in both spatial and temporal dimensions. Velocity is such a unit, and by its use the apparent disparity of space and time has been resolved and the idea of four-dimensional space-time can now be used in normative mathematical reasoning and also operationally in empirical science. In the latter field this concept clarifies much that was obscure.

In current mathematical theory a time dimension is added to three-dimensional space, giving integrated four-dimensional space-time. In behavior the integrative processes go on in four-dimensional space-time primordially. If consciousness emerges within the integrative process, then the activity is stepped up to a higher level and a fifth dimension is added to the original four dimensions. It may be argued further that in conceptual thinking, which employs language and other symbols of high-level abstraction, the process is stepped up to a still higher level, with the addition of still another dimension to the complex.

The word "relativity," as I use it here, has a wider and looser connotation than that of current mathematical physics. The "dimensions" to which reference has just been made are not those of classical physics which are (or may be) measured quantitatively. A dimension has been defined as any manifold that can be ordered. The definable ordinates employed if expressed quantitatively may be treated mathematically. Other possible systems of ordinates that cannot be expressed numerically may reveal dimensions that lie outside the range of conventional mathematical analysis. They may, for instance, be manifest qualitatively in terms of patterns for which no quantitative units of measurement are now available.

It should be emphasized also that Einstein's four-dimensional formulation of space-time and its mathematical corollaries evidently do not furnish an adequate frame of reference for human mentation. It may be a step in that direction in our search for some similar formulation applicable to still higher levels of integration.

The recognition of these successive levels of integration and of the number of dimensions involved explains why conscious processes cannot be measured in the units of three-dimensional space and one-dimensional time as these are perceptually known. The properties of each integrative level are unique and they cannot be reduced to those of lower levels. But there must be continuity of the vital processes at every transition from level to level, with perhaps a radical change in the mechanics of the process at the transition.

All that can be claimed for these speculations is that they may serve as suggestive working hypotheses in further research. They must remain unverified conjectures unless and until some metric is discovered that is applicable at both four-dimensional and five-dimensional levels. It is quite within the range of possibility that the apparent disparity of the conscious and the unconscious may be resolved by the discovery of some as yet unknown factor common to both of them, just as four-dimensional space-time was made available to empirical science when velocity was found to provide the appropriate unit of measurement. This may involve the discovery of some physicalistic principles as yet unknown and also, as suggested by von Neumann ('51, p. 24), some revision of current logical theory. For a brief history of logic and its application in current theories of cybernetics, with constructive comments on the mechanisms of thinking, read Reiser ('55).

In reference to the concept of space-time developed by Einstein and Minkowski, Margenau ('50, p. 149) writes: "New experiences have forced us to modify the conceptual texture in which space and time had been embedded. . . . Let us resist the temptation to think of this new space-time as less 'real.' It is a construct, to be sure, but so was three-dimensional space. . . . And if the truth must be told, you are in fact thinking in four dimensions every time you visualize an object as *moving in ordinary space.*"

In Chapter 16 of the same book Margenau recounts a bit of history which shows that the demand for reformulation of the mind-body problem in terms of principles as yet unknown is not unreasonable. He cites the problem presented by the apparently incompatible theories of the nature of light in classical physics—the particle-wave controversy. The solution came with the application of quantum mechanics to the observed phenomena, from which it was deduced that photons and electrons are neither particles nor waves. Light consists of traveling electromagnetic fields, the properties of which cannot be described in terms of classical mechanics. That is why no mechanical model can be constructed.

Quite apart from the preceding speculations, it is clear that when I say that I am a thinking body this implies that my body is different from every other body and that one of its distinctive properties is my private awareness. I know about my own body and I know about my own thinking just as I know about other things, and every object in our physical universe has its own distinctive properties that distinguish it from all other objects. My personal knowledge about these things is necessarily private, and I know enough about them to believe that they have substantial existence independently of my knowledge about them. My capacity for knowing implies a mechanism that does the knowing. I cannot know this mechanism as mechanism except through my perceptions, and perceptions are always framed in objective space and time. But conceptual knowledge as such is set in a different frame of reference. It is (or may be) timeless and nonspatial, and this is a property of a different and higher dimension than that of space-time—a property for which we have no unit of measurement in terms of space and time or in terms of integrated space-time.

Consciousness, then, is "a *unique co-emergent* with nervous organization" (Sellars, '38, p. 484), and it emerges at the successive levels of integration that we recognize subjectively as sensation, perception, and conception. The ability of mankind to acquire knowledge perceptually and conceptually gives to every individual his own most distinctive characteristics, and this acquisition is a magnificent achievement.

The distinction which we draw between awareness on the one hand and on the other hand the projection outward of some components of experience as things known about, including objects set in the frame of space and time, all observable behavior of ourselves and others, and all symbols of mental processes—this distinction is based on no philosophical postulates but is strictly operational as envisaged in both naïve common sense and in refined scientific analysis. And yet this distinction is a methodological artifact which results from the structural limitations of the human apparatus of perception. The knowings and the known are intrinsic components of a field of experience within which they are inseparable.

Mental work

If mental operations as subjectively known cannot be quantified in the metric of perceptual space and time, what is the status of mental work? We have all experienced mental effort, and the man who is mentally alert and active we call energetic. Can this effort properly be called work as the engineer defines the term? (What the engineer means by "work" has been explained on page 56).

In current physics the concept of energy plays a leading role. We know that heat and light are forms of energy and that there is a "mechanical equivalent" of this energy that can be measured in terms of standard units of energy. There is no specific kind of thermal or luminous energy. When physicists speak of various kinds of energy, the reference is to the *pattern* of its manifestation, that is, of the work done.

In any particular physical or chemical process, such as the burning of carbon in oxygen, the energy factors are measurable in numerical units, but that is not the whole of the story. There are complicating factors of pattern. Flames may appear. The energy of the light (which in turn is correlated with the color of the flame) must be entered in our equation, but there still remain qualitative differences between heat and light about which the equation tells us nothing. To the quantitative differences in terms of wave-length we must add differences in the patterns of their transactional relations with surrounding things, including the organisms affected thereby.

If, now, awareness emerges in the course of some particular kind of vital process, the energy expended in the metabolism may be measured in a suitable calorimeter, but this measurement tells no more about the mysterious quality of consciousness than the readings of a thermometer can tell us about the mysterious properties of luminescence.

That mental work involves the expenditure of energy has been demonstrated by the experiments of the Benedicts ('30), whose subjects solved difficult problems in mental arithmetic in the calorimeter. The amount of energy expended was small but measurable. What was measured here was doubtless the energy of chemical reactions and related electrical and other physical processes in the nervous (and perhaps muscular) tissues. These physico-chemical processes probably do not differ essentially from other metabolic activities of the nonmental functions, and so they are measurable in the same units. There is, then, no such thing as a specific kind of mental energy which is different from muscular energy or thermal energy. Energy is just energy, no matter in what form it may be manifested. Nobody knows what energy is. We know only what it does. We know a great deal about that, but we still have much more to learn.

Mental work is bodily work in just the same sense that muscular exercise is work. The body is the instrument, in both cases, of a specific change in the *pattern* of energy manifestation. When a weight is lifted by muscular action the cause of the movement is not a dis-embodied contractility. It is a contracting muscle. When a problem in mental arithmetic is successfully solved the causative agent is not an intelligent ego who operates an inert mechanism. It is a living brain engaged in thinking. Mind does not move matter. It is mind-ing matter that does mental work just as it is contracting muscle that does physical work. It is bodily energy that is used in thinking, and it is the body that gets tired while doing the work.

There are two components in what is commonly called fatigue that have been analyzed in a book published by S. Howard Bartley and Eloise Chute ('47). One component is an objectively demonstrable impairment or exhaustion of the tissues, the other is a subjective feeling of tiredness. These are independent variables. There may be considerable impairment without the feeling of tiredness, and conversely one may feel very tired when there is no demonstrable impairment of any functions (page 398). Both components ordinarily are present, but they should be separately investigated. The authors advise that the name "fatigue" be applied only to the subjective feeling. When fatigue is studied as personal experience rather than by exclusively objective and quantitative laboratory methods, the results of the latter type of study take their appropriate places as means to be employed, not as ends in themselves. But, however the prob-lem is studied, it is clear that fatigue results from bodily work of some kind, and it is the whole body that gets tired, not the muscles only, or the brain only, or a disembodied ego. This supports Coghill's contention that mentation is a total pattern, not a partial pattern.

Hans Berger ('21) claimed that his experiments show that in mental work the energy transformation into psychic energy involves approxi-mately 20 mkg. per minute (quoted from Klüver, '49, p. 401). It seems more probable that these experiments demonstrate not a trans-formation of one kind of energy into another but a change in the pattern of energy manifestation comparable with that seen when energy as heat is changed to energy as mechanical work.

Just as muscular work may change the structure of the body and

the pattern of behavior, so mental work may determine patterns of
growth of cerebral tissue and so effect lasting changes in habits of
thought, personal attitudes, and character. This is what education is
for. The interplay between the subconscious and the conscious levels
of cerebral activity is two-way traffic. Mind emerges from the nonmental, and it in turn may control not only the behavior of the body
but also its structural organization. It is recognized by everybody
that disorder of bodily structure may disturb the mind. The converse
is equally evident, as painfully illustrated by the prevalence of gastric ulcer associated with chronic anxiety or worry. Equally striking
changes in the physical structure of bodily tissue and its chemical
processes have been induced by hypnotic suggestion. The ulcers or
hypnotically induced blisters are not caused by a nonphysical entity
called a mind but by a psychoneural bodily process that is organically
related with the other vital functions.

What is characteristic of mental processes is not the amount or
quality of energy expended. It is the pattern of performance, and
this cannot be measured in quanta of energy.

Summary

The historical development of the science of mechanics shows
three periods of revolutionary change: from Aristotle to Newton,
from Newton to Einstein and quantum mechanics, and a third
period now opening in which scientifically acceptable nonquantitative
methods play an increasingly large part. The recognition of four-
dimensional space-time, not only as a mathematical abstraction but
also operationally as the frame of reference for integrative processes
in general, opens an approach to the mind-body problem from postulates quite different from those of conventional physiology.

Consciousness emerges within behavior, and motility is the seedbed
of mind. In muscular movement, whether executed consciously or
unconsciously, space and time are not separately individuated. Integrated space-time is, therefore, a key factor in psychogenesis. From
this as a starting point separate dimensions of space and time are
individuated in the analytic series of sensorimotor reactions. In the
integrative series this individuation may not take place; and, if and
when consciousness emerges within it, another and higher dimen-

sion is added to the primordial four dimensions—a dimension which we apprehend as awareness. Each of these levels has its own distinctive properties which cannot be reduced to those of lower levels.

No common units of measurements for conscious experience and the objective world as known perceptually have yet been discovered. The energy expended in mental work is bodily energy. There is no such thing as a specific kind of mental energy.

CHAPTER TWENTY-TWO

Mental Functions

The mythological mind

We mind our own business more or less successfully and many of
the more primitive animals transact their business apparently without
minding it at all. This contrast is equally apparent in our own behavior because both kinds of effort are blended in almost all of our
conduct. The unconscious components of behavior are studied
with the methods of conventional physiology, and these must be
thoroughly understood because they are essential factors of everything we do and think. The fact that we do not have to attend to
these factors is to our advantage because it enables us to make the
most economical and profitable use of such intelligence as we possess
without wasteful expenditure of mental effort upon routine details
that can be more rapidly and efficiently performed unconsciously.
But the status of the conscious components of behavior is still in controversy.

Primitive mythologies which peopled the universe with supernatural powers who may arbitrarily interfere with natural processes
survive to our time in a great variety of forms, and in all scientific
and philosophical discussions which in any way involve the functions
of the nervous system they have been and still are especially tenacious
and obstructive. The wide gaps in our knowledge are bridged by
hypothesis, and the tendency is to reify if not to deify these abstractions and to endow the artifacts which we have constructed by exer-

cise of scientific imagination with some occult individuality and creative power. Too often we have been seduced by the fallacy that having found a name for a problem we have its solution. The fabulous monsters of ancient mythology have been supplanted by rationally fabricated concepts which set the direction of our experimentation and the course of our thinking. The temptation to personify these concepts and their symbols is very strong. Gene, neuron, reflex, conditioning, instinct, gestalt, complex, libido, id, superego, and so on—these are verbal symbols which express abstractions of certain common features of wide experience. These symbols and the concepts for which they stand are useful and necessary tools of research, but to permit any one of them to crystallize into a dogma is to bar the way to further progress. They must be kept fluid and subject perhaps to as radical change as that which was made in the case of the dogma of the indivisible atom of nineteenth-century physics. Above all, they must not be endowed with any efficiency as causal agents, for natural processes are not controlled by abstractions.

The individuality of things suggests a fundamental pluralism, the matter-energy relation and the body-mind relation suggest a dualism, but the orderly universe that we actually observe is inexplicable by either of these hypotheses.

Animism

The reaction against dualistic mythologies has usually taken the form of a philosophy of nature based on one or the other of two incompatible basic postulates. Materialism assumes that physical substance is the primary thing which somehow may produce a nonphysical something called the mind which floats free and has no further part to play in the processes of nature. Idealism regards the mind as the primary or ultimate reality and matter as a secondary and perhaps illusory product of mentation. The one type of dichotomy is as unscientific and as sterile as the other, for the physical structure and the functions performed by that structure cannot be split apart by any such arbitrary dialectical analysis. Mind and body do not exist separately. There may be a body without a mind, but we know nothing about any mind apart from a body, although a physical body as defined in current physics does not necessarily include any particulate matter. Human nature cannot be understood unless the integrity of this vital process is recognized.

As a dynamic realist I must accept the reality of my subjective experiences and also of the outer world of which I have experience. I must, then, be some kind of an idealist and some kind of a materialist —perhaps what Sellars ('44) calls a "reformed materialist" (cf. Simpson, '49)—but I must be both of these, not one or the other.

In the current literature of behaviorism the reaction against the mysticism of traditional dualism takes the form of an aversion to anything that smacks of a mentalistic interference with the flow of the vital process as this is observable objectively, an aversion that appears explicitly or implicitly in the publications of many experimentalists in this field.

In Hebb's admirable account ('49) of the neurophysiological components of behavior he seems to be dominated by the fear of "slipping momentarily into animistic thinking." The danger is real; there can be no doubt about that, for uncritical animistic thinking has been responsible for endless confusion in both biology and psychology. But just what is meant by animism in this connection? The idea that mind is an entity detachable from the bodily organization that generates it and experiences it must be rigorously excluded from all scientific inquiry. Such a mind cannot be an *agent* in behavior, nor can it be regarded as *the* cause of any behavior. Nonetheless, mentation *as a vital process* has a significance for behavior whether the inquiry is conducted from the standpoint of biology or of psychology. An animism recognizing both that mental processes as subjectively experienced are real events which influence conduct and that search for the mechanisms employed in these transactions is a prime function of physiological psychology has no mystical contamination whatever.

From this I think it follows that Hebb unduly restricts the field of inquiry when he writes: "Though it has been tried before now, an explanation cannot be half neural anatomy and half consciousness. They are different levels in a logical hierarchy. A problem recognized at one level can be solved by recourse to a more fundamental set of conceptions, but an hypothesis cannot well comprise two levels, take in two universes of discourse at the same time."

This argument might be dialectically acceptable if it were not for the fact that the levels in question are not merely figments of logical analysis but have objective existence in a hierarchy of biological processes. This hierarchy must not be dismembered in either logical analysis or biological explanation; for what we want to explain is the relationship between the two levels. The "more fundamental set of conceptions" sought must of necessity include the relevant features of both levels.

If one chooses to restrict his inquiry to either one of these levels, there is no ground for criticism, for the transactions between the levels cannot be understood until the essential features of both levels are well known. The great merit of Professor Hebb's contribution to the organization of behavior lies in the skill with which he "presents a theory of behavior that is based as far as possible on the physiology of the nervous system," to quote from his introductory sentence. This is all to the good, and his physiological theories are so well documented by citation of experimental evidence that frequent reference is made to them in these pages. But he has not succeeded in his avowed purpose of restricting the discussion to the physiological level. When he writes (p. 140) "In the present chapter, accordingly, the 'higher' processes of consciousness and insightful behavior will be discussed together with the 'lower' factor of instinct, and, more briefly, the relation of these to emotion and motivation," he frankly abandons his initial premise that "an hypothesis cannot well comprise two levels." His later chapters are concerned explicitly with the relation between these levels and the mechanisms involved.

I meet other puzzling incongruities in reading Hayek's *The Sensory Order* ('52). This author uses an original and stimulating analysis of sensory processes as basis for a systematic inquiry into the foundations of theoretical psychology. The sensory order of things and events is contrasted with the physical order, the former defined as events perceived in terms of sensory qualities, the latter defined exclusively in terms of their mutual relations with one another regardless of their sensory qualities. The sensory order is called "mental," and conscious experience is regarded as merely a special instance of the more general mental order. The author's aim is to show that the kinds of relationships observed in the sensory order are strictly equivalent to those observed in the physical order. This is also true of the "phenomenal order" of conscious experience, and he maintains that the discovery of these similarities between the two orders is as far as we can go toward a solution of the mind-body problem. This he regards as adequate because, he says, "the difference between what are commonly regarded as merely 'mechanical' and as mental processes respectively is not one of kind but merely one of degree."

To this I object. Awareness does differ in kind from nervous conduction and muscular movement just as these differ in kind from each other. The similarities mentioned are real, and there are differences in degree of complexity of these similar series of events. But the differences in kind are actually there in the observed events; and they are not fully explained by the author's skillful proof of similarity of relationships in the physical and the phenomenal order.

I accept without qualification his final conclusion, "that *to us* mind must remain forever a realm of its own which we can know only through directly experiencing it, but which we shall never be able fully to explain or to 'reduce' to something else." But I have to confess that the intricate dialectic which leads him to this conclusion leaves me unsatisfied and in some respects it seems to be inconsistent with the argument that precedes it. What we want to find out is the nature of the nexus between the physical order of vital processes and the colligated and qualitatively different phenomenal order of introspective experience. The fact that the nature of this relationship is still unknown does not mean that it is unknowable and that the problem is insoluble. If no known mechanical principles suffice for its solution, let us search for others.

For a long time I have contended that properly controlled introspection has a legitimate status in the methodology of science and that this status is not limited to psychology. Writing as a biologist ('15) I said, "Possibly the new psychology may learn to get along without consciousness; but biology cannot do so, for it is evidently a real factor in at least the higher stages of evolutionary history, and this factor cannot be ignored in natural science." The nature of the causal relationship between the conscious components of human behavior and the physical processes involved is discussed by Grünbaum ('52).

Conscious experience influences conduct and is therefore a factor of behavior. Indeed, it has the basic properties of behavior in its own right, for the conscious act is a bodily act which is observed introspectively just as other kinds of behavior are observed by extraspection. As Boring has emphasized ('55, and works there cited), introspection therefore has the same scientific status as all other methods of observation and, like all the others, is subject to the hazard of faulty interpretation (page 23).

Psychology is a biological discipline, but it should be a psychobiology and not merely a subdivision of physiology. What we must do now is to bring together these artificially separated domains of experience—the subjective and the objective—and build a coherently integrated psychobiology.

Mind is minding

Although the energy expended in mental effort is quantitatively small (page 280), intelligence is the most precious acquisition on our planet and when efficiently and judiciously used it yields the largest profit. As we shall see, the specific properties of mind are better described in terms of patterns of performance and patterns of relations rather than quantitatively in terms of energy or anything else. This has long been recognized by some and is now accepted by our most competent authorities.

In the examination of mind we are looking not at a particular kind of thing but at a distinctive kind of process. What we observe is a minding body, not a body that makes a separate entity called a mind. When we watch a running horse we do not say that the muscles create an entity called movement. So also when we observe a thinking man we must not separate the action from the actor. A vital process, we repeat, cannot be split apart in this way.

We are prone to conceal gaps in knowledge under a mantle of equivocal verbiage, and mind can be defined to fit a wide variety of philosophical hypotheses. Traditionally mind is identified with consciousness. So many different definitions of "mind" and "consciousness" have been suggested that it would be desirable, if possible, to avoid both words in favor of "awareness" as less ambiguous.

In this book mind is defined in the traditional way as awareness. This is logically simple, for the awareness is present in any act or it is not. The accompaniments and precursors of awareness are recognized for what they are, that is, as physiological processes. We may call them subconscious acts or mind-stuff, but not mind as here defined. Of course, this is not a satisfactory definition, and I know of no way to define awareness, which must be individually experienced to be known. But we have experienced it, and so we can adjust to one another without bothering about definitions, and ways have been found to discover verifiable relationships of these subjective experiences which can be used as objective indicators and subjected to scientific analysis.

Unfortunately the word "awareness" is sometimes used as loosely as the word "mind," as illustrated by one philosopher's employment of it as a more neutral word than "consciousness": "The magnet becomes aware of a piece of iron when moved into its neighborhood, and acts accordingly" (Boodin, '43). I know nothing about a magnet's awareness but I know a great deal about my own. The distinctive properties of awareness, as the term is here used, can be known only through introspection, and this again is an ambiguous word. One psychologist tells me that in his opinion introspection is always in verbal terms, and, since verbal symbols are fabricated by bodily organs, if we can learn how these organs operate we shall have the whole story written in objective language. This to my mind is not supported by the experiments of Maier and many others (page 402) which show that rats sometimes behave in ways that cannot be distinguished objectively from human rational conduct, and that they can even abstract behavioristically those common features of a complex situation that we call "triangle" and "square," though we have no evidence that the rats have any ideas or verbal symbols connected with these acts. The evidence that monkeys and apes learn and think in terms of symbols is clear-cut, and they do it without the aid of language. These animals act as if they know what they are doing, though they may have no understanding of how they do it or why. We cannot deny them some sort of awareness and this, if present, can be known only to the animal introspectively.

In my own experience I am sure that there is much awareness that is not verbalized. The moot question of the relation of symbols to human mentation is critically discussed, with citations of much evidence, in Section VI of Jacques Hadamard's *An Essay on the Psychology of Invention in the Mathematical Field* ('45). From his own experience and that of many other qualified thinkers he writes: "I insist that words are totally absent from my mind when I really think. . . . I think it also essential to emphasize that I behave in this way not only about words, but even about algebraic signs. I use them when dealing with easy calculations; but whenever the matter looks more difficult, they become too heavy a baggage for me. I use concrete representations, but of a quite different nature. . . . As to words, they remain absolutely absent from my mind until I come to the moment of communicating the results in written or oral form, or (very exceptionally) for relay-results." And on page 142 he prints a letter from Albert Einstein, who says, "The words or the language, as they are written or spoken, do not seem to play any role in my mechanism of thought."

All the evidence now available in the field of comparative psychology seems to point toward the presence in many infrahuman animals of a simple, sensorimotor, affective, and conative awareness of what is going on which has its expression in reinforcement, inhibition, and directive guidance of behavior. These patterns of behavior and the primitive type of awareness probably colligated with them may be present in all animals; and they are progressively elaborated, in forms that are recognizably similar to human mental processes, in animals which possess more or less well differentiated cerebral cortex. It seems probable, therefore, that, although awareness is an emergent in the evolutionary series, it did not appear as a sudden mutation, but was gradually individuated from some more generalized type of integrated experience. All that we know about psychogenesis in the human infant points in the same direction.

Much of the trouble which gives rise to controversy is semantic, for we have no vocabulary in any language, so far as I know, which is adequate to designate the observed or conjectured antecedents of human mentation as these are manifested in the inorganic realm, in plants and unicellular animals, in isolated fragments of a multicellular body, in the several parts of a growing embryo, or in the separate organs of an adult body. The terms commonly employed in describing these supposed primordia are borrowed from the psychological vocabulary of human conscious mentation, and this necessitates redefinition of these words with results that are sometimes startling. Thus Whitehead speaks of the "subjective aim" of electrons and Agar ('53) ascribes to single cells, and indeed to all living aggregates of cells, "feelings," "perceptions," "purposes," etc. He says explicitly that "all perception involves cognition, conation, and affective tone," and he explains at length and repeatedly that these terms in this context carry no necessary implication of any awareness factor whatever. His definition of perception illustrates this: "An act of perception is the establishment by the subject of its causal relation with its external world at that moment." And this causal relation is not necessarily consciously perceived by the subject.

It is perhaps unfortunate that in describing "mentation" in other animals than ourselves we seem to be obliged to use words which have strong subjective nuance, for this inclines us almost inevitably to ascribe to lower animals mental capacities patterned after our own—the vice of anthropomorphism (Schneirla, '49). And yet there seems to be no other way open to us. The only way we can examine these things is the human way. The best that we can hope to do is to use our own awareness judiciously in the interpretation of animal behavior, being careful to transfer the quality of this experience to the objective world only in so far as we have empirical evidence for it. As this evidence accumulates, our definition of terms becomes more precise; the time will come (soon, we hope) when such anthropomorphisms as "perception" by a protozoan may be replaced by more appropriate descriptive terms. This is why, in dealing with primitive animals, I prefer to say that their behavior exhibits integrative experience rather than "mentation." I consider it unfortunate to borrow words so freely from human psychological vocabularies, as La Barre ('54) does in his interesting book *The Human Animal*, where he grants to plants and insects a knowing ability, or "adaptive knowledge," with resulting confusion of categories. Let us revise our vocabulary and if necessary enlarge it to meet the requirements of expanding knowledge.

Although it must be recognized that language is not an indispensable tool of thought, it remains true that most of the mental processes of men actually use verbal symbols, not only as vehicles of communication, but also as instruments of rational processes that do not come to overt expression. People vary in this respect. Some are pre-eminently verbalizers; others do a much larger part of their thinking in terms of visual, auditory, or other patterned abstractions that do not take verbal form; but some form of symbolism seems to be an essential component of all kinds of mentation above the level of simple sensation (pp. 308, 401). For a discussion of the role of language in human evolution see Pannekoek ('53), and for the neurological mechanisms involved see Lashley ('51).

In this connection Lashley ('49, p. 38) remarks that "it is not the invention of the symbols which makes possible the function" of high-order generalizations such as are used in language. He shows clearly that simpler generalizations can be made without language, but I repeat my conviction that some form of symbolism is requisite and that without the invention of language symbols the human type of mentation is impossible.

Awareness cannot be "reduced" to physicochemical categories or adequately described scientifically by ever so complete an explanation of the mechanism employed. This is as impractical as it would be to try to describe the properties of an electrical current in terms of those of the dynamo that generates it. The vital process which generates a conscious experience if viewed objectively is seen to be a physical mechanism in action. The properties of this action, again viewed objectively, are special kinds of metabolism which differ in some as yet unknown way from the metabolic patterns of unconscious bodily functions. There is a step-up of pattern here which is similar in principle to that which occurs at the transition from the level of inorganic process to that of vital process.

Another property of this unknown pattern of metabolism cannot be observed objectively at all. It can be apprehended only by the particular individual concerned, by whom it is recognized introspectively as an awareness of some kind. Such a twofold manifestation of the same process is not unique in biology. It is seen, for instance, in the process of nervous conduction, a metabolic process which includes chemical changes in the nerve fiber and changes in its electrical potential. The one process is manifested in two ways which must be investigated by quite different methods. It will not do to ignore either one of them and say the conduction is exclusively chemical or exclusively electrical. Similarly the psychobiological processes of the brain have qualities that are observable perceptually as metabolic functions and other qualities that are observable only introspectively, and the difference between these manifestations of the one process can never be explained by ignoring it. It will not do to say, as many biologists and psychologists now do, that the mind-body question is a pseudoproblem, that "there is no such problem."

It is contended by Lashley ('49, p. 29) that the nature of conscious experience as distinct from physiological processes is a pseudoproblem and that those who still maintain that mind, where it appears, performs a unique function in integrating behavior have not "indicated the nature of this function or defined the behavior which is its unique product." And yet his own conclusion (p. 40) regarding the evolution of mammalian behavior is that "the major changes are rather the result of the development of intelligent foresight and the inhibition of action in anticipation of more remote prospects." Are not intelligent foresight and conscious anticipation of remote prospects unique and definable functions? The awareness itself, although not definable in terms of conventional physiological criteria, is an experienced event which has observable integrating efficiency and which is demonstrably in organic relationship with preceding and following organic processes.

The discovery of the lawful order of these relationships is not a pseudoproblem nor is it to be lightly dismissed as an insoluble problem, as is done by Johnson ('45), who has subjected the basic concepts and presuppositions of psychophysics to logical and mathematical analysis, with the conclusion that "the so-called problems of psychophysics, namely, of deducing or inferring what other individuals than ourselves may sense and feel, are not genuine, but spurious. In other words, they are forever insoluble." His arguments and conclusions may be accepted if by solution we mean a rigidly logical and mathematical demonstration that follows of necessity and quantitatively from available factual evidence. But operationally we all know from our own experience that body and mind do stand in lawfully ordered relationship, and we have practical demonstration that the laws of this relationship can be investigated scientifically. We also know that we can and do see into other people's minds sufficiently well to make practical judgments about their mental attitudes and consciously directed behavior. These judgments are accurate enough to enable us to do business with them and often to predict their future conduct. In a similar way we can form some conjectures, though with far less probability, about the mental processes of some subhuman animals, well enough, indeed, to predict their behavior and adjust to it. No dialectic, however logically impregnable it may be, can nullify these incontrovertible facts. The appropriate scientific attitude is to accept them and try to discover the psychophysical principles which explain them. Nothing is gained by postulating in advance the limits of the knowable.

The scientific status of mentation has given psychiatrists a world of trouble which can all be avoided by following the simple rule laid down by Adolf Meyer (Lief, '48, p. 387), who said in 1912: "To make the

so-called introspective material an object of science, we certainly do all
we can to pin down the evidence for its existence and nature and to
prove it before others as well as before ourselves by just as searching evidence as physics demands for sound waves or electromagnetism. In the
measure that the introspectively most evident reactions obtain evidence of
objective validity in the interplay of objective events can they become a
valid topic of the science which describes what its objects are and do. . . .
We are still looked at with suspicion when we claim that the emphasis
on the so-called psychophysical parallelism is no longer obligatory, and
that if we make a contrast it should be that of mental and nonmental
biological reactions and not the illogical contrast of mental and physical."

The mental is also physical and some physical events have mental
properties. This dual nature of human experience, in which the experiencing self is polarized against the things experienced as the
subject set apart from the objects, finds a counterpart at lower levels
in a similar double nature of everything else. Every definable thing
is polarized in its relations to the other things of its surroundings.
This dynamic polarization of the thing as the focal center of transactional relations with other things is a common characteristic of the
world as we know it. The thing is a mechanism, and no mechanism
can operate in isolation from its surrounding field. The entire field
of this interaction is, indeed, an integral part of the mechanism
(pages 57, 439).

Now, the human person is a mechanism set in a wide field with
which it is always in transactional relations. Some of these transactions are on the physiological level and some are on the psychological,
and all of them are vital processes. The transactions between the
person and his surroundings which are carried on consciously must
operate through the instrumentality of physiological processes—sensory and motor analysis and complicated central processes of adjustment. When the equilibrium of this dynamic system is disturbed, as
occurs when an object is perceived, the physiological components of
the process are open to public inspection but the mental components
—the awareness of the perception—are not.

When the mental process reaches the level of self-consciousness it
is conscious of itself as the actor and it cannot at the same time be
directly conscious of the field of its activity as one with that activity.

The consciousness cannot be the function of a structure and at the same time know that structure as structure. Thus the subjective comes to be sharply set off from the objective in conscious experience. This sharp contrast is of the same sort (at a different level) as that which sets the organism apart from its environment and (at a still lower level) as that which gives every definable thing its individuality as opposed to the dynamic field within which it is set.

I have suggested ('05, p. 434; '39, p. 104; '45, p. 68) that the clear-cut polarization in consciousness of perceiving subject and perceived object is perhaps a methodological artifact arising from the inherent limitations of the finite mind and the practical use we make of introspective and extraspective experience. This is supported by the fact that it seems to appear rather late in human psychogenesis (page 308). Structure can be known only indirectly through sensation and movement in space and time, and what can be learned in this way is determined by the structure of the organs used. Our conceptual mental processes are set in a different frame of reference and use a type of nervous structure which has properties quite different from those employed in sensory and motor analysis. This is the reason why mind and matter cannot be directly equated in terms of any presently available units of measurement.

Just as awareness has its own distinctive qualities, so does every other recognizable kind of vital activity—respiration, locomotion, and life itself. These have not been made out of nothing by any kind of miraculous intervention, and we can bring to light the successive steps of their fabrication by natural processes. It remains true, we repeat, that the private and often incommunicable character of human mentation is the greatest obstacle to a thorough scientific investigation of it. My thoughts are my own, but so are my reflexes. My awareness is just one of those things, like my specific gravity and my physiognomy, that distinguish me as a person from all other things. These are things that I accept, however imperfectly I understand them. Life is a mystery which we do not yet fully understand. Mind is still more mysterious. We do know that mental processes must be in harmonious attunement with the realities of our world of objective experience or we quickly perish.

Summary

Mind is not something acting upon the body to make it go. It is the body in action. My mind is not something that I have. It is something that I am, just as my body is, for I am a minding body. The pattern of mentation is distinctive. So is the pattern of reflex. And each of these patterns belongs exclusively to the individual who makes it. The reflex is open to public inspection; any awareness of the reflex or of anything else is not, although the mental process may be publicized by language and other expressions. The most characteristic feature of mental action is that it can be known only introspectively.

Mind is here defined as awareness. In so far as subjective experience can be colligated with the physical organs employed and with their functions, including gesture, language, and other symbolisms, these objective data may be used as indicators of the related mental processes, and by this indirection legitimate sciences of introspective psychology and comparative psychology have been developed.

The body makes the mind, but the mind is not a product made by the body as gastric juice is made by the stomach. It is the body in action, a peculiar pattern of action of a special kind of bodily apparatus, just as walking is another pattern of action of a different kind of apparatus.

CHAPTER TWENTY-THREE

A Biological Analysis of Mental Processes

A neurologist looks at his own mind

The only way to get secure knowledge about mind is to experience it, and because one cannot experience other people's minds his own mental experience must be the ultimate court of appeal. Regardless of the amount of inferential knowledge about other minds that one has, all this information must be interpreted and evaluated in terms of one's own personal mental processes. Having had mental experience for more than eighty years and having devoted more than half of that time to study of the bodily organs of the mental life, I have expressed some opinions about the nature of mind and the apparatus of mentation. A few sentences from my Mellon Lecture at the University of Pittsburgh in 1939 are quoted here, and other passages from this address appear in subsequent pages.

I have made up my mind that this mind of mine is something that I myself have made. It has grown up with me. It is part of me as truly as is my body. It is not something added to my body to make it go. It is not something that I have. It is something that I am. It is an active part of me, something that I am doing. There are no mental states, only mental acts. What the psychologists call the content of my mind is the pattern of this performance of mental work by bodily organs.

Our minds, then, are not given to us by kindly fairies or handed down to us ready-made in the genes or by tradition in social heredity. However we may be influenced by hereditary organization, by social pressure or mob psychology, it remains true that every mind inheres in a single person; it is something that the individual has made and that he alone can use. It is this personal attribute of mind that makes us so jealous of it.

Our minds bother us. Our most serious troubles are mental, and many problems of practical life and of science would be simplified if the mind were given a holiday. Many people take such holidays more or less deliberately with results not always fortunate. Some objective psychologists have done their best to lay the ghost, but it will not down. It does not do any good to try to solve a difficult problem by ignoring the troublesome factors or by identifying mind with some quite different action, with adaptation, or with all totalizing or integrative functions. And panpsychism is a speculative excursion of more interest to metaphysics than to science.

As a neurologist my interest is an inquiry into the natural history of mind, the part it plays in the vital economy. We want to see how far we can go in the exploration of the mental life without overstepping the boundaries of the natural and the requirements of good scientific method. We want specific and detailed answers to the questions, first, What are the bodily organs of the mental processes? and, second, Exactly how do these organs operate in the performance of mental work? The neurologist can supply a great deal of information about the first topic. The right answer to the second question is that we do not know, but the knowledge already available about the bodily apparatus employed in mental processes and recent developments of new methods and instruments of precision encourage the hope that this second question is not insoluble.

It is possible to find out what parts of the body are actively engaged when we perceive a flash of light, when we are hungry or angry, or when we imagine a muscular movement without actually executing it. We do not yet know all about any of these processes, but it is a great gain to have identified some of the organs involved and to be able to record quantitative measurements of some of their activities. We are beginning to know just where to look for other essential facts.

The patterns of mentation

It has been customary to recognize three kinds of human mental processes. These are cognition or knowing, affect or feeling, and conation or willing. Throughout the present work especial attention is directed to the cognitive factors of behavior; but it must be kept in mind that the classification which separates cognition from the other kinds of mentation is somewhat artificial and arbitrary, for in actual thinking the three kinds of processes are blended in varying proportions. They are most clearly distinguished in the higher mental processes, and as we pass from these to the simpler and presumably more primitive types they tend to merge into a generalized type of awareness in which the three kinds are not clearly distinguishable. The following general statements summarize a few principles that are more fully considered elsewhere in this book.

Among the various components of mentation in man and other animals, intelligence has been most thoroughly studied in comparative psychology because its manifestations in behavior are readily accessible to observation and experiment. But what intelligence really is has never been satisfactorily explained (Chapter 28). The answers proposed are so diverse and conflicting that we must first clarify our own definitions of some terms and consider some general principles.

Sensation, perception, learning, intelligence, and reasoning comprise a man's intellectual life, his cognition or knowing, in distinction from his emotions, impulses, and volitions. The importance of perception in behavior has been emphasized, because most of our knowledge about the nature of the world to which we must adjust our conduct is perceptual knowledge. This knowledge provides the essential foundation for the study of the higher cognitive processes. Ranked in order of their complexity and probably also of the time of their appearance in psychogenesis, the following precursors and components of human cognition are commonly recognized:

First, there is differential *sensitivity* adapted for analysis of the various modes of energy manifestation that act upon the body. This is seen in many inorganic mechanisms, such as a set of self-registering meteorological instruments which makes a separate record of changes in temperature, humidity, atmospheric pressure, and so on. In the living body the sense organs are the primary analyzers and the resulting analysis gives us the modalities of sense.

If there is awareness of this analysis, the subject experiences a *sensation*, which may be a generalized feeling of well-being or malaise or may be individuated as a specific modality. Subjectively the sensation may seem to be a simple elementary experience, but the process of sensing can be analyzed experimentally. It is rarely, if ever, a simple or purely cognitive experience, for it usually has an affective quality and there is always a conative or expressive component, either as a present response or as a "trace" left by previous responses. There is, as we have seen, probably no awareness without some kind of active response to the stimulus. The sensation is an act, not a passive reception.

In *perception* the active component of the sensation is accentuated and the activity is consciously directed outward toward the source of the excitation. The subject attends to the thing perceived, and attention involves a bodily attitude, a dynamic posture or tension directed toward the object sensed. This directive quality may be present on the plane of mere sensitivity or sensation, and in the lower animals this is probably always true. But in perception the experiencing subject is recognizably set apart over against the object of experience. In this distinction between sensation and perception we follow the usage in Baldwin's *Dictionary of Philosophy and Psychology* (Macmillan Co., 1902, Vol. 2, p. 277), where we read: "The word sensation connotes only subjective state produced by an external stimulus without implying any awareness of an object. . . . To have a perception is to be aware of an object by means of a present sensation."

In all motile animals there is some capacity for adjustment of the body and its members to the spatial relations of environing things and for timing these adjustments in appropriate sequence. This is accomplished in a great variety of ways, which may involve the co-operative action of several senses and complicated motor mechanisms. In the lower ranks of animals these movements are made tropistically or reflexly and perception as defined here is not necessarily involved. In higher animals perception is a cortical function.

If a mammal is deprived of its cerebral cortex, visual discrimination of the spatial relations of things is seriously impaired, and in primates it is totally lost.

In perception the sensation has meaning and the "I" as knower is polarized in distinction from the thing known. This is the dawn of *intelligence*. It has been clearly demonstrated experimentally that perception (and the derived intelligence) is *learned*. It is not innate, although the pattern of its manifestation is in large measure determined by the inherited bodily structure, which in turn has been organized during preceding racial experience. Patterns of adaptive behavior which by natural selection or otherwise have been impressed upon the genetic organization of the species reappear in each generation as racial memories or neurograms which determine the limits within which perceptual learning is possible and also the manner of its expression.

Sensitivity and sensation are pre-eminently analytic. In perception the analysis is carried further and a synthetic factor is added. It is the latter which gives to perception its distinctive quality. In perception there is recognition of the relation of things to one another and to the perceiving subject. This involves a judgment. In this integrative process the subject is the focal point of reference and the distinction between subject and object is clearly defined in consciousness.

The *perceptual knowledge* so acquired can now be manipulated subjectively. Common features of heterogeneous experience are abstracted and generalized as ideas or *concepts*, for which symbols are devised. The symbol becomes a datum, an object of regard, at a higher level of integration than the percept, and as such it is the instrument of thinking at this higher level. Thus the subject acquires *conceptual knowledge*, which provides the mental tools of all rational thinking at higher levels. These tools are not energies or structural organs or any other physical things. They are patterns of performance which are recognized subjectively as ideas. The psychical, accordingly, is defined in terms of the process of the experience rather than of its content.

This contrast between perceptual knowledge and conceptual knowledge was drawn sharply by Sellars ('38) in an epistemological analysis of the mind-body problem, and I have applied it operationally in my biological approach to the same problem (Chapter 13; cf. '49, p. 170).

The structure which fabricates the idea and its symbol is a stable component of the body, but the idea is a transient manifestation of the operation of the appropriate structure in the requisite pattern. These patterns of performance leave structural traces (of unknown nature) in the organization of the nervous system. These neurograms may be reactivated by appropriate stimulation. This recall may not rise to the level of awareness, in which case it may activate an automatic habitual response. If awareness of it is present, it is apprehended as a memory.

It should be emphasized that the distinctions here made between sensation, perception, and conception are relative, not absolute. Current psychological research reveals so many factors common to all of them that the lines between them are less sharply drawn than formerly. There are, however, real differences that must not be ignored. We are examining them here in the biological frame of reference.

The scope of psychobiology

Biology is usually defined as the science which deals with living bodies in all their relationships. The boundaries of this domain are fuzzy at both ends. There are mesoforms between living and lifeless bodies, and where shall we draw the line between psychology and physiology? The trouble is that the psychologists themselves cannot agree on what their science is about. Klüver ('49) gives a graphic portrayal of the difficulties encountered in attempts to frame an acceptable definition. There are so many kinds of psychology that at present we can do little better than accept Cattell's characteristic statement: "Psychology is what the psychologist is interested in *qua* psychologist." In a recent paper ('55a) I have commented upon psychology as a biological discipline, and we are here examining it from that standpoint. However psychology is defined, it has biological relationships, and the function of psychobiology is to clarify these relationships.

In my essay "The Natural History of Experience" ('45) I wrote that psychobiology justifies itself scientifically by its objectives and methods of attack upon the problem of experience. Since all creatures have experience, psychobiology may be defined for our present purpose as the scientific study of the experience of living bodies, its method of operation, the apparatus employed, and its significance as vital process, all from the standpoint of the individual having the experience. A few paragraphs from that paper are quoted here.

The difference between the physiological and the psychological attitude toward any experience and the resulting behavior comes out clearly when we consider the process of adjustment as the operation of a polarized equilibrated system, with the integrated living body at one pole and at the other pole the total external and internal environment. An experience is a disturbance of this dynamic equilibrium, and it endures until some satisfying balance is restored. The experience itself adds a new factor and so participates in establishing the new balance. Both physiology and psychology must understand the structural configuration of the operating system, organic and environmental, and its method of operation. The physiologist views the entire process as adjustment—the correlation of bodily changes with current events—either adjustment of the animal as a whole to environment or of part with part within the vital economy. He views the process as a spectator from the outside, and the individual facts acquire meaning as they are set into the frame of the total situation. There is a fitness of environment as well as a fitness of organism (Henderson, '13).

The psychologist examines the same events, but he views them from the inside, that is, from the standpoint of the individual having the experience. In viewing behavior objectively his horizon is more restricted than that of the biologist, for an experience is a personal matter and the psychologist's primary interest is its effect upon the person himself. He is more concerned with the *action* of the organism than with the reaction as a whole. In the examination of his own experience he has the benefit of an awareness which he aims to understand in all of its relationships. All other kinds of experience must be studied by the methods of objective science, and here he tries to put himself in the place of the person or animal having the experience, to see the situation from the other's point of view.

Psychological interest centers in the individual, in the person having the experience, in the motivation of his behavior, its pattern of performance, and the satisfactions resulting from successful adjustment. This satisfaction may or may not be consciously apprehended, but it is always the end toward which the behavior is directed. A satisfaction is a value. So we conclude that the major interest of all psychological research is to gain a better understanding of the intrinsic values of life and the enhancement of these values. To the objective psychologist this may sound like a *reductio ad absurdum*. Perhaps so, from his standpoint. But no adequate psychobiology can be developed from a premise which denies the significance for behavior of conscious motives, feelings, purposes, and satisfactions. From this it follows that the domain of psychology extends beyond the conventional limits of biology; but my contention here is that these limits have been artificially restricted and that conscious experience as a vital process must be given its due recognition in the fraternity of biological sciences. Here it should be emphasized again that experience must not be regarded as something existential in its own right. An experience is not an entity. It is an act, a *behavior*, and it cannot be understood apart from its context in the total pattern of the behaving individual's action system.

The frame of reference within which the preceding formulation is set is, of course, only one out of many that may be, and have been, chosen. Yet the experience of the behaving subject seems to be the focal point of interest in the basic postulates of psychology, now widely accepted, as these have been concisely formulated by Vinacke ('48).

Summary

The processes of knowing (cognition), feeling (affect), and willing (conation) are blended in varying proportions in all mental acts and these kinds of human mentation tend to merge into a more generalized awareness as we pass to the more primitive animals.

Primitive sensitivity becomes sensation if awareness of it is present. Sensation advances to perception when it acquires meaning in terms of the relations existing between things sensed and the perceiving subject, and these relations can be experienced only through action oriented toward the object sensed. This is the dawn of intelligence, and, since intelligence is the most reliable guide to human behavior, it and perception will be examined critically.

Psychobiology is primarily concerned with the experience of living bodies, examined in all of its relationships from the standpoint of the individual having the experience. The relationships of conscious experience to unconscious experience reveal the origins, the mechanisms, and the biological significance of mind in the vital economy.

CHAPTER TWENTY-FOUR

The Beginnings and Growth of Mind

Panpsychism

The problems of psychogenesis can be approached in two ways, either by examination of the growth of mental capacities in the individual or by inquiry into the origin and development of these capacities in evolutionary history. Some of the difficulties encountered in the latter approach have been mentioned. The embryology of mind is more accessible to direct observation and experiment, yet no mental abilities can emerge during the course of individual development except those for which the necessary structural organization has been provided by preceding evolutionary processes and so laid down in the genetic endowment of the individual. No animal can learn to talk and to solve quadratic equations unless he has inherited the cortical apparatus requisite for construction and use of the mental symbols employed. And no animal can learn to fly unless he has inherited wings or a brain so organized as to be able to invent a practicable substitute for them. So it is apparent that the phylogenetic history of mentation is the more fundamental aspect of psychogenesis.

Because the mentality of subhuman animals can be known only by inference from their structure and behavior, many comparative psychologists define mind in terms of these objectively manifest criteria; and, since some of these properties of the living body and its behavior can be followed back through the animal series in successively simpler forms as far as the most primitive organisms known, mentation is regarded as a property common to all organisms. Some go further. Since precursors of the vital properties can be found in the inorganic realm, mind is predicated as a universal component of our cosmos as a whole. If the premises and definitions are granted, this conclusion seems logically defendable.

But these doctrines of panpsychism side-step the crucial issue, namely, the unique and evidently significant properties of awareness as such, and we have no way of finding out at what stage in the evolutionary process (or in embryological development) these unique properties are present. Such scanty evidence as we now have inclines me to favor an "emergent view of consciousness" (Sellars, '43), rather than a radical panpsychism. Mind, like gold, is where we find it and, like gold, its presence is sometimes masked by the enveloping matrix. But gold is gold, wherever it is, and we gain nothing but confusion by defining awareness in objective terms only and then confining our search to the objects colligated with it. Though the origins and early qualities of the conscious life are inaccessible to us, its later manifestations in man's close relatives among the primates can be recognized, as illustrated in the next chapter.

Panpsychism is an attractive hypothesis which can be defended (and has been by very able advocates) on philosophical grounds, but the scientific evidence for it is weak and inconclusive.

Among the many expositions of the general doctrine, one by A. Campbell Garnett ('42) aims to show that the theory of emergence of the mental from the nonmental "is not consistent with the strict demands of scientific method," but that "the life and mind of the human organism are an organic part of the life and mind of a world organism." That the mental and the physical "are fundamentally integrated in one organic whole" throughout the cosmos is acceptable to this author as a postulate for a naturalistic philosophy. The argument is ingenious, but to a naturalist (meaning me) who is not a philosopher the dialectic is not convincing.

Immediately following the article just cited is one by Paul Henle ('42) entitled "The Status of Emergence," which seems to provide ample philosophical justification for a naturalistic concept of emergence. It seems to me that the hypothesis of emergence, as Henle explains it, is preferable to a radical panpsychism (which ascribes mind even to an electron, as some do), not only because of its "logical simplicity," but primarily because it accords better with such factual evidence as we have about problems of psychogenesis.

Psychogenesis

Returning now to the embryology of mind, we note that the child's earliest conscious experience is obviously of very generalized quality. It is a total pattern within which the several components of the adult mental life are gradually and progressively individuated. Even the fundamental distinction between himself and the rest of the world is not recognized at birth, but this knowledge is slowly acquired by experience. My infant nephew was seated on the floor one day munching a biscuit and at the same time watching the wriggling of his toes. On a sudden impulse he reached out his hand and offered a bite to his great toe. He had not yet learned much about himself.

In short, nothing strictly mental is heritable as such. The pattern of the organic substrate is given in the genetic organization, and this sets definite limits to the potentialities for mental development. These potential mental capacities can be actually realized only through the personal experience of the child.

If the child is born without the normal equipment of sensory and motor organs, this is a serious handicap, for these are necessary instruments for the acquisition of experience. Fortunately, however, deficiency of one member may be compensated by acquisition of unusual skills by the other members. A child born without hands can learn to write with his toes. Children born deaf can learn sign language, those born blind can read Braille, and the mental accomplishments of some who are both blind and deaf are often spectacular. The mental retardation, however, of those unfortunates who are born with deficient cortical apparatus of semantic learning and hence of efficient reasoning ability is irremediable, though many of these mental defectives may be trained under skillful guidance to be productive and self-supporting within the limited range of their competence.

In the early months of the child's postnatal development his mental processes are apparently limited to concrete experiences on the plane of sensorimotor thought and accompanying pulses of emotion and impulse, a plane which is comparable with the adult mental life of his playmates, the cats and dogs. At this age he learns to recognize signs which are significant for his behavior—parental gestures, words, and so on—and to respond to them with similar signs. These signs become symbols which at first are abstracted from a particular thing—"da" for daddy, my daddy. Generalization, that is, the abstraction of common features from diverse particulars, such as "father" for all daddies, comes later, and further growth of intelligence depends largely upon his ability to integrate heterogeneous experience in a hierarchy of symbolisms, each of which stands for an abstraction, an idea. The acquisition of language, the use of words as symbols of abstract ideas rather than signs of particulars, marks the stage of development which sets mankind apart from all other animals. The invention of articulate speech provided the instruments which were essential for all subsequent growth of intellect and reasoning. It also made possible a moral culture beyond the capacity of any brutes. Ideas of good and evil, of right and wrong, thus symbolized were incorporated into the social structure as moral codes.

The significance of this critical stage of mental development has been shown very clearly by several experiments in which a human infant and an infant chimpanzee were reared together under conditions as nearly identical as possible. One of these has been published (Kellogg and Kellogg, '33), and others are in progress. The infancy of the chimpanzee is shorter than that of the child and so it is not surprising that in the early months the baby ape surpassed the child in speed of learning many things. A newborn chimp named Viki was reared by Dr. and Mrs. Hayes in their home as nearly as possible like a human child until she was six years old (Hayes, '51; Gray, '55). She learned to use tools very cleverly, and at five years of age she could pick out pictures to match the real objects portrayed. She learned to speak a few words with difficulty and could understand many more, just as a dog does. But she could not be taught a true language, so she was quite unable to pass from the simian to the human level of education.

The growth of children's mental capacities has always been watched with interest by their elders, and beginning about fifty years ago serious attempts have been made to put child study on a scientific basis. The earlier observations were descriptive and impressionistic; as the data were accumulated increasing attention was paid to methods of quantitative study and to the correlation of changes in patterns of behavior with the growth of their bodily organs. One of the most productive of these programs is that of the Yale Clinic of Child Development, the director of which has published his conclusions about the beginnings of the human mind (Gesell, '45). As Gesell emphasizes, the examination of postnatal behavior does not really begin at the beginning, for the moment of birth marks merely one critical point in a continuous process of development which includes the forty weeks of prenatal life and an indeterminate period of ancestral evolution. General surveys of this field have been published by Carmichael ('54) and in the symposium edited by Barker, Kounin, and Wright ('43).

The study of prenatal human behavior is difficult for obvious reasons. A firm foundation for these studies was laid by Coghill and research in this field is now very active. In various mammals, including man, these studies reveal successive additions to the complexity of nervous connections correlated with every change in the pattern of overt behavior. Although the importance of this relationship has been questioned (by Lashley, Kuo, and others), the further the study of the mechanics of growth is carried the more evident it becomes that demonstrable changes in nervous patterns accompany changes in the stable and standardized components of behavior. These local changes, of course, must not be regarded as isolated events. They must be set in their appropriate relations with the total organization.

Prenatal human behavior has been systematically studied by Hooker ('36, '39, '43, '52). He reports that at fourteen weeks of fetal life there is an important change in the pattern of behavior. The fetus is no longer marionette-like or stereotyped in the character of its movements, which are thereafter graceful and fluid, as they are in the newborn. At this time the higher integrating apparatus of the thalamus and perhaps also the thalamo-cortical connections have reached a stage of differentiation which probably marks the beginning of functional capacity. These higher levels of the brain mature much later than do those of the lower brain stem and the complication of their internal structure continues for many years after birth, probably as long as learning capacity lasts.

It is obvious that no nervous mechanism of central adjustment can perform its functions until the nerve fibers which connect its several parts are in functional connection. By microscopic examination of a series of brains of known functional age it is possible to discover what central organs are added to the existing structure at each stage in the complication of the action system. This gives reliable information about the organs employed in the performance of these functions as they successively mature. The cortical associational tissues are the last to become functional, and, unfortunately, the details of the sequence of development of these tissues are not yet sufficiently well known to give a reliable basis for correlation of the higher mental processes with the related nervous organization.

The methods just described, supplemented by a wide variety of experimental procedures, can reveal the locations within the brain of the nervous organs which execute the simpler components of the behavior pattern, particularly those of reflex and other stereotyped systems. The apparatus which serves the integrating functions has not been adequately described. Many fields where these functions are predominant can be circumscribed more or less precisely, but the details of the mechanisms employed are imperfectly understood. This deficiency is remediable, and in fact this problem is now under active investigation.

It is possible to discover by observation and experiment at just what stage in the growth of an organized system of nervous elements the system can perform its characteristic function—a specific local reflex, a complicated act of locomotion, or whatever. It has been seen that after the several nervous elements involved have reached this early stage of functional competence they continue to grow for an indefinite period. This growth may take the form of repeated branching of the nerve fibers and the elongation of the branches, so that each nervous element acquires a progressively larger number of anatomical connections with different functional significance. In this way the apparatus of a rigidly stereotyped pattern of response may be transformed into or supplemented by a more labile and modifiable pattern adapted for conditioning of reflexes and other individually acquired abilities. This is an early stage of development of the apparatus of nervous integration, including learning.

This embryological development recapitulates in broad outline the series of progressive changes displayed by the phylogenetic development. Though the two series are by no means closely parallel, each contributes much toward the understanding of the other, and the same general principles can be seen in both of them. The most notable feature of both series is the obviously directive nature of the observed sequence of changes. There is progressive complication of behavior and its mechanism, and the objective toward which these changes point is more efficient expression of the intrinsic capacities of the organism in the interest of a wider range of adaptive adjustments and of ensuing satisfactions.

Motility is the cradle of mind

That mind emerges within overt behavior and is primarily conative has been advocated by many philosophers and psychologists and supported by a wealth of biological evidence. Not long ago Professor Sheldon ('41) wrote, "The whole trend of modern psychology emphasizes the conative aspect of conscious life," and "Consciousness arises in connection with motor activity."

Overt behavior is movement of some sort. Movement is primordial and mentation arises within it not to cause behavior but to regulate it, direct it, and improve its efficiency. Conscious emotive experience reinforces the action system with additional driving power, and in proportion as intelligence guides the direction taken in its expression, the efficiency of the behavior is improved. In both embryological and phylogenetic development, intrinsically activated motility precedes reaction to external stimulation. The body acts before it reacts. In embryogenesis myogenic movement precedes neurogenic action. Muscles can act and react before they have any nervous connections.

Motility as self-expression is the dominant motif in all of Coghill's writings. His psychology and philosophy are as dynamic as his physiology. His definition of "mentation" is broader than the usage here adopted, for it includes much that I would assign to the premental or subconscious. He said, "Behavior is overt mentation," and "The earliest or elemental mentation probably arose with motor function." The latter statement I accept, the former I would qualify, for if mentation is defined as awareness, as I do define it, there is no evidence that all behavior is overt mentation.

Feeling, Coghill said, is elementary mentation, "the matrix of all mentation," and the feeling to which reference is made here is below the level of awareness. When awareness does emerge it probably has the same qualities which Coghill ascribed to more elementary preconscious feeling, namely, a strong conative factor (feeling of effort), associated with sensibility (primordial intelligence) and affect (satisfaction or dissatisfaction), though these components may not be clearly individuated. Elemental volition is the feeling of effort in movement. This is the primary component of Coghillian "mentation" and probably also of mind defined as awareness. The affective component of elementary feeling may be characterized as feeling tone, because it is associated with effort. "Emotion," he said, "is psycho-organismic posture charged with feeling, or motivated feeling toward an object." The intimate relation of elementary feeling, including sensibility, emotion, impulse, and volition, to tonus and posture was emphasized by Coghill. He wrote "Tonus, according to my idea, is the basis of posture as a total pattern in relation to attention."

The dean of British physiology, Sir Charles Sherrington, whose aphorism heads this section, laid especial stress upon the motor and postural factors of mentation, and, like Coghill, he recognized the matrix of mind, if not mind itself, in even the most primitive animals which exhibit motility. A few detached sentences from his remarkable book *Man on His Nature* ('52) are quoted here, but for their full import they must be read in their original context.

"There seems to be no lower limit to mind" (p. 265). "Mind, recognizable mind, seems to have arisen in connection with the motor act. Where motor integration progressed and where motor behaviour progressively evolved, mind progressively evolved" (p. 213). "The motor act as conative would seem to have been the earliest nurse of infant mind. . . . Does it not begin with urge to live?" (p. 193). "Motor behaviour would seem to be the cradle of recognizable mind. . . . Moreover the motor act is that which seems to clinch the distinction between self and not-self. The doer's doings affirm the self" (p. 324). "The awareness attaching to these motor acts relates the conscious 'self' to the acts as doing them. . . . The muscles besides being motor instruments are sense-organs. The muscular act therefore affects sense. There is perception of the act. Sensual perception has, as always, spatial reference. . . .

But there is in the conscious motor act an awareness also of the 'I-doing.' This latter awareness is not derived from sense. It is the 'I's' direct awareness of itself acting. A difference between it and the awareness derived from sense is that while that which derives from sense has, as we said, spatial projection, this which is not derived from sense has no spatial projection. It is awareness of the self 'doing' but it is not projected" (p. 325).

The distinction drawn in the last passage quoted is the same as that which I emphasize here as the most significant difference between perceptual experience and conceptual experience. Another distinction drawn by Sherrington—that between the anticipatory and the consummatory phases of any reaction—is significant here. The interval between reception of the stimulus and final action may be short or long, and during this time the posture or motor attitude is set and directed toward the appropriate motor activity. This is a critical period of active tonus and active inhibition during which the conscious components of the reaction (if any) emerge. These components may include sensory quality, intensity, affect, and conation in various combinations, and all of the thinking that follows. The consciousness is thus tied in with posture, motor attitude, and the final action as an integral part of the expression.

It seems probable, then, that conscious participation in any action arises within an inhibitory state, a stage of uncompleted movement expressed as attitude, an active tonus which first blocks overt expression. This is followed by release of some particular activity directed toward the object of regard. This accords with the belief long ago expressed by Dewey that consciousness emerges from unconscious action in problem situations, that doubt is the parent of thought. As long as life's processes go on smoothly without undue friction no attention is paid to them. The problem situation checks behavior. Intelligence begins with inhibition, just as reflex does, and the next step is the release of some pattern of behavior; it may be exploratory overt movement, a conscious search for clues, or a purposive action directed toward an objective selected by insight. Thinking in even its highest efficiency consists very largely in the inhibition of irrelevancies.

The history of the evolution of the brain teaches that its primary function from the beginning is the regulation of the transformation of patterns of sensory experience into patterns of motor response. Appropriate behavior is the end to be achieved. Sperry ('52) emphasizes this and supports it by the evident fact that the vertebrate brain was first designed for the regulation of overt behavior rather than for mental performance, and even at the culmination of its elaboration in man the primary concern of the brain continues to be the management, directly or indirectly, of overt behavior. This he carries to its logical conclusion: "The evolutionary increase in man's capacity for perception, feeling, ideation, imagination, and the like, may be regarded, not so much as an end in itself, as something that has enabled us to behave, to act, more wisely and efficiently." But, it may be objected, this seems to leave no place for man's higher "spiritual" values, his rational, esthetic, and moral achievements and the satisfactions that they yield. To this I would reply that these things have no value at all to the man who cherishes them or to anybody else unless something is done with them or about them. If they have no expression in conduct, they are negligible from any standpoint whatever. In other words, all mental activity is to be regarded as means to an end, and the end is conduct that yields the highest quality of satisfaction.

The importance of tonus and posture in the regulation of both unconscious and conscious behavior has long been recognized. Alexander Bain, who was a pioneer of modern dynamic psychology, taught that of all our senses the muscular sense is the most important; and the idea of the primacy of motility in perception, though a century old, is now receiving renewed attention with improved methods of experimental study.

The motor factors of mentation have been experimentally demonstrated in cognition, conation, and emotion. In the latter domain the differences of interpretation of the observed facts as reported by James, Lange, Cannon, Sherrington, and many others are reconciled in Nina Bull's attitude theory of emotion ('51), with abundant evidence derived in part from experiments upon hypnotized subjects. She concludes that "the 'body language' of the musculo-skeletal system is not merely expressive movement—a sensitive indicator of psychic processes—but includes a generative function dependent on its preliminary attitudinal phase. It is only logical that action deferred with a consequent prolongation of the preparatory motor attitude requires a continuous discharge into visceral as well as endocrine activity. The 'reverberations' of the total organism can then register centrally as felt emotion."

She distinguishes latent, motor, and mental phases of attitude and concludes that the conscious component of emotion does not precede its expression as commonly supposed, nor does it follow the final action of expression as William James suggested, but it belongs at an intermediate stage in its anticipatory phase where motor attitude is to be thought of as uncompleted movement.

Langfeld ('31, p. 105) cites similar statements by Bain and Ribot about thought processes in general, the latter author saying "a thought is a word or an act in a nascent state—a commencement of muscular activity." Josiah Royce ('03, p. 351) insisted that our motor or kinesthetic experiences form the very core of consciousness. The various forms of the mental life develop within action and are, therefore, special developments of action. "Thought is either action or nothing." Arnold Gesell ('45, p. 46) writes: "The embryology of behavior can be envisaged in terms of *posture*." This may be either static or dynamic. "Postural attitude issues into postural action. . . . The embryogenesis of mind must therefore be sought in the beginnings of postural behavior."

In one of Coghill's last publications ('41) he stated three principles which were derived from his work and have been supported by much subsequent research. These are (1) that of the integration of the whole organism in the performance of particular functions, (2) that of proprioceptive sensitivity as a factor in determining posture, (3) that of the primary importance of posture in determining muscular action. "In posture," he said, "the individual is as truly active as in movement. . . . In the course of development of behavior of Amblystoma the earliest partial reactions are postural." But these earliest postural reactions of the limbs are parts of a total reaction "and the sensory factor is in the proprioceptive system. The stimuli arise wholly within the organism. . . . Posture, therefore, is a forerunner of action and must be regarded as basic to it."

These principles can be accepted in their entirety except for one incidental statement in the quoted passage. Coghill's statement that "the stimuli arise wholly within the organism" applies to the movements of early larvae of Amblystoma under the conditions described. It must not be generalized. Since the quoted statement was written it has been shown experimentally that in adult animals the so-called proprioceptive stimuli may arise either within the body or externally. The eyes, the skin, and other exteroceptive organs play a major part in many reactions which are commonly described as proprioceptive, particularly those controlled by movements of the head.

The cerebellum was described by Sherrington ('48) as "the head ganglion of the proprioceptive system," and we now know that cerebellar control of posture and movement involves not only the specific proprioceptors (semicircular canals, muscle spindles, etc.), but also visual, auditory, cutaneous, and other organs of sense that are classed as exteroceptors. Both unconscious and voluntary movements are subject to this cerebellar control. In view of the fact that Sherrington in 1906 originally defined the proprioceptive system in terms of the kind of response evoked rather than of the organs of sense involved, it has been suggested by Larsell that it is fitting to call this system "proprius" rather than "proprioceptive." (For further discussion of these topics see Herrick, '49, chapters 11 and 12; Herrick, '47; Herrick and Larsell, '48.)

The phylogenetic development of postural adjustments has been reviewed by Dart ('47), with a critical survey of the literature relating to the physiological and therapeutic control of posture and the correction of malposture. He draws a distinction between posture and poise. Posture, he says, is a static concept, implying a fixed pose or habitual attitude of the body or its members. Poise is dynamic; it is the fluid running of a smoothly executed movement in which the several components are in momentarily changing balance. In particular, the activation and the inhibition of the muscles involved must be so adjusted as to work in dynamic equilibrium without interference. In any local movement there is active inhibition of the antagonist of every activated muscle, and in addition to this there is general inhibition of all conflicting movements.

The development of the postural factors of behavior in the chimpanzee has been critically examined by Riesen and Kinder ('52). This sequence of events is compared in detail and quantitatively with the corresponding series in the development of the human infant as recorded by Gesell. Posture is behavior, and it plays a significant and different part at successive stages of development of the individual and in the different species of the evolutionary series.

Increase in mental capacity, especially among the higher primates, seems to be correlated with refinement of the motor equipment. This is shown with especial clarity at the transition from brute to man when hands were transformed from organs of arboreal locomotion to instruments for the use of tools. It is a significant fact that in those South African extinct species (the Australopithecinae) which had some bodily structures intermediate between fossil apes and fossil men the differentiation of the structure of the limbs proceeded at a more rapid rate than that of the brain (Clark, '47a).

This intimate relationship between the apparatus of expression and intellectual advancement continued at an accelerated rate up to our time. The industrial expansion and a large part of scientific progress of our culture are directly dependent upon the invention of more efficient tools, for tools are now important organs of expression. The invention of language as the pre-eminent tool of communication marked the beginning of the distinctive human cultural pattern, and the improvement of the apparatus of communication in all its various forms is largely responsible for the revolutionary cultural changes now going on.

The primacy of motility in psychogenesis seems to be well validated. The conscious experience of the human adult cannot be so simply oriented. The earlier motor theories of consciousness are reviewed and criticized by Langfeld ('31), who supplements them by "a response interpretation of consciousness," in which consciousness is identified with the entire response, both afferent and efferent, although probably it does not arise unless there is an incipient or consummated discharge into efferent pathways. This way of looking at the conscious process emphasizes its quality as a total pattern, and it is supported by the evidence that the nervous processes involved are circular reactions involving the engineering principles of the "feed-back." The application of these mechanical principles will be given further consideration, for we must agree with Langfeld that "organization and dynamic relations must remain mere terms, suggestive for further investigation, until we know more about the processes of the nervous system."

Summary

The beginnings of mind (awareness) may be sought in the embryogenesis of the individual or in the phylogenesis of the race. Because no mental abilities can be acquired by the individual except those for which adequate bodily organs are provided in the genetic organization of the species, the evolution of mentation is of more fundamental significance for psychogenesis than is its embryological development. Notwithstanding this fact, for the practical problems of control of behavior the postnatal development of the individual is of more immediate concern, because here the various factors involved are more readily observed and more easily regulated.

The three conventional properties of mind—intelligence, emotion, and volition—seem at the beginning to be blended in an undifferentiated general awareness best described as "feeling." This primitive awareness emerges within action, and its recognizable properties are individuated progressively as the action system is expanded and diversified. So long as smoothly running standardized innate patterns of behavior adequately meet the requirements no mental participation is needed; but in problem situations where free expression is inhibited conscious control may determine the course of action taken. This control is a blend of emotional and rational factors.

During the period of arrest, while attitudes and postures are established and attention is directed to the object of interest, mental processes are generated, and these may give emotional drive and intelligent guidance to the ensuing action. In the more primitive animals the fitness or appropriateness of this action is determined mainly by innate components of the action system, with little (if any) conscious control. In mankind successful conduct can be assured only by keeping the animalistic impulses and emotional drives under the control of intelligent direction.

CHAPTER TWENTY-FIVE

Evolution of Mind

The limitations of method

The preceding inquiry into the early stages of the development of mind might appropriately be followed by a survey of the entire series of animals from the lowest to the highest, listing the factual data relating to the precursors of mind and its progressive refinement. This would require a large volume—and when all the recorded facts were assembled the conclusions that could be safely drawn would be disappointingly meager.

It is true that the evolution of mind-stuff, that is, the precursors and instruments of mentation, is an open book, though but little of it has yet been deciphered. But these facts are not enough to give us knowledge of what mental experiences these animals actually have, for we cannot discover these experiences by simple observation because the necessary introspective data are inaccessible to us. Although direct frontal attack upon the problem of the evolution of mind as awareness is impracticable, the problem, as we have seen, may be approached by indirection. This approach is profitable only in the case of the higher animals whose nervous systems and behavior are sufficiently like the human to provide an adequate basis for comparison.

The successive emergence of new patterns of behavior in different species has been recorded and the cerebral structure of the animals exhibiting each of these patterns has been examined and described in minute detail. Comparative neurology and comparative psychology thus working hand in hand have brought together an impressive series of relationships that show many instructive resemblances between the phylogenetic and the ontogenetic development of behavior and the colligated bodily organs. The details recorded in these studies are very technical and much of this literature is intelligible only to specialists. These anatomical and physiological studies, in all ranks of animals, give us no reliable evidence regarding the conscious experience of the animals, or, if they have any awareness of what is going on, what kind of awareness it is.

We have adequate evidence that the conscious experiences of all men have some broad features in common, that some of these are confined to mankind, and that others we share with at least the higher members of the animal kingdom. The further animal behavior and the structure of the apparatus employed deviate from human patterns, the less secure these inferences become. If the operating structure has no counterpart in the human body we can draw no safe inferences about what kind of awareness, if any, is colligated with it.

Most fishes, for example, have a system of cutaneous sense organs of the lateral lines widely distributed over the whole body, and the nerves supplying these organs are in many species the largest that they possess. These organs evidently play a major role in the control of the behavior of the fish (page 335); but if the fish has any conscious experience of their function, we have no way of learning what the quality of that experience may be. It is quite possible that the fish has no awareness at all of the activation of these highly specialized sense organs, for in the human body the structurally similar semicircular canals of the internal ear and also the other proprioceptive sense organs normally perform their important functions of maintenance of posture and balance quite unconsciously. The correlation of specific kinds of mental work with the related organs and their physiological properties can be made with precision only on human subjects.

In the present state of knowledge the starting point in the evolution of mind as awareness cannot be determined. The difficulty may be illustrated by the problem of the mentality of insects. The complicated behavior of many species of insects simulates human pur-

posive action so closely that it was explained by many of the early
naturalists as "lapsed intelligence." The theory was that these marvelously perfect adaptive adjustments were at first individually
learned and intelligently directed toward the desired end and that
subsequently this learned behavior was somehow implanted in the
germ plasm and so fixed as an inherited instinct. We now have
ample proof that this is not what happened. The biological mechanisms of directive evolution are sufficiently well known to make
it clear that at no stage of the process, at this integrative level, was
any intelligent directive required. The rule of parsimony demands
that intelligence must not be invoked if simpler lower-level principles are adequate. Moreover, the brains of insects are much smaller
and simpler than those of all vertebrates, and they are organized
on a radically different plan. The structures which in the brains of
higher vertebrates are known to be requisite for the high-grade
mentality postulated by the lapsed intelligence theory are totally
lacking in the brains of all insects and in all their ancestors. The
insect's instinctive behavior is explicable on biological principles at
the physiological level. This is not to deny that insects may have
some kind of conscious experience. I think it probable that they have,
but if so we have no way of finding out what it is like, other than
inferences drawn from critical study of their behavior.

Mental integration

All mental acts that we know anything about are total patterns
of integrative type. The search for the origin and biological factors
of mental evolution, accordingly, should begin with the general properties of the integrative apparatus. In my description (Chapters 8
and 9) of the distinctive characteristics of integration as contrasted
with analysis it was shown that the mechanical principles of the
most significant integrative processes must be formulated relativistically, in a broad and loose connotation of this term. These principles
are exemplified clearly in the functions of the nervous system.

Consciousness as we experience it seems to be a high-level integration of some kind of nervous processes, the exact nature of which
is still to be discovered. There may be simple types of consciousness
that emerge from lower levels of nervous organization or from the

nonnervous integrative apparatus of the simplest animals, but the evidence about this subject is scanty and equivocal. Moreover we have no exact information about the nature of the vital processes involved in any conscious act or of the mechanical principles of the operation.

Notwithstanding these disconcerting gaps in our knowledge, some general principles of integrative action find their clearest expression in the higher levels of conscious experience. To cite a notable example, the consciousness of the self as an integrated personality is set over against our knowledge about the not-self, and this is basic for perception and all mental processes derived from it. We can recognize some of the factors of these processes and trace the course of their progressive individuation and elaboration. Some of these factors are strictly physiological; others can be recognized only introspectively; and these factors can be separated only heuristically, for in actual operation they are inseparable. The essential and indissoluble integrity of the unconscious and the conscious factors of mentation must not be lost sight of for a moment, for otherwise we are lost in a tangle of unrelated and meaningless details.

This may be illustrated by another example. In traditional usage all mental acts, all kinds of awareness, are called "subjective" in distinction from the nonmental things and events of which we are aware. But some recent authors define this word more broadly. If every individual organism is regarded as a subject, then many of the integrative processes can be called subjective regardless of whether performed consciously or unconsciously.

The earliest steps in the individuation of the mental factors from the nonmental are still obscure, but the later stages of the prehuman evolution of mind can be observed in the anthropoid apes. After a brief inspection of the primate mind, we shall direct attention to a few selected factors of human mentation that are basic for further inquiry into the mechanics of the thinking process.

The primate mind

The cortex of a chimpanzee is highly elaborated, although it has only about one-fourth the superficial area of that of a man. Here, if anywhere, one would expect to find transitional stages between the animal type of intelligence and the human. In this we are not disappointed, for the experiments of Yerkes and Nissen ('39) reveal obscure but recognizable evidence of symbolic processes. They say: "It is our opinion, based upon the results of varied and long-continued training experiments, that symbolic processes occasionally occur in the chimpanzee; that they are relatively rudimentary and ineffective." Another interesting conclusion is that "some of the vertebrates are capable of symbolic response to spatial but not to non-spatial cues," whereas man adapts as promptly without spatial cues as with them. Precise and rapid adjustments in space are provided in the action systems of almost all animals and this apparatus is efficiently organized very early, so that spatial cues are readily available.

Other experiments have proved beyond question that both apes and monkeys can use a simple form of symbolism (Wolfe, '36; Carpenter and Locke, '37; Cowles, '37; see also the summaries by Yerkes, '43, chap. 10, Schneirla, '48, Howells, 54). In one series of experiments the animals were taught to use poker chips of different colors as money, which they earned, hoarded, and expended for food in a vending machine in about the same way that human children do. Chips of different colors purchased each its own kind of food, and the animals quickly learned the purchasing power of each of the tokens. In a popular account of these experiments Professor Beach ('47) writes: "Little children learn to prize money long before they know the relative values of different coins. Many a four-year-old clamoring for a nickel has been entirely satisfied when given a penny instead. Dr. Wolfe's chimpanzees had readily learned to choose white poker chips in preference to worthless brass slugs, but was their mentality equal to the task of dealing with 'coins' of different values?" The experiment was successful. "When given a choice, they came to spurn the white chips as long as they could get blue ones with twice the buying power." These animals were able to grasp the meaning of symbols and to use them efficiently, though it is emphasized that the symbols employed were of the simplest order and far below the level of those required for articulate speech. Man is the only animal that has a true language.

For many years Dr. Yerkes and his associates at the Yerkes Laboratories of Primate Biology, Orange Park, Florida, have been searching for evidence of the presence of distinctively human mental capacities—reason, imagination, symbolism, and the like—in these our nearest relatives among the animals. Their observations have been fully reported in several books (Yerkes, '29, '35, '43) and many special papers. A good popular description is given by Gray ('55). They cannot be summarized here save to mention that Dr. Yerkes finds experimental evidence of a rudimentary form of "ideational process" in the chimpanzee, "an appearing neural process from which human insight, full-fledged and unmistakable, has developed. It is rather a promise or intimation of understanding than anything more complex psychologically" ('43, p. 170). He adds further (pp. 195–96): "In the behavioral categories symbolized by the terms sense, perception, memory, imagination, the superiority of the chimpanzee over all observed Old and New World monkeys is definitely indicated. . . . Really significant differences in sense or receptivity between ape and man have not been discovered. . . . The ape is at the beginning of a road on which man has advanced far, although slowly and haltingly. . . . Most of our human psychobiological processes or characteristics can be discovered in chimpanzees, many also in monkeys; but often indeed recognition of them is difficult." These conclusions are supported by the works of the authors previously cited and many others, among which those of Köhler ('18) and Zuckerman ('33) merit special mention. For a general summary see Nissen ('46).

The "human insight" to which Yerkes refers is dependent upon capacity for thinking in terms of symbols and can go only so far as symbols are available. Without language this capacity is restricted to very simple processes of reasoning. If the animal is already familiar with the particulars of a complex situation, a new arrangement of them may present a problem that a dog or a monkey can solve instantly or after a momentary pause. A mental survey of the situation may reveal the correct answer before any overt movement is made. This method of economizing physical work by expenditure of a smaller amount of mental work is the secret of success in all human industry, and its rudiments are clearly present in many of the other higher animals.

One would like to let the matter rest here and say that behavior which gives evidence of insight is unquestionably motivated mentally. But our human experience shows that the case is not so simple. A man may make an important decision after long and critical reflection, or he may jump to a conclusion instantly on a "hunch." The hunch may be right, but the man can give no account of any reasoning process involved in reaching it. One may go to sleep at night puzzled by a vexatious problem and upon awakening in the morning find himself in possession of the correct solution with no knowledge of how he got it. Here is intelligent behavior characterized by insight, but the symbols which were undoubtedly employed were manipulated entirely below the level of awareness. Something of this sort may be going on in the brains of rats and monkeys when they use symbols in patterning their behavior.

Signs as defined below (page 401) are used in many inorganic mechanisms, one of which is the ordinary burglar alarm, and in animal behavior we find all stages of transition from this simple mechanical device to the most complicated hierarchies of symbolisms that are used by mathematicians and philosophers. So the claim (White, '40) that "man uses symbols; no other creature does" and that "there are no intermediate stages" is obviously contrary to fact.

It is evident that neither symbolism nor insight can be used as an infallible index of mentation, and, as will appear beyond, problem solving and learning are not reliable measures of mental capacity. There are instances where all these processes can be shown behavioristically to be present without evidence of an accompanying awareness.

The evolutionary history of the primates as summarized by Simpson ('49, chap. 7) indicates with high probability that the earliest members of this order (lemurs and their allies) had no better brains and presumably no higher intelligence than did their contemporaries in other mammalian orders. What they did have that was distinctive was a unique pattern of cortical organization which remained fundamentally unchanged during the subsequent evolutionary development of this order and which had unique possibilities for elaboration of cerebral tissue capable of intellectual work of unparalleled efficiency.

The most important distinctive feature of the cortical organization of the higher primates is the facility it provides for the development of individual initiative and personal differences in the way the developing animal uses the data of experience in the learning process. Nissen ('46, p. 556) expresses the opinion that individual variations in respect to intelligence, drive, emotional threshold, and other mental capacities seem to be as great in the large apes as in man. In a large colony of chimpanzees there are as many "personalities" as there are individuals. In another context (p. 569) he says that the differences in intelligence shown by the various species of primates (even excluding man) are perhaps as great as those among all the other mammals together. Man's larger and more plastic brain "is perhaps less a specialization than a potentiality for further development along a new dimension of progression: a development which, instead of proceeding by germinal variation and mutation, progresses by the pyramiding of cultural accretions."

Man's closest relatives, the anthropoid apes, are so similar to man in all the features here under consideration that their mentality can be inferred from their behavior with reasonable assurance of accuracy. We also have good evidence that some other animals have sensations, emotions, and memories similar to man's and also more or less intelligence. This evidence becomes less and less convincing as the animal series is surveyed from the anthropoid apes down the scale to the more primitive animals. The proximate ancestry of human mentality can be traced with precision only a short way back in phylogeny. But not all animal experience falls within the purview of consciousness, and in both individual and racial development the unconscious components of experience precede the conscious components.

In the series of stages in the evolution of behavior as viewed objectively there are few wide gaps in our present knowledge. The continuity of the series of changes in both overt action and internal structure as we pass from the inorganic through the ranks of the animal kingdom up to and including mankind may be regarded as established. The apparent interruptions of this continuity are successively closed as our knowledge of the facts is enlarged. The three most puzzling saltatory changes in this series are marked by the transitions from the inorganic to the organic, from aquatic to terrestrial habitat, and from brute to man. These apparent gaps are rapidly being narrowed by the discovery of "mesoforms," or transitional stages. The first two of these gaps have been considered in preceding chapters. The gap between ape and man has not been completely closed, but recent paleontological discoveries have brought to light so many intermediate forms of extinct species of apes and fossilized specimens of primitive man that we may confidently expect that the main features of human ancestry will soon be clarified, so far as bodily structure is concerned (Clark, '55). The ancestry of man's peculiar mentality, his "spiritual life," is not so well understood.

The three factors which seem to have played the dominant part in the transition from anthropoid to human types of behavior and experience are: first, the assumption of the erect posture, with the liberation of the hand from the function of locomotion and the resulting elaboration of skill in manipulation; second, the invention and use of tools of increasing variety and complexity; and, third, the acquisition of speech and other symbols of ideas that facilitate communication of knowledge and its transmission from generation to generation. The second and third of these factors are discussed in an interesting little book by Pannekoek ('53).

Most men have more than twice as big a brain as any ape. This gives them the capacity to be more than twice as intelligent and also ability to do more than twice as many silly things and to do them with vastly greater efficiency. The apes get along very well in their native habitats if not interfered with by man, but men seem to be unable to live peaceably with one another and so they destroy themselves by their own stupidity.

Summary

Mind as awareness can be directly known only introspectively, and animals that lack language can communicate their mental experiences to us very imperfectly. There is evidence from behavior that the higher apes possess recognizable rudiments of most of the human mental processes; but without the symbolisms of language these rudiments are simple and the ape is incapable of the human type of reasoning. The use of symbols to designate abstractions of general features from heterogeneous experience is a useful indicator of mental competence. In apes and monkeys this ability is well developed, although at a low level, and in rats it is demonstrably present.

Because the lower ranks of animals can tell us nothing about their conscious experience and because their structure and behavior are so different from man's, it is impossible to determine (on the basis of presently available evidence) at what stage in animal evolution any awareness of what is going on first appears or what the most primitive minds are like. All inferences which may be drawn from behavior about animals' minds are speculative, and the further the behavior deviates from the human pattern the less reliable are these speculations.

CHAPTER TWENTY-SIX

Sensation

The senses

Analysis of the cognitive factors of behavior naturally begins with the simplest of them, the sensations. These, as already indicated, may be vague and generalized or very specific and specialized. The steps in the progressive differentiation of the several systems of sense organs during phylogeny can be seen in surviving representatives of the several stages, as will be illustrated by a few examples.

The organs of sense and their related nerves are the channels of communication between the objective world and the central nervous system. The motor nerves and their end-organs provide the mechanism for appropriate responses. What may be the appropriate response in any particular situation is determined by the central adjusting processes and other factors.

The habitat and way of life of an animal and the kind of motor responses to stimuli that prevail are, accordingly, inseparably related with the receptive aspect of the sensation. The selective quality of the sense organs is determined by the use to be made of them. A species that lives in a totally dark cave has no use for eyes. The eyes, accordingly, atrophy. Birds are pre-eminently visualizers with large eyes and acute sight, and their organs of smell are reduced to vestiges. Dogs, on the contrary, live in a world of odors and adjust their lives accordingly. Their behavior is controlled far more by things smelled than by things seen.

When my daughter was a little child we lived in the country. She would sometimes wander away out of sight of the house; noting her absence, I would step outside and look around, then perhaps call her name. If I heard no answer I would then call out the dog, her usual companion, and say, "Iris, find Ruth." The collie wasted not a moment in looking or listening, but instantly ran in ever-widening circles with nose to the ground until she picked up the scent of the child's footprints and then dashed off assured of a successful search. So every animal's behavior is adjusted to his way of life and the organs available for satisfying his needs.

No animal is sensitive to all the kinds of energy that play upon its body. A selection is made of those stimulating agencies that are significant for the particular environment to which the species is adapted, and sensory equipment is provided for these modalities of sense and no others, no two species of animals having the same sensory equipment. The dog lacks color vision but the sense of hearing is more acute than ours. The ears of the bat are sensitive to supersonic vibrations far beyond the human range of hearing. Differentiations of this sort will take as varied forms as there are habitats and modes of life for which the bodily structure must be adapted. Graphic illustrations of the range of these adaptations are given by Griffin ('53) and La Barre ('54, chap. 2).

This gradual specialization of the several sensory systems from a primordial general sensitivity accounts for many puzzling features of human sensations, particularly the ways in which the different senses co-operate, play into each other's hands, and may even be interchanged in some situations. There are some curious discrepancies between the modalities of sense as we recognize them subjectively and the underlying physiological processes, as illustrated, for instance, by our inability to discriminate between the taste and smell of many familiar foods. Several other human senses are not clearly differentiated in consciousness, though their organs are structurally different and perhaps far apart in the body.

Factors of sensation

Sensing is an analytic process, and the primary function of the sense organs, as Sherrington long ago pointed out, is "to lower the threshold of excitability of the arc for one kind of stimulus and to heighten it for all others." All protoplasm is sensitive to a large number of physical agents and quite insensitive to many others. What constitutes an adequate stimulus for any sense organ depends on the structure of that organ and its connections. These factors vary within wide limits in different kinds of animals and to a less extent in different individuals of the same species.

The conventional list of five senses of man must be expanded to more than a dozen modalities, and each of these is a complex of several qualities. In a recent letter to me S. Howard Bartley called attention to the interrelationships and intermodal reciprocities among our senses and added this comment: "Instead of there being a number of discrete sense departments, the number we can catalogue is arbitrary and dependent upon the number individuated out. It is only in following conventional language and thought that we speak of the senses as separate or as entities, the products of which may be to some extent combined. 'Senses' arise in the first place only by individuation. This being granted, it is no wonder they have so many properties in common. Such common properties ought to seem less spectacular and amazing than their differences" (cf. Hayek, '52, pp. 83-86).

Various definitions and classifications of the senses are in vogue, depending on the criteria employed. Four factors must be taken into account:

1. Physical criteria. Each receptive organ is sensitive to some particular manifestation of energy within a more or less restricted range of quality and intensity.

2. Anatomical criteria. The structure and connections of the sense organs determine what physical processes are adequate stimuli for each kind of organ.

3. Physiological criteria. The type of response normally evoked plays an important part in determining the modalities of the sense organs and their distribution in the body. Thus Sherrington classifies the sense organs as exteroceptors, interoceptors, and proprioceptors, depending upon whether the typical response is to external events, visceral and postural changes within the body, or automatic regulation of the action of the skeletal musculature.

4. Psychological criteria. Introspective experience is what we ordinarily rely upon to distinguish the modalities of sense. This is usually adequate, but not always. As just mentioned, some savors cannot be distinguished from odors subjectively, and without making a physiological experiment one cannot tell whether the sensation results from stimulation of the tongue or the nose.

The peripheral analysis of the modalities of sense by the sensory end-organs may be more or less refined, and this analysis is preserved throughout the courses of the peripheral sensory nerves to their "primary centers" in the central nervous system, each of which is a receptive field for all excitations of one or more of the sensory modalities. These primary centers are so interconnected with one another and with higher centers of control as to facilitate the correlation and integration of sensory experience and its resolution into a prognosis for appropriate courses of action. Most of these central processes of correlation and adjustment are carried on at subconscious levels, either because their patterns are predetermined by the inherited structure of the brain or because they have been automatized as habits.

The human body is sensitive to many kinds of stimuli to which response is made unconsciously. Most of the proprioceptive responses are of this sort. The receptors in muscles, tendons, semicircular canals, etc., are called sense organs, but their excitation ordinarily does not give rise to sensations. This unconscious response implies sensibility below the level of sensation. In this sense it may be called extra-sensory, but it would be inexact to call it extra-sensory perception, for perception, as the term is used in this work, is by definition subjective. Although most of the complicated processes of muscular co-ordination, digestion, and circulation are not perceived, they nevertheless play vitally important parts in patterning what is perceived and in all higher mental processes. Our bodies may also be sensitive in still other ways about which we have as yet no adequately controlled scientific knowledge.

The literature on the senses and their organs is very extensive. My general conclusions have been summarized elsewhere ('24, chaps. 3 and 4; '31, chap. 5), but since those books appeared much new information has been recorded. Adrian ('47) reviews the sense organs from a different point of view. For a recent survey see Geldard ('53). These details cannot be summarized here. The intricate relations of the temporal and spatial factors in all nervous and mental operations are illustrated by a few selected examples in this and the following chapters.

Temporal and spatial factors

Each of the senses possessed by any species of animals has a limited range which varies somewhat from one individual to another. Vision and hearing are the most highly differentiated senses of man, and these are adapted for the analysis of natural rhythms, rhythms of high frequencies in the former and of much lower frequencies in the latter. Both visual and auditory organs have been evolved from simpler apparatus adapted to respond to much lower frequencies of vibration. The organs of vision were at first able to register merely the intensity and direction of illumination, but they early acquired the ability to register also the relations of things in space, and this is the cardinal function of the eyes in all vertebrates. The organs of hearing are similarly specialized for registering and analyzing the temporal relations of events. Both of these senses have other special functions in addition to these, and other more generalized senses co-operate with vision and hearing in the analysis of the spatial and temporal relations of things. The origins and evolutionary history of these senses and their organs are now known in broad outline, though many details are still obscure.

The natural rhythms to which the human body is sensitive vary from a single mechanical impact upon the skin, through physical vibrations sensed by touch, sound waves sensed by the ear, and light waves sensed by the eye. Beyond this range of conscious sensations the body responds unconsciously to higher vibration frequencies— ultraviolet and x-ray radiations and other higher frequencies to an unknown limit.

In man the tactile receptors of the skin respond to mechanical impacts ranging from single contacts to rhythmically repeated contacts up to a rate of about 1,552 vibrations per second. The ear is sensitive to mechanical vibrations perceived subjectively as tones with a range of about 9 octaves. The exciting stimuli are vibrations ranging from about 30 to about 20,000 vibrations per second, with wide individual variations at both lower and upper limits. The skin is sensitive to vibrations sensed as radiant heat ranging from 3×10^{12} to 8×10^{14} per second. The eye is sensitive to vibrations ranging from 4×10^{14} to 8×10^{14} per second.

The figures given in the preceding paragraph show that the same rates of vibration may give rise to both tactile and auditory sensations, a fact that can be easily verified by lightly touching the sounding board of a piano when a bass note is struck. The vibration rates sensed as heat and those sensed as light also overlap extensively. It is, therefore, not surprising to find that both the organs of hearing and the organs of sight have been derived in the early stages of their evolution from sense organs of much simpler structure and generalized function. These primitive organs as seen in some invertebrates take the form of budlike cutaneous papillae (termed sensillae) provided with sensory hairs. They may serve the sense of touch or the chemical senses, or they may have still other functions, and several of these functions may be combined in the same organ. The "feelers" (vibrissae) of cats and rats are highly specialized sense organs derived from such primitive endorgans.

All fishes and aquatic amphibians are provided with an elaborate system of cutaneous or subcutaneous "lateral line organs" which are widely distributed over the body and serve as distance receptors (page 321). Their sensory hairs respond to vibrations of the water and so may be used to locate the distant source of the stimulus, which may be a moving enemy or a swimming animal good for food. These organs are so sensitive that a blinded salamander larva can capture prey with their aid almost as efficiently as by visual response (Scharrer, '32; Detwiler, '45). The lateral line organs of fishes are sensitive to vibrations of water similar to sound waves, but of slower rate than those to which the ears of the same fishes are sensitive. Although fishes' ears lack the cochlea, they are true organs of hearing within a restricted range.

In frogs and other terrestrial amphibians the larval lateral line organs atrophy at metamorphosis, and no vestiges of these organs are found in any class of vertebrates above the Amphibia. Frogs possess a rudimentary cochlea and a primary cochlear nucleus in the brain, which is derived by a curious transformation from the

lateral line nucleus of the larva (Larsell, '34; Herrick, '48, p. 135).
The cochlea is the organ of tone analysis. It is larger in birds than
in reptiles and is elaborately developed in all mammals. Although
hearing is primarily a time sense, it retains some efficiency for localization of the source of the sounds, a property of the tactile organs
from which the auditory apparatus was differentiated. On the phylogenesis of the ear see Guggenheim ('48). Wever ('49) gives a
critical review of hearing.

Some responses to the spatial relations of things are made by all
organisms. Many green plants turn toward the sun (heliotropism)
and their roots grow downward (geotropism) and in any direction
toward water (hydrotropism). In the human body many bacteria
and all white blood corpuscles have affinities, which are probably
chemically activated, for specific organs or local conditions. In all
animals the prime function of tactile sensibility is localization of
things.

The eye is pre-eminent as a distance receptor. Undifferentiated
protoplasm is sensitive to light, and in the course of evolution a
great variety of specific photoreceptors has been elaborated. In
the most primitive animals which lack nervous systems the whole
body may be sensitive to light. In some free-swimming unicellular
species a pigmented "eye-spot" is embedded in the protoplasm to aid
in the orientation of the animal with reference to the source of the
light. In some worms which lack eyes the head end of the body
is more sensitive to light than the rest of it, and in other species
of worms eyes of simple structure are present in the leading segments. These eyes have been specialized from simpler organs of general sensibility by the formation of photosensitive pigment and some
other relatively minor structural changes. All stages of this transition have fortunately been preserved in the adult body of a species
of leech described by Whitman ('92). In Clepsine, cutaneous sense
organs, or sensillae, of generalized function are present in all of
the posterior segments of the body. More anteriorly these are gradually transformed from segment to segment into well-developed
eyes at the anterior end.

Insects have both simple eyes, comparable with those of worms,
and paired compound eyes. The latter may be enormously large.

Their complicated structure is wholly unlike that of vertebrate eyes. Some mollusks are without eyes; some have simple eyes variously placed where they will do the most good, those of snails being on movable stalks. The eyes of squid and octopus are large and superficially resemble those of vertebrates, though their structure and development are radically different.

The paired eyes of all vertebrates are similar in development and fundamental structure, and they differ in these respects from eyes of all other animals. In evolution they were not derived from any specialized invertebrate type but arose independently from eyeless ancestors. The marine lancet, Amphioxus, is the closest surviving relative of the extinct ancestors of the vertebrates. These small wormlike animals burrow in the sand and have pigmented photosensitive "optic cups" embedded within the posterior segments of the spinal cord but absent in the anterior part of the body, which is insensitive to light. It is probable that the immediate ancestors of vertebrates were wormlike glassy-clear free-swimming animals with similar pigmented cups at the anterior end of the body and that in the early vertebrates this pigmented part of the brain was evaginated to form the retina (Parker, '08). The retina of all vertebrates is really a part of the brain, and its extremely complicated structure (Polyak, '41) is a sensitive photoreceptor which analyzes mixed light into its component elements. For a comprehensive survey of vision and its organs see Walls ('42).

In all orders of vertebrates except the crocodiles the pineal body (epiphysis) is a dorsal outgrowth from the middle of the brain (epithalamus). In some of the lower orders the pineal body or the associated paraphysis is transformed into a functional "parietal eye," which occupies a foramen between the parietal bones on the top of the head. This foramen is large in fossil skulls of some of these lower orders. This fact, together with the central connections of the parietal nerve within the brain, has suggested to me ('48, p. 250) that possibly in ancestral vertebrates the parietal eye was differentiated before the lateral eyes were well developed. The lateral eyes give a wider field of view and better localizing efficiency, so after their appearance the parietal eye became vestigial or disappeared.

Summary

Sensitivity becomes sensation if the individual has any awareness of the response to stimulation. The simplest and probably the most primitive sensations are generalized feelings of malaise or well-being. This generalized sensation is an active process in which cognitive, affective, and conative factors may be blended. From this vague awareness the specific modalities of sense are individuated. The cognitive factors are recognized as qualities and intensities of sensation. The qualities may include localization of the part of the body affected, the source of the stimulus, and the spatial and temporal relations of the things sensed in so far as these relations determine the orientation of the body with reference to the source of the stimulus. An affective factor is usually recognizable; the sensation is gratifying or unpleasant. This quality is the germ from which the emotions are developed. The feeling of effort is primordial, and in all sensation there is a motor component whether or not it is recognized as such. Volition stems from this component of sensation.

Sensations are primarily analytic functions. They sort out of mixed experience the several factors which are significant for appropriate adjustment to existing conditions. The number, kind, and arrangement of the sense organs, accordingly, are very diversified in the various species of animals in adaptation to their habitats and ways of life. The evolutionary history of the organs of vision and hearing is reviewed because of the importance of these senses in our perception of the spatial and temporal relations of things.

Chapter Twenty-seven

Perception

Criteria of perception

So much of human behavior is motivated by perceptions of what is going on in our surroundings that the mechanisms of perception and their limitations must be well understood. There is ample experimental evidence that perception is not merely an indispensable instrument for the acquisition of knowledge, but is itself a behavior. Sensory stimuli as such have no significance for the organism. Their meaning is acquired only by doing something with them or about them, that is, only through experience of the results of behavior performed in response to them. Such experience may be acquired biologically in the course of evolution by natural selection or otherwise and so incorporated within the hereditary organization of the species; but the responses controlled in this way are not perceptions; they are reflexes or instincts. There is no perception unless these inherited patterns of response are supplemented by personal learning, with awareness of the thing perceived in its relations in space and time to the perceiving subject. This perception may be regarded as a behavior because we know by experiment that the polarization of the perceiving self against the objects perceived must be learned by actual experience gained through the motor responses made to the setup of sensory stimuli received.

This has been demonstrated most clearly in the analysis of visual perception of objects seen as oriented in space relations. One perceives consciously, not the total stimulus pattern, but only highly selective portions of it; and the selection of things perceived is largely determined by past experience. I see a pencil lying before me on the table. I would not recognize it if I had not had previous experience with pencils and their actual use in motor acts. The pattern of the sensory experience is determined by the image of the object on the retina, but its meaning as a pencil has been acquired behavioristically. My estimate of its position, its distance and direction from the eye is made automatically, but this again is an acquired automatism.

The newborn infant knows nothing at all about his objective world. This information is slowly acquired by experience. He soon learns not to reach for the moon, and before long his perceptual judgments about the relations of things sensed come automatically and so he is able to make practical adjustments to his surroundings. These judgments, however, are not infallible. A large part of our routine experience and all of science are concerned with checking our perceptual experiences, one against the others, in order to distinguish reality from illusion and to learn what to do about it.

The test of the validity of a perception is its predictive value as a guide for action. "We must learn the reliability of a perception through experiencing its consequences in action" (Cantril, '49).

Sensitivity and motility are equally essential components of the perceptive process. The amount and quality of perceptual knowledge which it is possible for an individual to acquire depend on the sensory and motor equipment available. No two species of animals and no two individuals of the same species have exactly the same equipment, from which it follows that no two individuals live in exactly the same perceptive world. Mankind has invented ingenious devices which vastly extend the range of the sensory and motor organs with which we are naturally endowed and these are continually enlarging our perceptive capacity. For an over-all view of the mechanisms of perception consult Hebb ('49), Allport ('55), Granit ('55) and Sperry ('52). Sperry puts special emphasis on the fact that "perception is basically an implicit preparation to respond."

Temporal and spatial factors

However far the range of perception may be extended by artificial aids, some limitations of this range are inherent in the basic structure of the organs of perception. Some of these limitations may be overcome by conceptual manipulation of the perceived data. The human body has no organs capable of direct perception of cosmic rays or of the mental processes of any other person, and yet we have been able to learn a great deal about both of these things by indirect methods and skillful reasoning.

From the behaviorist's standpoint the most significant limitation of our perceptual capacity arises from the fact that everything perceived is set in the frame of three-dimensional space and linear dimensional time. As explained in preceding chapters, this imposes a peculiar limitation upon all perceptual knowledge which sets it off in sharp contrast against the other kinds of mentation. This distinction is basic because it rests on a similar difference in the properties of all analytic and integrative processes at the lower preconscious levels (page 322).

We now know that the patterns of relations of things in space as projected upon the human retina are transmitted to the brain by about a million nerve fibers as nervous impulses and there registered in corresponding spatial patterns in three places: first, in the superior colliculus of the midbrain, where some of the visual reflexes are organized; second, in the lateral geniculate body of the thalamus, where further integration of spatial discriminations is effected, and perhaps of color discriminations also (Clark, '47); finally, in the occipital lobes of the cerebral cortex, where retinal excitations are first projected in spatial patterns and then subjected to further analysis and integration. From this cortical area impulses radiate through the cortex and are thus brought into physiological relation with all other cortical activities that are relevant to the complex of visual excitations experienced. At this final stage of the perceptual process the spatial patterns are no longer registered as such anywhere in the cortical apparatus of integration, but, as explained in Chapter 32, the cortical associational processes are not bound to any stable structural arrangements of the nervous tissues.

Somehow in the course of these central activities the awareness of the sensation emerges, but this does not rise to the level of a meaningful perception of actual spatial relations unless cortical neurograms ("cryptograms") of previous motor responses to similar visual excitations are reactivated. It has been shown experimentally that the outward projection of the perception which orients things seen in their true relations in space is, in human beings, dependent upon past experience. It has been learned—unconsciously, for the most part—and this personal learning is built up on the foundation of a complicated system of inherited reflex patterns of adjustment.

A series of experiments which is interesting in this connection has been reported by Austin H. Riesen ('47, '50). Two newborn chimpanzees were reared in darkness until they were sixteen months old, an age which is psychologically equivalent to that of a two-year-old human child. Four other infant chimps were subsequently similarly tested, with additional controls. The experiments confirm the conclusion reached by clinical observations on children born blind and later given good vision by removal of cataracts, namely, that visual perception must be learned by motor experience. This is a much slower process in man and the chimpanzee than in lower species of animals which have been tested. The lower animals can make some of these adjustments immediately without practice, and vestiges of this innate capacity persist even in man (Lashley, '49, p. 35). The reduction of this inherited capacity is apparently the price we have to pay for our better ability to adapt to a changing environment. These facts, as Riesen says, may necessitate some changes in current theories of perception and learning. For a description of these experiments with critical comments see Hebb ('49, pp. 18 and 112).

The central processes involved in auditory perception are different from those just described, but they illustrate some principles common to both of them. Approximately 330,000 tones of all frequencies and intensities can be discriminated by the human ear. The cochlea has about 23,500 receptive hair cells, and their excitations are transmitted to the brain by about 25,000 ganglion cells and fibers of the auditory nerve. Within the brain the auditory pathway includes some fibers to the inferior colliculus, where reflex connections are made, and others to the medial geniculate body and thence to the auditory area in the temporal lobe of the cerebral cortex.

It is currently believed on the basis of experimental evidence that sound waves of high frequency are registered at the base of the spiral

organ of the cochlea, waves of low frequency at its apex, and intermediate frequencies between these. The experiments of Alexander
and O'Brien ('54) show that the apparatus of tone analysis is not so
simple as this. But, whatever may be the method of tone analysis, it
is clear that the temporal factors of sound waves are registered in
spatial patterns in the auditory area of the cerebral cortex. Tones perceived as of high pitch activate the anterior end of this area, those of
low pitch the posterior end. The dog's hearing is more acute than that
of man, and the auditory area in the temporal lobe of the cortex of
the dog is relatively much larger. Tunturi ('44, '45) has published
charts of this cortical area which show the cortical projection of
sounds of vibration frequencies from 100 to 16,000 per second. Just
as there is a point for point localization of the retinal surface upon
the visual projection area of the cortex, so there is a point for point
localization of the parts of the organ of Corti in the internal ear
upon the auditory projection area of the cortex.

Sound waves differ in their rates of vibration. These temporal differences are registered in the brain as spatial differences, and they
are sensed subjectively as tones which have neither temporal nor
spatial qualities. Our perception of elapsed time is not a simple
sensory datum. It is built up by synthesis of sensory data, often of
diverse sorts.

Just as the temporal factor in the discrimination of pitch is inextricably involved with spatial factors of nervous analysis and transmission, so in vision spatial discrimination is similarly involved with
time factors. Lashley ('51) has emphasized this intimate relation of
spatial and temporal factors in the integrative nervous functions, and
Clark ('47) writes: "The temporal factor in the timing of the arrival
of retinal impulses has so far received little attention, and yet it may
turn out to be of considerable importance in visual discriminatory
functions."

Thick fibers transmit nervous impulses faster than thin fibers (page
260). The optic nerves and the central tracts related with them contain both thick and thin fibers, and the timing of responses to retinal
stimulation is evidently determined in part by varying rates of
transmission in these fibers and by the complexity of the central
visual adjusting apparatus. I have described the arrangement of

thick and thin fibers of the optic system of Necturus ('41) and larval and adult Amblystoma ('41a, '42, pp. 228, 273), and subsequently ('44a) I discussed the possible physiological significance of the differences in rates of conduction of thick and thin fibers in the central adjustments of behavior in response to visual stimuli in these animals. These central connections are very intricate, and no final conclusions can be reached until the various factors of the problem are separately examined by adequately controlled experiments.

In these physiological processes time and space seem to be mutually interchangeable. This has been brought out by the experiments of Bartley ('42) in which temporal factors were so manipulated as to allow time to reciprocate with space in central neural activity. This reciprocal relation is even more clearly shown by the earlier experiments of Helson and King ('30, '31), the results of which they describe as the "tau effect." If three spots on the back of the hand or arm are touched lightly with the point of a pencil in quick succession, two spatial intervals will be defined by the three stimulations. It is found that the judgment of the length of these intervals depends more upon the time interval between the stimulations than upon the actual distances between places touched. It has been shown by another observer that the tau effect is reversible. Judgments of time intervals between the stimuli are influenced by differences in the spatial intervals between the spots touched.

Similar reciprocal relations seem to prevail among all the other senses. Not all modalities of sense stand in a simple one-to-one relation with the respective sense organs with which they are usually colligated. For example, the peripheral organs of smell and taste are widely separated in the body and their structure is different, yet many savors cannot be distinguished subjectively from odors.

It is not surprising to find that perceptual localization of things in outer space employs nervous organs and pathways that are precisely localized both peripherally and centrally. But neurologists were not prepared for the discovery that space factors and time factors seem to be mutually interchangeable at various physiological levels. This interplay of space factors and time factors evidently may go on at the physiological level (Wiener, '48, chap. 1), and it is carried much further at the conceptual level of consciousness, even to the point where both space and time are dispensed with in high-level abstractions. In discussing the interaction of temporal and spatial systems Lashley ('51, p. 128) writes: "Spatial and temporal order thus appear to be almost completely interchangeable in cerebral action." As explained later, the apparatus of integration in the cerebral cortex includes an elaborate scanning mechanism in which there is an interplay between temporal rhythms and spatial arrangements of the nervous elements (for summary and references see Brazier, '48).

The foregoing examples are selected from an enormous body of knowledge about the comparative anatomy and physiology of the organs of sense and the central adjusting mechanisms related with them, because they illustrate some of the factors that must be investigated if we would come to an adequate understanding of perception. Some of these factors are intuitive, that is, dependent upon inherited structure. Some of the learned factors have been so firmly habituated that they go on automatically at subconscious levels. Other factors are consciously attended to and can be known only introspectively. These factors are firmly integrated in the act of perception; but only those of the group last mentioned are accessible to us in awareness, so that the perception seems to be a simple datum of conscious experience.

Motor factors

A perception begins with an attitude or active posture of attention and if it does not eventuate in satisfying action it has no significance for psychological theory or for behavior. The reliability of a perception and its significance for present and future behavior can be tested only by action. The action may be an immediate motor response or it may be a mental process with no overt expression, but if one does not do something with a perception it has no lasting quality and it is negligible from every standpoint. What we need is not merely knowledge but wisdom, and wisdom can be acquired only by active experience, not by passive reception.

These factors led Cantril ('49) to this definition of perception: "A perception may be defined as an implicit awareness of the probable consequence an action might have for us with respect to carrying out some purpose that has value for us." To this he adds: "I believe it is safe to say that every perception is in itself a value-judgment process. . . . In most of our perceptions, of course, this weighing process goes on quite unconsciously." The motor components of attention and perception are similarly emphasized by Sperry ('52), who makes it clear that perception is basically an implicit preparation to respond, that is, the preparation of the animal for adaptive action.

These characteristics of perception were recognized by Helmholtz (chap. 26, pp. 1–37, vol. 3, of *The Perceptions of Vision*, in his *Treatise on Physiological Optics*, English translation published by the Optical Society of America, 1925). Cantril ('47a) quotes several passages from Helmholtz, including the following statements: "To many physiologists and psychologists the connection between the sensation and the conception of the object usually appears to be so rigid and obligatory that they are not much disposed to admit that, to a considerable extent at least, it depends on acquired experience, that is, on psychic activity. . . . The idea of a single individual table which I carry in my mind is correct and exact, provided I can deduce from it correctly the precise sensations I shall have when my eye and my hand are brought into this or that definite relation with respect to the table. . . . It is only by voluntarily bringing our organs of sense in various relations to the objects that we learn to be sure as to our judgments of the causes of our sensations."

Many others have recognized a motor or conative factor in both sensation and perception. More than a half-century ago my brother (C. L. Herrick, '96) wrote: "The consciousness of a sensation is probably never attained until there has been a kinesodic response to it and it is not unlikely that it is the reflected current rather than the direct one which enters consciousness. It is in this way that the storages of vestiges in the cortex may be explained in such cases where the original stimulus never reached consciousness." In an unpublished manuscript written shortly before his death in 1904 I find this passage: "Every time we feel a sensation we do something. . . . Perception, then, is the combined result of repetition of a familiar group of sensations with a reproduction of the group of reflexes or conscious responses before associated with them. It involves reidentification of the sensations and anticipation of the proper reflexes or efforts."

Montgomery ('07, p. 363) also recognized the conative factor in both sensation and perception, and he emphasized the part played by personal experience on a background of "phyletically pre-established correspondence" between sense-stimulating influence and our modes of perceptual awareness.

Tonicity, in the broad sense of the word, is as important for sensation as for muscular movement. Werner ('45) finds a common dynamic property which binds both sensory and motor processes. "This common factor is, most probably, tonicity. Normal and pathological evidence favors the theory that the perceptual space—of which visual motion is a special form —is organized, not as a purely sensory area, but as a sensory-tonic field." This tonicity is not static. It is an active process which is goal-directed.

The sensory-tonic field theory of perception developed by Werner and Wapner ('49) is based on the conception of a "field" of continuous interaction between the organism and the objects perceived. Physiologically considered, tonicity is a prerequisite factor of this interaction and the resulting integration. This tonicity may be manifested as posture (static) or movement (dynamic). Both forms of it are essential, and in my opinion the motor expression of it (past and present) is the most significant factor determining the actual content of the perception.

In a series of later papers, the results of which are summarized by Werner and Wapner ('52), experiments are described which clarify the nature of sensory projection and the way sensory, emotive, cognitive, and motor factors are actually interrelated in the act of perception. They find that the stimulus object always arouses sensory-tonic events which involve the total organism, not merely the receptive apparatus of end-organ and brain.

Werner and his colleagues recognize two classes of factors of perception distinguished in terms of homeostasis. (1) The one is characterized as homeostasis of the field comprised of the object and the perceiving body. The effects of "object stimuli" presuppose articulation between object and body in a field which embraces both. (2) The other is called internal homeostasis, the effects of which are organismic changes which occur whether an object is present or not. The first involves outward projection in terms of perceptual space and time. The second is wholly internal to the organism. Both of these factors are normally present in perception, and I would add that it is the second which is progressively elaborated at the higher levels of conceptual thinking. In 1924 Spitzer made a similar distinction between "oikotropic" and "idiotropic" nervous functions (for an interesting comment see Klüver, '51, p. 150). Granit ('55) gives an excellent description of the mechanisms of centrifugal control of posture.

Here again, as everywhere in our analysis of the processes of behavior, the contrast between innate and acquired functions is fundamental. If responses to frequently recurring complexes of sensory excitation are made reflexly, no perception is involved, even though the performer may be aware of what he is doing. Sensation accompanied by emotion (affect) and impulse (conation) may be called sensorimotor mentation. It has a directive quality, but it does not rise to the level of perception unless the directive includes components which have been acquired consciously by controlled personal experience. The perceiving subject consciously attends to the thing perceived, and this attention usually involves the activation of muscles as well as cerebration. The muscles may not actually contract, but the oscillograph records changes in their electrical potential which give evidence of their sublimenal excitation.

Although innate and acquired components are inseparably blended in every perception so that they cannot readily be recognized by inspection, it is possible to devise experiments which artificially separate them. An especially instructive setup of laboratory apparatus and clever experimental procedures at the Hanover Institute has successfully analyzed the act of perception of objects in visual space so that the several constituents of the process can be separated and their properties investigated. These experiments clearly show that there are in man some innate patterns of response to visual stimuli, but there is no intuitive recognition of either the location or the significance of an object which projects an image upon the retina. It is only as the body reacts to the retinal image by directive (purpose-like) movement that the sensory stimuli acquire significance.

Sets of the apparatus employed at the Hanover Institute and its predecessor, the Dartmouth Eye Institute, have been installed in several other institutions and a detailed description has been published by Ittelson ('52). The Hanover Institute has been articulated with the Institute for Associated Research of Princeton, New Jersey, and here this experimental program is now active, with adequate publication of methods and results. These results have significance of wide import for psychology and for the theory of knowledge in particular; see the comments upon them by Bentley ('50) and Bridgman ('54).

Lawrence ('49) has published a laboratory manual of general psychology in which special attention is given to the analysis of the process of perception. Several of the experiments devised at the Hanover Institute are described. Distorted rooms and other devices are employed to bring to light the implicit assumptions which are involved in all ordinary perception. Another report of these experiments is given by Ames ('51).

These experiments show that assumptions based on previous experience, that is, the observer's "assumptive world," play a significant part in determining the way he will act in all situations. Our perceptions furnish a reliable prognosis for action, in other words, for the kind of action that has the highest probability of being successful. It is concluded, further, that the processes involved in human behavior take place in a milieu more inclusive than that which can be defined in behavioral space and time.

The experimental program of the Hanover Institute has led Adelbert Ames, its director, to a conclusion that he expresses in this form: "Our disclosures also apparently show that our sensations, and therefore perception, action and purpose, cannot be understood in terms of three dimensional space. Mathematicians are pointing out that our disclosures can only be understood in terms of non-Euclidean concepts." He refers here to the work of Luneburg ('47), among others.

Perceptual space as objectified is Euclidean, but Luneburg is investigating visual space as perceived, not the spatial relations of objects. Visual space is a mental construct. We can construct a Euclidean map of the visual sensation of a point in binocular vision, but we cannot be sure that the map represents truly the sensed qualities of form and localization of the points on the map. Indeed, it is clear that this is not necessarily true. It is claimed that a psychometric co-ordination is impossible in terms of Euclidean geometry, but that it can be demonstrated in terms of a different metric, specifically, "that the geometry of the visual space is the hyperbolic geometry of Lobachevski." The ingenious experiments on visual perception by Köhler ('51, p. 233) lead to the conclusion that there is no constant geometry of visual space, for the cortical visual processes build their own space from one moment to another.

Integrative factors

Sensation and reflex are in the "specious present," but both of these have a past and a future reference. In perception this "time-binding" integration is enlarged and accentuated. There is integration of the present experience with memories (organic or conscious) of previous motor responses to similar stimulations and also an implicit reference to the motor adjustments involved in the determination of the spatial and temporal relations of the source of the stimulus to the perceiving subject. The perceptual experience has a past and a future reference; it is selective, directive, and purpose-like, though most of these processes go on below the level of awareness.

An essential feature of perceptual integration is the polarization of the perceiving subject against the things perceived, of the self against the not-self. This implies the presence of self-consciousness at a higher level of mentation than primitive undifferentiated "feeling," and this in turn is a prerequisite for that sharp contrast between perceptual knowledge and conceptual knowledge which has been emphasized in the preceding discussions.

The act of perception has an analytic component which faces outward toward the object perceived and a synthetic component which gives meaning to the thing perceived. The latter component requires some cortical participation in the process. The literature of clinical neurology and neurosurgery contains records of many cases in which the components of perception have been separately affected and so isolated for examination. Many cases of agnosia and related forms of aphasia show that perception involves memory, recognition, and judgment and that the several factors of these processes can be separately impaired by local cortical injuries.

In Margenau's inquiry *The Nature of Physical Reality* ('50) he writes on page 448, "The central distinction in our analysis of experience was between its immediate and its rational elements, between data and constructs." This is essentially the same as Sellars' distinction (which I have cited on page 162) between perceptual knowledge and conceptual knowledge. Both authors base the distinction primarily upon epistemological considerations. I make the same distinction drawn from the observed qualities of animal behavior and human experience, and I emphasize its operational value in the study of behavior objectively and of our subjective experience of it. The three of us reach the same conclusion, namely, that the distinction between data and constructs does not imply that they form "two clearly separable, mutually exclusive sets of entities with a dividing boundary definite enough to satisfy the desires of class-minded logicians. But the distinction is good enough for scientific purposes; . . . normal behavior is conditioned by the acknowledgment of a difference between thought and perception."

The "double knowledge" to which reference has been made above recognizes the twofold quality of perception. The neglect of the realities of the external world is the defect of the now current philosophy of knowing described as phenomenalism. This has been pointed out by Sellars (Sellars *et al.*, '49), who writes: "In what sense do we see and handle things? Intuitional notions of perception may well need to be rejected. But it is one thing to affirm that veridical perception involves complex attitudes, sensory processes, and interpretative operations, and quite another to say that we 'see' only our sensations—which is a misleading statement" (p. 84; see also pp. 80 and 100). A perceptual judgment is more than the apprehension of subjectively experienced sense-data. It must be projected outward operationally and realistically against a background of previous experience so as to reveal the congruence of the sense-data with the actualities of the things sensed.

The thirteen papers presented at the University of Texas Clinical Psychology Symposium (edited by Blake and Ramsey, '51) give a useful survey of current researches on perception and their applications in psychotherapy.

The "purposive" quality of perception

Directive movements, especially those controlled by feed-back mechanisms, are sometimes loosely called purposive, even if executed by a computing machine or a reflex mechanism. Thus Adelbert Ames has said that purpose in perception "is part of our very structure." Gerard ('49) writes: "The physiologist's whole life is concerned with problems of organic purpose, though he rarely likes to say it, particularly in public. We see purposeful behavior all through the body; it is the only way it makes sense to us. And then we look for the mechanisms to account for it."

The word "purpose" as used here without qualification and explanation has given rise to misunderstanding. Human purposive behavior involves "anticipation of a goal"; and if this anticipation is consciously directed toward the goal, as is usually implied when speaking of human purposes, then it must be recognized that patterns of purposive action are not innate but are acquired by learning through experience. This acquired capacity must not be confused with that goal-directed adaptive behavior which is developed biologically and is carried out with no conscious recognition of the goal to be reached.

The mechanism of reflex and instinctive behavior which is obviously directed in anticipation of a goal is wrought into the hereditary structure of the species and no learning is necessary for its perfect performance. It is a mistake to call such behavior purposive, however purpose-like it may appear to be. Schneirla ('49) emphasizes the importance of avoiding this mistake because the ascription of "purpose" to the lower organisms inevitably carries with it the implication of vitalistic or mentalistic conceptions that have no place there.

In human perception the "anticipation of a goal" which undoubtedly is present contains the two factors mentioned above: first, an inherited pattern of biologically adaptive response and, second, an acquired pattern which has been learned. It is only the second component that can properly be described as purposive, although the first component is doubtless the seedbed from which true purpose has emerged at the human level of integration. The sources of human purposive behavior can thus be followed back in the embryological and phylogenetic development of behavior as far as adaptive responses to sensory excitation can be recognized (Sinnott, '50). Hayek ('52, p. 121) discusses the mechanics of this operation, although he hesitates (unnecessarily, I think) to call it mechanical.

Summary

Perception is a mental synthesis of sensory data, motor experiences, memory, recognition, and judgment. Adjustment of the person to the spatial and temporal relations of things may be made reflexly or instinctively, with or without awareness of the act; but this is not a perception unless there is a conscious polarization of the perceiving subject against the things perceived, with awareness of their relations in space and time to one another and to the perceiving subject.

This perceptual knowledge is acquired by postnatal experience in which there is always a motor component with directive quality. Perception involves attention, which is selective and purposive and always preceded and accompanied by some motor expression. Perception, accordingly, is a behavior, not a passive reception.

The nervous mechanisms of perception include the entire apparatus of sensory and motor analysis and in addition cortical associational connections of great complexity. In the nervous processes involved, spatial and temporal factors are interchangeable and mutually convertible. Perceptual knowledge of space and time is an acquired judgment derived mainly from motor experience. Perception is at a level of psychological integration intermediate between sensation and conception. This is a strategic position, and adequate knowledge of perception should prepare the way for further study of intelligence and all the other cognitive processes that depend upon perceptual knowledge.

The part played by perception in the motivation and control of behavior cannot be discovered by examination of the conscious components of the act alone, and the nature of perception can be revealed only by experimental analysis of the act while in process. In this functional approach the perception is tied to action, to the end toward which the action is directed, and to value-judgments (conscious or unconscious) that appraise the significance of the acts performed for defining the relations of the percipient to the things perceived.

CHAPTER TWENTY-EIGHT

Learning and Intelligence

Intelligence and learning contrasted

Intelligent behavior has been so variously defined that it must first be stated explicitly that intelligence is here regarded as a conscious function. Reflex and instinctive behavior may simulate intelligent behavior so closely that it is difficult to distinguish them objectively; but if there is no awareness of means and ends, no consciously purposive direction of the course of action, the behavior is in this discussion regarded as unintelligent by definition.

Learning is a quite different function which may be done unconsciously or intelligently. Both learning and intelligence are patterns of constructive activity. They are creative in the sense that they involve the acquisition of something new. It is, accordingly, not admissible to define either learning or intelligence in terms of inborn latent capacity, for unless the available capacities are actually exercised nothing is learned and no intelligence is manifested.

Intelligent thinking as experienced subjectively is accessible to scientific observation and measurement only by indirection, but intelligent behavior is open to public inspection. The problem is to find definable criteria and units of measurement. Human and animal intelligence has often been gauged in terms of learning ability; but this criterion must be used with caution, for intelligence cannot be equated with learning. It is not rate of learning or range of learning that characterizes intelligence. It is the use that is made of what is learned. I have known some very learned men who were surprisingly unintelligent. Accumulative knowledge is dead stuff, useful and necessary food for thought; but intelligence is more than knowledge—it is the actual use of knowledge constructively in problem situations.

If a problem is solved by aimless exertion until the right answer is chanced upon, the animal has learned something. He has acquired useful behavior, though very little or no intelligence may have been used or gained. If, on the contrary, the problem is solved by "insight" or by "thinking it through" before action is begun, we call the act intelligent. Since intelligence is fed by knowledge and all knowledge must be acquired by learning, we must attend first to the learning process.

Learning

An enormous amount of well-directed research has been devoted to the learning process in men and other animals, with results which so far are disappointing. About twenty-six years ago an experimental psychologist, after many years of distinguished research directed specifically to this problem, said to me that no laws or principles regarding learning had been formulated that have not been questioned by competent authorities. At that time he wrote: "The whole theory of learning and of intelligence is in confusion" (Lashley, '29, p. ix), and this statement is as true today as it was then. For documentation of the statement see the first four chapters of Halstead's *Brain and Intelligence* ('47). These disagreements arise in part from limitations of the methods used and in larger part perhaps from differences in the attitudes and presuppositions of the observers.

On the basis of much animal experimentation Maier ('39, '40) insists that learning must not be confused with problem-solving. The latter, he says, is a reasoning process, quite different from learning, and he enumerates five separately measurable processes which characterize the learning function. In his analysis ('29, '37, '38) both learning and reasoning are defined behavioristically, disregarding any mentalistic factors. Since in my opinion reasoning is essentially a mental process, I would formulate the problem differently and reach a different conclusion.

Many psychologists think that conditioning of reflexes is the simplest process that merits the name of true learning. Pavlov regarded conditioning as a strictly cortical function, but subsequent research has demonstrated it in a great variety of animals which lack the cerebral cortex, even as far down in the animal series as the flatworms. The conditioned reflex is an acquired total pattern formed by central association of two or more partial patterns of local action. The local reflex typically arises within a field of generalized activity and is progressively restricted. Conditioning also emerges from a wide field of activity which is then restricted on the sensory side by narrowing the zone of adequate stimulation and on the motor side by limiting more precisely the movement evoked. This factor of conditioning is essentially the same as that observed in all learning by trial and error and in much habit formation.

The biologists incline to define learning more broadly than do most of the psychologists. Thus Child ('24, p. 249) wrote: "The whole course of development is a process of physiological learning, beginning with the simple experience of differential exposure to an external factor, and undergoing one modification after another, as new experiences in the life of the organism or of its parts in relation to each other occur. . . . There is no evidence of any fundamental physiological difference between the general protoplasmic memory as expressed in physiological gradients and their effects and the higher forms of memory characteristic of the central nervous system." Here development is interpreted in terms of memory and learning.

Gesell's studies of child development led him to a similar conclusion, for he says ('45, p. 194), "Learning is essentially growth." Carmichael ('54, p. 160) concludes that "it is not possible save for pragmatic reasons to say at any point that growth has stopped and learning has begun." The thesis that "learning in its broadest sense connotes development of behavior" was elaborated in more detail by Coghill, and I have elsewhere ('49, chap. 17) quoted extracts on this subject from his published works and manuscript lecture notes. Coghill regarded the neuropil of the vertebrate nervous system as the critical tissue in all learning processes from the simplest to the most elaborate. With this I agree, and much attention has been devoted to its study.

Learning, however defined, involves first the acquisition of something new and then "progressive automatization in a growing nervous matrix" (Coghill, in a personal letter). Learning thus passes over into habit and, as age advances, the action system (of both body and mind) becomes less flexible and more stereotyped; but learning may continue as long as the living tissue is sufficiently pliable to make new internal adjustments in response to the exigencies of life.

In learning, a novel feature is introduced into the situation and there is a selection from all possible modes of behavior of some one of them, a selection made in terms of previous personal experience (as contrasted with racial experience in the formation of instincts). The "trace effects" of previous experience of the consequences of different actions are enduring rather than evanescent. These characteristics distinguish learning from fatigue, sensory adaptation, and facilitation by repetition. The trace effects to which reference has just been made are allied with, and perhaps derived from, the inorganic phenomena of hysteresis.

The evolution of the learning capacity is thus seen to be a continuous process, with emergence at successive levels of new patterns which are progressively better adapted to promote the welfare of the individual. At which of these levels the emergent should be called true learning is a question of semantics. In a brief biological survey of learning ('38a) I provisionally described learning as a more or less enduring change in the pattern of behavior brought about through the personal experience and reactions of the individual. This I now think is too broad a statement because it would include fatigue and other processes which lack the selective and novel features of learning. As I now see it, the broadest biological conception of learning includes processes of three classes or levels of integration:

1. Primitive or protoplasmic learning, that modifiability of behavior or habituation which involves an enduring change in pattern of performance resulting from the individual's experience. All organisms exhibit some measure of this sort of adjustment to their changing needs, plants less than even the simplest animals. In this general sense all protoplasm can learn.

2. Sensorimotor or neural learning, the exercise of which requires a differentiated nervous system. In its simpler forms this does not differ essentially from the first type except in greater complexity and potentiality for further elaboration. Intrinsic factors prevail here and the activity is stereotyped; yet the acquisition of this skill is evidently facilitated by exercise and modifiable by temperature changes and other environmental influences. In more highly elaborated forms sensory experience, trial-and-error, and practice play a relatively larger part. This type of learning culminates in conditioning of re-

flexes. It is acquired slowly, with much waste motion and fumbling, but ultimately it may yield a very efficient performance.

3. Semantic or cortical learning, which works with mental symbols of various grades of abstraction. This involves at least the rudiments of ideation and culminates in human rational thought. This type of learning is intentionally directed with more or less of "insight" and intelligent control of the process, and it may be very rapid. Learning of this kind cannot go far without the aid of language, for its tools are symbolisms of various grades.

A fourth level of learning has been recognized by Murdock ('49) at the human grade of social development. At lower levels learning is an individual accomplishment and what the animal learns dies with him. In human societies a new and very potent factor is introduced by the acquisition of language which facilitates communication of learned skills to others and their transmission by tradition and written records to all succeeding generations. Relatively stable patterns of social structure are thus perpetuated in increasing number and complexity. In this way diverse cultures arise and each cultural pattern is transmitted by social heredity indefinitely, so that "societies as well as individuals learn. Social learning is synonymous with cultural evolution."

These classes of learning have no sharp borders. They intergrade and each higher stage contains also the lower together with something additional. How far down this scale of modifiable behavior it is expedient to extend the connotation of the word "learning" is debatable. Schneirla ('49, p. 268) places the lower limit at the flatworms. Certainly in the lowest ranks the learning capacity is less than in the higher, yet I think it is important to recognize that we are dealing here with a continuous evolutionary process, a vital activity that is coextensive with life.

The learning process is ordinarily directive and it is an organized activity, never a mere random fumbling. Krechevsky ('32) insists upon this and writes: "We must change our description of the learning process so as to recognize the existence of organized and systematic responses at *all* stages of the process." "The rat, when placed in an unsolvable situation, does not respond in a helter-skelter chance fashion, but makes a series of integrated, unified attempts at solution.

These systematic responses are partly, at least, initiated by the animal himself and are not altogether merely a resultant of the immediately presented external situation."

Intelligence

Learning, as we have just seen, is a directive physiological process within which, in its higher forms, an intelligent factor emerges. In the course of the education of the human child the learning process is guided and dominated by intelligent control. Although intelligence is thus genetically related with learning, these two processes must not be identified, and intelligence cannot be directly measured in terms of learning ability, as has often been attempted. Some other criteria for the analysis and evaluation of intelligence must be sought.

Intelligence has been defined as ability to solve problems, but that includes too much and too little. Many problems are solved without intelligence by computing machines and insects, and perhaps the most significant characteristic of intelligence is ability to invent problems. This capacity for imaginative or creative thinking marks the highest level of integration in the organic realm.

Our definition of intelligence as a mental process has some corollaries that should be made explicit. Mind is minding, not something separable from the minding body. Intelligence, then, is not a detachable thing that can be drawn off, measured, and manipulated like a pint of blood. As a vital process it is tied in with other vital processes of diverse sorts. Intelligence is derived from knowledge, and the nature of the intelligence is largely determined by the amount and quality of the knowledge available. Knowledge is a product of knowing, which again is a vital process. And knowledge itself, as the word is used in this context, is a process, not an inert thing.

In common usage the word "knowing" has other meanings that are irrelevant here. We say the honeybee knows its way about, but whether it has any awareness of what it is doing we cannot be sure. The "wisdom of the body" (Cannon) is a figure of speech that does not carry any implication that the parts of the body know that they are acting "wisely," that is, in conformity with the needs of the body. The knowledge with which we are concerned here must be consciously apprehended as such in order to be available for use in the intelligent activity. Since consciousness itself is always a vital process, the knowledge used must be active knowing, not an accumulation of static knowledge. The "accumulative knowledge" stored in the brain (as memory traces, neurograms, schemata, engrams, or whatever you choose to call it) is not available to intelligence unless it is reactivated so that the latent memory is vitalized into action of the appropriate nervous tissue. Because all mind is minding, consciously apprehended knowledge is knowing and so as a vital process it enters into the larger integrative process of intelligent thinking.

Knowing is a transaction between the knower and the known, and in all perceptual knowledge one of the parties of this transaction is the object known. In naïve experience these parties—the knower and the known—are polarized one against the other; but underlying this apparent duality there is an inseparable relationship which must not be split apart. In all our search for the essential nature of intelligence, its factors and its mechanisms, attention must not be diverted from the fact that we are dealing with a unitary vital process and not a detachable entity and the further fact that in this vital process the knower and the known stand in reciprocal transactional relation —a relationship which must not be sundered by epistemological or any other kind of dialectic.

Mechanisms of learning and intelligence

The nervous mechanisms employed in learning and intelligence, so far as these are now known, are described by Hebb ('49) and Eccles ('53). Hebb's analysis of the data brings out an important principle which clarifies much that was obscure.

In the development of the learning process, in the individual and also in phylogeny, two stages are distinguished—stages which differ radically in rate and pattern of learning and in the mechanisms employed. The very young of higher animals and the adults of very primitive animals show a stage of early or "primary learning," to which in the higher mammals there is subsequently added a stage of late or higher learning.

The second stage is called by Hebb "conceptual learning," and it should be noted that his definition of the concept is broader than mine. His "concept" is defined behavioristically, but just how it is defined is not clear to me. The concepts which he ascribes to rats I prefer to call symbols. They are organized patterns of assembly of neurological processes that go on at a lower level of abstraction than that of the concept and which may or may not have a conscious component. I define the concept psychologically as a synthesizing mental process of higher order, a process which employs symbols (verbal or other) of simpler ideas and integrates these around a central "core" (as defined by Hebb, p. 133). Percepts and various other psychobiological processes when so assembled and integrated may in turn be symbolized (verbally or otherwise) and so employed as tools of rational thinking. An interesting and plausible hypothesis of the neurological mechanism of such an assembly as given by Hebb is described here in Chapter 33.

These two stages of development are not sharply separated. The higher type of learning is gradually acquired, but in the adults of men and the large apes it is clearly different from the primary learning of these same animals in infancy.

Primary learning develops directly from the innate inherited capacities, that is, from the reflexes and instincts. In very primitive animals where these inborn capacities predominate, the learning may appear to be very rapid, but this appearance is deceptive because most of this behavior is not individually learned and the learning capacity may be very small. In animals higher in the scale where real learning plays a larger role, the learning process of this type is rather slow. It is acquired by trial and error with much fumbling or by conditioning of reflexes. This, which I have called "sensorimotor learning," may be done by adult animals which have no cerebral cortex or cortex of simple structure, and it is the only kind of learning possible in very young animals of the higher ranks.

The late, or higher, stage of learning, on the contrary, may be far more complicated and yet done much more rapidly. This is because it is a cortical function, and the cortex of the higher mammals is a vast storehouse of memory "traces" or "engrams" of previous experience which can be drawn upon to give meaning to the presently experienced perceptions. An unfamiliar situation or a difficult problem may be resolved into appropriate action almost instantly by "insight," or the problem may be solved after a more or less prolonged reasoning process which is primarily a cortical associational activity. The cortical functions may be carried out more rapidly than the conditioning that is characteristic of primary learning. This type of learning culminates in what I call the cortical or "semantic" learning of mankind.

An interesting and surprising peculiarity of cortical learning of the higher levels is that it is accompanied by an actual retardation of the rate of primary learning. The first type of learning is slower in higher mammals than in lower and slower in adult man than in the infant. It is pointed out by Hebb that in the adult animal the efficiency of the higher learning process is roughly proportional to the relative mass of associational cortex, or, otherwise expressed, to the ratio of the total associational cortex to the total sensory cortex.

Measurement of intelligence

Intelligence, I repeat, is here defined as a mental process, that is, a psychobiological activity. The biological aspects of it can be measured in numerical units with precision, but the introspectively known aspects of it are refractory to such measurement, as has been mentioned in several contexts. In the domain of values, for instance, we found no practicable measuring rule for the satisfactions experienced when real values are acquired (Chapter 12), and similar obstacles are encountered in every other kind of conscious experience. Moreover, the various attempts to measure intelligently controlled behavior studied objectively have so far failed to meet the rigorous requirements of scientific method. The chief difficulty arises from the fact that there is no agreement among the observers about what it is they are looking for.

If, as is often done, intelligence is defined as innate *capacity* for "all-round intellectual ability," then the "intelligence tests" now in current use shoot wide of the mark, because what they measure is *performance*, not capacity. The inborn capacities of the person or animal tested may lie quite outside the range of the tests used, and indeed these capacities may not have had an opportunity to mature to functional efficiency because of unfavorable environment. The inherited structure provides the organic substrate for the growth of biological intelligence and determines its limitations, but the intelligence itself is the fruition of that growth. It is not latent capacity. It is creative work.

Recognition of the two stages of the learning process as defined by Hebb enables him to separate two corresponding components of the intelligence quotient (IQ). There are two types of intelligence. Intelligence A is the innate intelligence potential, which comes to expression first in primary learning. Intelligence B is dependent upon the extent and efficiency of later or higher learning, which in turn is determined very largely by the cultural environment. The usual types of intelligence and aptitude tests measure performance at a particular age in a specific culture and may be valid and very useful for estimating the actual level of comprehension, learning, and problem-solving for that age in that particular culture, that is, for estimating Intelligence B. But such tests may be invalid and indeed pernicious if taken as a reliable estimate of Intelligence A. Halstead ('47, '51) has been successful in separating "biological intelligence" (the A type) by comparative study of normal persons and those with injury of the brain.

The tests in current use give us quantitative reports of "psychometric intelligence" in which the genetic factors (Intelligence A) and the acquired factors (Intelligence B) cannot be distinguished. One way to separate these factors is by extensive selective breeding experiments—and such experiments are impractical in a human population. One clue is given by the observed fact that an examination of 150 pairs of identical and fraternal twins shows that identical twins are much more alike in each of the primary mental abilities than are fraternal twins, indicating that inheritance plays an important part in determining mental capacity. This question has been tested experimentally on rats at the University of California. The factor studied was ability to learn to run a specially designed 17-unit maze. Tryon ('29) found that when a heterogeneous population of rats is chosen as the initial parental group they differ widely in their learning scores. The "bright" and the "dull" parents were selectively bred for several generations, with rigid controls, and statistical analysis of the scores of the offspring shows conclusively that this mental ability is inherited, in part at least. "The results are consistent with what would be anticipated if this trait were produced by multiple genetic factors." Riesen and Kinder's experiments ('52) shed additional light upon the relations of "nature" and "nurture" in the development of infant chimpanzees.

The general principles drawn from statistical analysis and mathematical treatment of the data accumulated in programs of mental testing have proved to be practically useful, though only within restricted fields. These performance tests, when skillfully composed and used, measure something that correlates with the requirements of the situation for which the test is designed.

In industry the use of appropriate aptitude tests and correlation of the scores with actual production is saving enormous waste of manpower. Aptitude tests of high school and college students correlate closely with subsequent rank in class of the students tested, and they give invaluable guidance in the choice of a vocation. From World War I until now the administrators of our armed forces have been studying the use of aptitude tests for classification of the personnel for various types of service with gratifying results. And now the Selective Service is applying similar methods in the administration of the draft for military service. Tests given by the military Educational Testing Service to 339,000 college students registered for the draft indicated that their scores correlated fairly well with those previously recorded by the College Entrance Examining Board and the American Council on Education for many of these students (Chauncey, '52).

Valuable as these tests are in practice, it must be admitted that we do not know just what it is that they measure.

It has been clearly shown that most of the intelligence and aptitude tests now in common use are heavily weighted in favor of a "middle-class" economic and cultural group and are unreliable and unfair to people of different economic status and cultural training. To correct this bias a research team has been engaged for several years upon a series of new IQ tests, the Davis-Hess "culture-fair" tests, which aim to reduce so far as possible the factor of cultural opportunity and to reveal "mother-wit," or real genetic differences in native ability. Some of the results of this extensive research have been published (Eells et al., '51).

None of the tests so far employed reveal a single index of general intelligence, such as has been sought by Binet, Spearman, and others for more than fifty years, but the presence of a general factor is not excluded. It is possible to devise batteries of tests which bring to light not a unit character of mental competence but several specific factors of intelligence which can then be subjected to mathematical analysis and experimental study. More than twenty-five years ago Thurstone began a program of "multiple factor analysis" of intelligence to see how many specific kinds of ability can be identified. A battery of fifty-six psychological tests was devised, each test designed to reveal some particular type of mental ability. Several hundred presumably normal people were given the entire series of tests; when the records were assembled the correlation was determined for each pair of tests in the whole battery. For each pair of tests the correlation reveals the extent to which those who succeed in one task tend to succeed in the other. The very laborious mathematical computations involved brought out the fact that twelve factors were sufficient to account for all significant correlations of the abilities represented in the fifty-six tests. These abilities, then, are regarded as primary factors of intelligence. Some of them are well-defined, others are more obscure, and there is, of course, more or less overlap of the several factors in every experiment.

The results of these inquiries as reported by Thurstone ('47, '48) show that the method is fruitful. Much remains to be done to clarify the factors already isolated and to discover others. Special tests have been devised for the factor analysis of young children, motivated partly by the thought that methods of instruction may eventually be adapted to the mental profile of each child. Analysis by Guilford ('55) of individual differences among young, superior adults, in accordance with multiple factor theory, shows that at least forty dimensions are required to account for the patterns of intercorrelations among scores from tests involving intellectual tasks. This program of factor analysis is now finding applications in the practical areas of education and industry, enabling us, as Thurstone says, "to differentiate our treatment of people by recognizing every person in terms of the mental and physical assets which make him unique as an individual."

This is what we are after in all programs of mental testing, job analysis, and personality studies—the discovery of the unique qualities of the individual person, his capacities, aptitudes, and limitations, not those of the fictitious average man. For this we need certain norms or standards of reference that can be expressed in mathematical form and that provide useful guiding principles. These principles can be discovered only by skillful analysis of the actual records of performance made by large numbers of people. Given these records and the requisite technical skill (including especially mathematical proficiency), principles emerge in accordance with which the individual record can be judiciously appraised.

The principles applied in mental testing and factor analysis have been discovered empirically by statistical and mathematical treatment of the raw data. What we want to do next is to translate the quantitative records of "psychometric intelligence" into biological intelligence as it is actually exhibited by people. To this end well-validated factors can be separately investigated under experimental conditions which permit quantitative expression of their relations to one another, of the effects produced upon them by various normal and injurious treatments, and of the amount and location of the brain tissue requisite for their normal functioning.

Reports of such inquiries have been published by Halstead ('47, '51), who has devoted himself to a search for the number and kind of factors that can be separately recognized and measured in a population comprising "normal" healthy people and others with various types of lesions in the brain, including surgical removal of some of its parts. These people were given a battery of neuropsychological tests which yielded a four-factor description of performance on the tests. These factors were systematically investigated in all cases studied. In cases of brain injury the four factors were variously affected and the measurements for the different factors were combined in the form of an impairment index.

A different approach to the problem of measuring the factors of mental pattern in individual persons has been devised by Stephenson and colleagues ('53). Their "Q-technique," instead of checking performance against statistical norms, establishes correlations between qualities of performance (including mental acts) shown by each person rather than between the tests used. These data (including again the subjective as well as the objective behavior) can be dealt with as objectively as any psychologist can deal with the behavior of a rat or an aphasic patient. For a review of the vast literature of mental measurements, see the *Yearbook* edited by Buros ('53).

Summary

Comparison of learning and intelligence shows them to be quite different types of function. Both are total patterns of directive processes which involve the acquisition of something new. They cannot be defined in terms of latent capacity, for they exist only when available capacities are actually exercised.

Biological learning is here defined very broadly to include three stages of progressive expansion of that primordial modifiability of behavior that results from the individual's personal experience and leads to selective and enduring change in the pattern of behavior. The stages listed are: (1) protoplasmic learning, (2) sensorimotor or neural learning, and (3) cortical or semantic learning.

Intelligence is here regarded as a purposively directed mental process with awareness of means and ends. Its pattern and the limits of its competence are set by inherited structure and by opportunities for self-culture available. Acquired knowledge is the raw foodstuff of intelligence, without which no growth is possible. Intelligence integrates knowledge and gives it direction and is rarely, if ever, devoid of interest and affect, for, like all other high-level mental processes, it is a complex integration of many diverse factors. No single index of general intelligence is available, but methods of multiple factor analysis open promising fields of statistical and experimental research.

Two stages in the development of learning processes are distinguished: first, an early stage of primary learning which makes direct use of inborn reflex and instinctive capacities, and, second, a following stage of higher or cortical learning which employs symbols of various grades of abstraction. Two types of intelligence are related with these two stages of the learning process.

CHAPTER TWENTY-NINE

The Origin and Evolution
of the Cerebral Cortex

Brain and mind

The cerebral cortex is the indispensable apparatus for carrying on all the higher mental processes at the conceptual level. No invertebrate animals have cortex of the vertebrate type, and it is lacking also in the most primitive members of the vertebrate series. It appears rather late in evolutionary history and also is the last part of the developing human body to reach full maturity. The lower animals which have no cortex lead very successful lives. Their ways of life are different from ours but adequate for their needs.

The cortex is something added to a full equipment of everything necessary for successful living at a high level of efficient and very complicated behavior. The most striking illustration of this is found in the song birds, which have large and very complicated brains and only mere rudiments of cerebral cortex. In contrast, more than half of the human brain is cortex and parts directly connected with it. This cortex adds something to the behavior patterns which birds lack.

What is this cortex and what is it for? A comparison of bird culture with human culture shows that our cortex is the organ of civilization. It gives to man his unique capacity for production of marvelous mechanical inventions so that he can fly better than any bird. And it equips him for far more precious rational, imaginative, esthetic, and moral achievements.

This cortical endowment with its mysterious properties of conscious participation in its own operations was not bestowed upon us miraculously. It grew up with us naturally, and the history of its evolutionary development contributes to an understanding of the vital processes that give us conscious experience.

Cerebral and cerebellar cortex

The word "cortex" as a technical neurological term is applied to any thin layer of gray substance (a cellular fabric) which is spread superficially over an inner core of white substance (a fibrous fabric), as the bark of a tree covers the underlying woody fiber. In the human brain, cortex is most elaborately developed in two places, the cerebellum and the cerebral hemispheres, in both of which it is a secondary derivative of the older stem portion of the brain and is folded up above it.

Cerebellar cortex is the dominant regulator of the action of all skeletal muscles and so was called by Sherrington ('48) the "head ganglion of the proprioceptive system." The pattern of action of these muscles is determined elsewhere and the cerebellum has nothing to do with that. As the engineer would express it, it is a servomechanism. It controls the execution of these acts by regulation of the strength and timing of contraction of the separate muscles involved. This regulation is entirely involuntary, for it is effected on the outgoing or efferent side of the nervous circuits. The size of the cerebellum varies with the amount and nature of muscular activity. It is small in sluggish species and very large in active fishes, in birds, and in all other vertebrates with rapid movements requiring accurate control.

The cerebral cortex is radically different in structure and significance for behavior. It emerged from the brain stem rather late in phylogenetic history and was progressively enlarged and complicated in proportion as individually acquired, or learned, patterns of behavior assumed more and more dominant control over the reflex and instinctive patterns. It sets the pattern of intentionally controlled conduct, and in mankind it is the apparatus of all the higher conceptual processes of ideation, reasoning, imagination, and esthetic appreciation.

The cerebral cortex is broadly connected with the cerebellar cortex through the cortico-pontile system of fibers, so that the cerebellum exerts regulatory control over all voluntary movements just as it does over involuntary action. Cerebellar and cerebral cortex are the most highly differentiated parts of the apparatus of integration and their integrative actions are fundamentally different. The cerebellum is connected with the sensorimotor circuits of the brain stem, as the electrician would say, in parallel, not in series. It exerts regulatory control over these systems by differential reinforcement and inhibition of the active muscles as required from moment to moment to ensure the appropriate co-ordination of their contractions. In terms of government, the functions of the cerebellum are strictly administrative, not legislative. The cerebral cortex is the supreme legislative assembly, determining courses of action in the light of objectives sought and means available. Its activities from its inception are at a higher level of integration than are those of the brain stem or cerebellum.

Origin of the cerebral cortex

Structurally the cerebral cortex is a layer of gray matter, composed of nerve cells embedded in a mat of neuropil, which in man is about an eighth of an inch thick and is spread over the convoluted surfaces of the cerebral hemispheres. This superficial gray matter, accompanied by the underlying white nerve fibers connected with it, is wrapped around the brain stem like a cloak or mantle and so is called the pallium.

The nervous structures concerned with local reflexes, instincts, and other stable components of behavior may be arranged in separate clusters ("nuclei") distributed in the brain stem, or they may form large solid masses, like the corpus striatum. Cortical tissue is spread in thin sheets to facilitate two related functions, first, precise localization of sensory and motor analytic processes and, second, the correlation or association of the several localized functions to ensure integration of behavior in patterns adapted to give the response appropriate to the existing situation. Both the stable inherited patterns of behavior and the more labile acquired patterns involve both analytic and synthetic nervous functions in mutual interplay. The simple amphibian brain, as illustrated in Figure 1 (page 246), has no cortex, but the pallial area where cortex is developed in the higher brains can be recognized. It is the dorsal convexity of the small cerebral hemisphere, that is, the part which has been dissected off from the right hemisphere in the illustration. Figure 3 shows a cross section through the amphibian cerebral hemispheres and the arrangement of some of the typical nervous elements. The pallial area has three subdivisions with different arrangements of the nerve cells and the related nerve fibers.

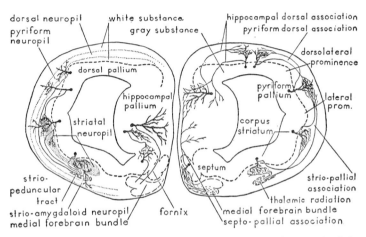

Fig. 3.—Diagram illustrating typical neurons of the cerebral hemispheres of the mud puppy (Necturus) as seen in cross section. × 16. Compare Figure 4(A), which shows a similar section taken farther back through the interventricular foramen. The outer border of the gray layer is marked by a broken line. Descending fibers are drawn in the left hemisphere, ascending and pallial association fibers in the right. After Herrick ('34).

From this simple beginning the successive steps in the evolutionary development of the cerebral cortex can be followed with precision. The first well-differentiated cortex appears in the reptiles, where we find three major subdivisions which correspond in position and fibrous connections with the three subdivisions of the amphibian pallium, as shown by A and B of Figure 4. In the mammals these three

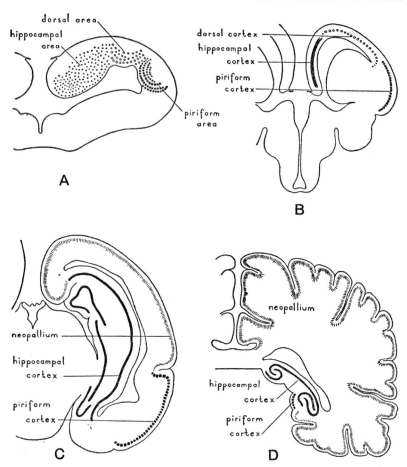

Fig. 4.—Diagrams showing approximately the relative extent of the
olfactory and nonolfactory pallial fields as seen in cross sections of various
vertebrate brains. A. A primitive amphibian (Necturus), with the entire
pallium dominated by olfactory influence. × 12. There is no layer of
superficial cortex.   B. The box tortoise (Cistudo), with three areas of
differentiated cortex—medially, the hippocampus (archipallium); laterally,
the piriform cortex (paleopallium); and dorsally, a generalized cortex
which is the precursor of the neopallium. × 7. The medial and lateral
areas have extensive olfactory connections.   C. The Virginia opossum
(Didelphis), with the olfactory cortex (hippocampus and piriform) much
more extensive than the nonolfactory neopallium. × 4.   D. Human,
with great enlargement of the neopallium and reduction of the olfactory
parts of the cortex. × ½. After Herrick ('33).

cortical fields are progressively enlarged and differentiated, with re-markable differences in the amount of this enlargement and the character of their specialization (Fig. 4, C and D). In the course of this evolutionary development the cerebral hemispheres increase in size and complexity of internal structure far more than does the rest of the brain (Figures 5 and 6).

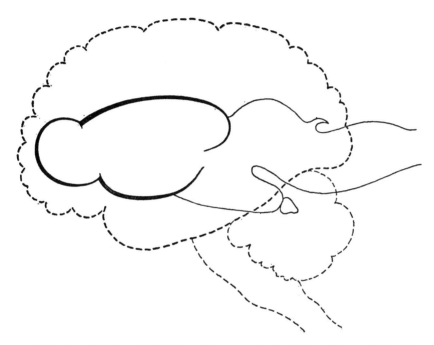

Fig. 5.—Outline of the lateral aspect of the brain of an adult sala-mander (Amblystoma) upon which is superposed in broken lines a similar outline of a human brain, to illustrate the relations of the cerebral hemis-pheres to the brain stem in the two species. In both cases the outlines of the cerebral hemispheres are drawn in thicker lines. The two outlines are not drawn to the same scale. The salamander brain is drawn about six and a half times its actual length and the human brain two fifths of actual size. If the human hemisphere were drawn to the same scale as the sala-mander's hemisphere, it would be more than a yard long. Compare Figures 1 and 9.

The embryological development of the human brain repeats in broad outlines the evolutionary development of the genus Homo,

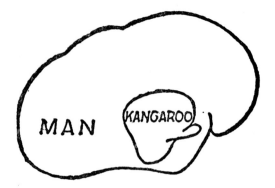

Fig. 6.—Outline projections (side view) of the relative sizes of the cerebral hemispheres of a man and a kangaroo of about equal body weight. The human brain weighs forty-eight ounces, the kangaroo's brain weighs two ounces. After Sir Richard Owen.

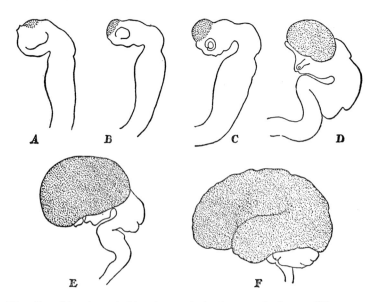

Fig. 7.—Sketches of side views of the human brain at different stages of development to illustrate the relative extent of the cortical area (stippled). The ages of the prenatal stages (A to E) are approximate. A, two weeks; B, three weeks; C, four weeks; D, eight weeks; E, six months; F, adult. After Herrick ('24).

although with many deviations. Figure 7 shows six stages of the development of the human brain from fetal age of two weeks to the adult, illustrating the progressive increase in the relative size of the cerebral cortex.

In early embryonic stages of the development of the brain all the cells are crowded close to the inner wall next to the ventricle. Here they multiply, move outward, and finally in the brain stem they are variously grouped to form clusters, or nuclei, which are localized and interconnected in ways appropriate for the functions to be performed. In amphibian brains this outward migration is seen in only a few places. In the pallial field it has begun only in the hippocampal area (Fig. 4, A); but in higher species all the cells move out to the external surface and there form a continuous sheet of gray matter. They are variously specialized and arranged in layers in patterns which vary from place to place.

The many structurally different cortical areas that have been described are of two classes—the projection areas and the areas of association or elaboration. The former are the primary areas which are the first to be differentiated in embryological and phylogenetic development. Each of them is connected by projection fibers with some subcortical part of the brain stem which has a specific analytic function, either sensory or motor. The association areas are interpolated between the projection areas and serve to bind all parts of the cortex together by association fibers.

The correlation of the visible structure with the functions performed proves to be very difficult. These difficulties are considered in subsequent chapters, and here we summarize some features of the evolution of the cortex which contribute to the solution of these difficult problems.

Factors of cortical evolution

In the vertebrate series the first well-differentiated cortex appears in the reptiles. In the turtles this cortex is a thin sheet of cells of special form spread throughout the pallial areas of each cerebral hemisphere. This area is the simple, smooth, dome-shaped roof of the lateral ventricle, which is arched over the basal, or stem, part of the hemisphere. This cortex shows the typical structure and major subdivisions seen in higher animals, here reduced to lowest terms. Search for the origins of this structure and the agencies responsible for its differentiation takes us first to the amphibians and lungfishes, which have obvious rudiments of it, and to the sharks and some other fishes, where simpler rudiments can be recognized.

In the more active fishes, including the game fishes sought by sportsmen, the overt behavior is dominated by the sense of sight. Such fishes are visualizers, with large eyes, and the primary visual center in the roof (tectum) of the midbrain is correspondingly enlarged. All other exteroceptive sensory systems are connected with this optic tectum by large tracts of fibers so that this area in the middle of the brain contains the adjusting apparatus for most of the animal's customary reactions. For this reason it might be expected that the apparatus for more complicated behavior at higher levels of integration would have been differentiated in this region. This, however, did not happen. In fact, the optic tectum in all mammals is smaller and more simply organized than it is in many fishes and in the frog, also a good visualizer.

The reason why the higher integrative cortical apparatus was not differentiated from the tectum of the midbrain is found in the fossil record of vertebrate evolution, which shows that none of the highly specialized fishes were the ancestors of land-living animals. On the contrary, the earliest amphibians were descended from generalized fishes allied with living ganoids and lungfishes. These were mudfishes of simple structure and sluggish habit. The eyes were small, the olfactory organs very large. Smell was evidently the dominant sense, and the olfactory centers at the front end of the brain were enormous. When, in the Devonian period, these fishes emerged from the water to live on land as amphibians their more diversified behavior required enlargement and further differentiation of the brain, and because they were poor visualizers, this specialization was not in the midbrain but in the larger and physiologically dominant olfactory area of the forebrain.

The olfactory field of the cerebral hemispheres is a complex center of correlation, where olfactory stimuli are related with diverse other kinds of sensory influences brought into it by fibers which ascend from sensory centers at lower levels of the brain. This olfactory field at the anterior end of the brain is the dominant center of control of all behavior of these primitive vertebrates, and for this reason it was the seedbed for further structural differentiation as the patterns of behavior were stepped up from one integrative level to another. Here rudimentary cortex had its beginnings.

In surviving species of primitive fishes and amphibians the basal parts of the hemispheres control the simpler and more rigidly stereotyped reflexes. The dorsal or pallial parts do not differ greatly from the basal parts, but such minor differences as there are point in a direction toward the cortical differentiation that is found here in reptiles. The evidence for this is complicated and technical.

Three critical periods in the evolution of cortex may be distinguished. First, at the transition from amphibians to reptiles a simple pattern of definitive cortex was firmly established. Second, when the mammals diverged from the reptiles the cortex was greatly expanded and structurally complicated. Finally, when man emerged within the primate order this expansion was accelerated at an unprecedented rate, with corresponding efflorescence of the life of reason. The following outline may suffice to indicate the trend of this evolutionary movement to those readers who are familiar with the internal structure of the human brain. There is further discussion of these principles in several of my published works ('21, '26, '27, pp. 306–22, '33a, pp. 248–56, '33b, pp. 176–201, '33c, '34, '34a, '48, chaps. 7, 8).

In lungfishes and amphibians the hollow cerebral hemispheres are expanded in form similar to that of the human brain in the second month of fetal life (Figs. 1 and 7). From the basal parts of the hemispheres many fibers stream backward into the hypothalamus and motor field of the midbrain. In addition to this primitive path, there are other connections between the olfactory fields of the hemispheres and lower centers that are concerned with the more complicated olfactory reactions. These secondary connections are in two series related with the medial and lateral walls of each hemisphere respectively.

In the amphibian hemisphere the medial and ventral parts are broadly connected with the hypothalamus by fibers passing in both directions. These connections provide for correlation of the olfactory sense with the gustatory and visceral senses and for discharge from the hypothalamus of appropriate excitations to the viscera. In a similar way the lateral and dorsal parts of the hemisphere are connected by ascending and descending fibers with the thalamus and midbrain, where the olfactory sense is brought into relation with the exteroceptive and proprioceptive senses. Fibers which descend from the thalamus and midbrain to lower levels of the brain may activate all skeletal muscles. The ascending and descending connections between the thalamus and the hemispheres are in addition to the more primitive reflex circuits of the lower levels of the brain, and they regulate these lower functions at a higher level of integration. The descending fibers from the cerebral hemispheres correspond roughly with the sub-cortical components of the extrapyramidal systems of fibers of the human brain.

There is, accordingly, in these primitive brains a well-defined localization of function in the hemispheres—olfacto-visceral functions medially and olfacto-somatic functions laterally. This is a fundamental distinction, and the analysis of function goes little further than this. The several senses —touch, vision, hearing, etc.—are not separately localized in the hemispheres. This situation is similar to that found in the medulla oblongata, where visceral and somatic sensory centers are well separated but centers for the separate senses are not (page 245), and the explanation is the same. Since most of the activities of these animals are mass movements of the entire musculature, refined central analysis is unnecessary.

In amphibians the connections between the hemisphere and the thalamus are small, but those with the hypothalamus are very large. Correlated with this is the interesting fact that the medial part of the pallial field (the primordial hippocampus) has a characteristic structure which is clearly a first step toward differentiated cortex and that this peculiar structure is found nowhere else.

When this arrangement is compared with the simple cortex found in reptiles, we observe first one notable difference. The amphibian pallial field has two well-defined subdivisions, medial and lateral; the reptilian has three, medial, lateral, and dorsal (Fig. 4). The medial and lateral cortical areas of reptiles both receive many olfactory fibers and, like the corresponding amphibian areas, are connected respectively with the hypothalamus and the thalamus. The medial area gives rise to the mammalian hippocampus and the lateral area to the piriform cortex (region of the uncus in man). The dorsal area is progressively emancipated from olfactory influence, and it has large thalamo-cortical connections (sensory projection fibers) and electrically excitable motor cortex giving rise to a small pyramidal tract.

In fishes and amphibians the ventral, or stem, part of the hemisphere is more highly elaborated than the dorsal, or pallial, part, and most of the hemispheric control of behavior of these animals is effected in these basal centers. This is because the behavior of these animals is organized for the most part in reflex and simple instinctive patterns. In the most primitive living amphibians (e.g., the mud puppy, Necturus) no fibers ascend without interruption from the thalamus proper to the pallium, but small numbers of such fibers are seen in the frogs and much larger numbers in reptiles and all higher animals. These thalamo-cortical projection fibers play the critical role in the evolution of the cortex, and progressive localization of function in the cortex goes hand in hand with the segregation of specific nuclei for the several sensory and motor functions in the

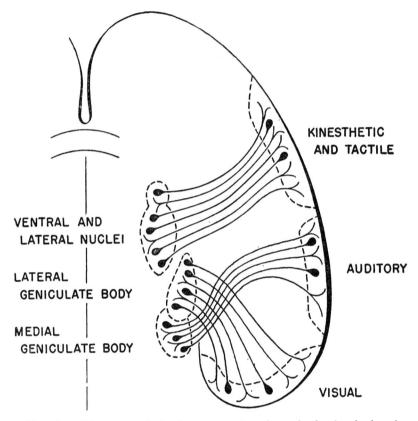

Fig. 8.—Diagrammatic horizontal section through the forebrain of a primitive mammal to show the relations of the thalamic centers for touch, vision, and hearing to their cortical projection centers.

thalamus. Figure 8 shows the primitive arrangement of three chief systems of sensory projection fibers.

The facts just summarized make it clear that the principles in accordance with which cerebral cortex emerged within an olfactory field are to be sought in the reciprocal relations between the brain stem and the cerebral hemispheres. Since both hypothalamic and thalamic projection fibers are present in the higher amphibians, the question arises—why do not frogs have any cerebral cortex? I do not know the complete answer, but I think a clue may be found in the fact that in all amphibians, including frogs, fibers from the olfactory bulbs reach all parts of the hemispheres and olfaction is predominant in all behavioral adjustments which are controlled by the pallial part of the hemispheres.

In the mammalian thalamus and cortex separate fields are set apart for reception of each modality of sense—smell, sight, hearing, touch, etc. —and the most characteristic feature of cortical functions is the interplay among these different types of sensory experience, for which an elaborate mechanism is set up in the associational systems of nerve cells and fibers. Separate localization of each sensory and motor component of this dynamic system is essential for efficient operation, because the apparatus of these different sensory functions must be separately placed in the cortex in order that associational connections can be made among them.

The reason why frogs have no cortex is, then, to be found in the fact that the several sensory systems represented in the thalamus and pallium are not sufficiently well segregated and separately localized to provide an adequate mechanism for the cortical type of associational interplay among the several modalities of sense. In the amphibians a first step toward this segregation has been taken by the well-defined separation of the hypothalamus and related primordial hippocampus, on one hand, from the thalamus proper and related corpus striatum and overlying piriform pallium, on the other hand. But this localization of these two broad classes of behavior alone does not go far enough to satisfy the requirements of the cortical type of adjustment. More refined analysis of sensory experience and more sharply defined localization of the several modalities of sense in the thalamus and pallium are prerequisites for cortical differention and the cortical pattern of integration.

The brain of the frog does not conform with these specifications. Even the distinction between the medial visceral and the lateral somatic pallial fields is weakened by the presence of dominant olfactory influence in both of them. Between these two pallial fields of the frog there is a dorsal zone of "general pallium" which provides a wealth of associational connections between the two bordering pallial fields; but this zone too is under dominant olfactory control. In no part of the amphibian pallium is there precise and exclusive localization of function. They do not require it because total patterns of behavior predominate in all amphibians. (The presence of well-defined cortex in the lungfishes—Rudebeck, '45—is exceptional and the explanation must await further knowledge of the connections of these cells.)

The simplest reptilian brain exhibits the minimal essentials for typical cortical differentiation in the pallium, namely, at least three areas with distinctive patterns of sensory connections, areas from which somatic-motor and visceral-motor projection fibers take origin, and a more or less elaborate system of associational nervous connections, which is the integrating apparatus. The higher reptiles have somewhat larger and more complicated cortex, but in none of them is there any considerable advance from the simple structure just described.

At the transition from reptiles to mammals in the Triassic period another advance step was taken. The cortex was greatly expanded, more separately localized sensory and motor areas were differentiated, and the amount of associational tissue was greatly increased by thickening of the cortex and its more complicated stratification, with several layers of cells and fibers. In the lower and earlier mammals (monotremes and marsupials), the olfactory areas of the cortex were the first to enlarge. As shown both by casts of fossilized skulls of this period and by comparison with the most primitive living mammals, the early mammals had very large hippocampal areas (archipallium), large but less differentiated piriform lobes (paleopallium), and much smaller nonolfactory cortex (neopallium). In higher mammals these relations are reversed, owing to the great increase in size of the neopallium (Fig. 4, page 372). In all mammals the piriform area retains strong olfactory connections. The hippocampal area has extensive olfactory connections in amphibians and reptiles; but in mammals these are reduced and in primates they are almost eliminated. The final step in cortical evolution, at the advent of the genus Homo, was marked by rapid expansion of the associational apparatus of the neopallial cortex.

The essential features of the successive steps in the evolution of the brain are now well known because fortunately there are living representatives of each stage in the existing fauna, and the fossil record is complete enough to enable the paleontologists to determine the relationships of these living representatives to their extinct ancestors and to reconstruct the main lines of phylogenetic development during the whole period of vertebrate evolution. Although no fossilized brains have been preserved, casts of the skull cavities of extinct vertebrates show many instructive details of the size and shape of the brains which originally occupied those cavities. Furthermore, in the embryological development of human and other higher brains the most significant steps of this evolutionary history are recapitulated in recognizable stages.

The fossil record shows that primitive reptiles, now extinct, were the ancestors from which two lines of progressive evolution diverged. One of these lines leads to the present birds, the other to the mammals. In the higher reptiles the stem portion of the cerebral hemisphere (corpus striatum complex) is enormously enlarged and the cortical part, although larger than in the more primitive turtles, nevertheless retains its reptilian simplicity of structure. In the mammals, on the contrary, the stem portion of the hemisphere is diminished to less than the reptilian size and complexity and the cortex is greatly enlarged and diversified, progressively so as we pass from lower to higher species of mammals.

The bodies of birds are more highly specialized than are those of any mammals, and their behavior is far more complicated than that of any reptiles. Their cerebral hemispheres are larger than those of reptiles, but their cortex is less differentiated. In some species the cortex is so far reduced as to be scarcely recognizable. Why is this? The answer is found in the internal structure of the hemispheres and the correlated behavior.

The birds' cerebral hemispheres are composed almost entirely of the enormously enlarged corpora striata, which are concerned almost exclusively with stereotyped reflex and instinctive behavior. Birds, like insects, are very successful animals. The number of species is large and the several species are adapted to a wide range of environments. They mark the culmination of an evolutionary trend of very distinctive nature, characterized by highly elaborated instinctive and emotional behavior, a type of action system essentially thalamo-striatal rather than cortical, with a rather low order of intelligence.

Mammalian evolution shows a trend in a different direction—toward increasing adaptability and educability of the individuals along with diversification of species. In the more primitive surviving mammals these capacities are not outstanding, but they nevertheless possess larger and more complicated cortical tissue than any sub-mammalian groups, with potentialities for further development that are practically unlimited. This cortical gray expanded very rapidly during mammalian evolution and with accelerated speed when the hominids surged forward in a direction different from that taken by their primate relatives.

The evolutionary trends which have reached their highest expressions in avian and mammalian behavior, though differing radically in method and final patterns, have this in common: both mark the highest points yet reached in the process of cephalization, that is, the integrative control of all bodily activities from a single center of dominance which faces forward toward further advance in the same direction.

Those parts of the human brain which regulate the clear-cut intelligent and esthetic components of our behavior developed late in the phylogenetic history of the race and in the embryology of the individual. They do not replace the pre-existing nervous system that successfully executes complicated reflex and instinctive activities but are added to these more primitive nervous organs, using them and supplementing them in such a way as to extend the range of successful adjustment and give it a flexibility that the more rigidly stereotyped reflexes and instincts lack.

Summary

Cortex is extensive in the cerebellum and the cerebral hemispheres. The functions of the cerebellar cortex are administrative, regulating the execution of movements the patterns of which are determined elsewhere. The cerebral cortex is the supreme arbiter of intentionally controlled conduct. When the evolution of the cortex is reviewed, the history of its progressive differentiation sheds some light upon the significance of the complicated structure of the human brain.

Two physiological factors have co-operated in shaping the course of this differentiation: (1) increase in the number and specificity of ascending and descending projection fibers passing between the cortical field and lower centers of the brain stem; (2) progressive elaboration of the intrinsic associational apparatus within the cortex itself. The first factor refines the analysis of sensory and motor experience; the second factor is integrative.

The turtles have the simplest typical cortical structure seen in any animals now living. They have three primary cortical fields: (1) the hippocampus (achipallium), concerned with olfactory-visceral functions; (2) the piriform lobe (paleopallium), with olfactory-somatic functions; (3) the neopallium, with non-olfactory functions. This basic pattern is preserved in all higher brains, with, in the human brain, extraordinary complication of each of the three primary cortical fields.

CHAPTER THIRTY

The Structure of the Cortex

Comparative anatomy and physiology

The enormous amount of descriptive detail about the structure and physiological properties of the brains of many kinds of animals from fishes to men was for a long time a mass of heterogeneous facts of uncertain significance. This confusion was due in part to the inadequacy of the methods of study available and too often to erroneous preconceptions which closed the mind to the real meaning of the observed facts. During the last few decades these obstacles have been so far overcome that progress has been rapid and the prospect of further advance is heartening.

The broad outlines of the history of the evolutionary development of the brain are now well known. The general trend of events in the history of the evolution of behavior has also been observed and recorded. The correlation of these two series of facts which would reveal the nervous mechanisms employed by the various patterns of behavior is well advanced only with respect to the simpler reflex and instinctive factors.

It is obvious that the behavior of different kinds of animals is closely correlated with differences in their equipment of sense organs and of the organs of motor response. The corresponding differences in the internal structure of the brains of these animals have been accurately described; but we have few reliable data about the correlation of animal intelligence with the corresponding nervous apparatus.

[384]

One difficulty is that we have no generally accepted standards for measuring animal intelligence. Another complication arises from the fact that the internal texture of the brains of animals of the same species varies within so wide limits that what constitutes the normal or typical structural pattern for the species cannot be accurately described. It is, accordingly, difficult to determine whether any of the observed differences are correlated with any learned patterns of behavior. Unfortunately this individual variability of histological structure is more pronounced in the cerebral cortex than in other parts of the brain. Lashley, who has contributed the most exact information on this subject, concludes ('47) that "individual variation in brain structure within a species is of the same kind and often equal in extent to that between species." This is most conspicuously true in the human species. The differences between the average size and shape of brains of different races of men fall well within the limits of the individual variations within each race. These differences can be observed and measured.

From the behaviorist's standpoint, the ratio of the mass of the cerebral cortex and parts immediately dependent upon it to the total weight of the brain is of special interest. It is obvious from simple inspection that the relative mass of the cortex corresponds in a general way with the grade of learning capacity and intelligent behavior. This is graphically illustrated by the difference in the relative sizes of the cerebral hemispheres of a man and a kangaroo of about equal body weights, as shown in Figure 6 (page 374). But it is very difficult to quantify these correlations.

The learning processes are especially favorable for such studies. It is clear that learning capacity increases progressively from lower to higher mammals and that this increase is dependent upon enlargement and especially upon structural differentiation of the cortex. Among the lower mammals the behavior and correlated cerebral structure of the rat have been most thoroughly studied. Similar studies of other animals, and especially of monkeys and apes, reveal the successive steps in the elaboration of more learning ability and more intelligent behavior. A few examples of the results of these studies are cited below.

These studies of learning, intelligence, and the correlated bodily organs of subhuman animals have brought to light many fundamental principles; but, because human mentation and the human brain are different from those of all other animals, no amount of observation and experimentation on these other animals can fully elucidate the problems that are of primary interest to physicians, psychologists, and sociologists.

It has been mentioned (page 326) that the brains of the lemurs and other lower primates are small and no more highly differentiated than are those of the lower members of other mammalian orders. In primate evolution the progressive enlargement of the brain was relatively rapid and this was due almost entirely to increase in the amount of cerebral cortex. This increase was accelerated with unprecedented rapidity when the manlike apes stepped down from the trees, assumed an erect posture, and separated their way of life from that of the other anthropoids.

There is evidence that these changes in the structure of the body and the shift from arboreal to terrestrial habitat were not initiated by an increase in the size and internal complexity of the cortex, but that, on the contrary, the cortical differentiation followed changes in the skeletal and muscular systems in adaptation to the changed patterns of behavior. The ape became a biped before he became a man.

Measurements of the skull capacity of fossil apes and men show that during the preceding million years there has been a progressive increase in the size of the brain from an apelike ancestor to modern man (Connolly, '50; Thrapp, '50; Clark, '50, 55; Watson, '53; Howells, '54). The protohuman ape men of South Africa had skull capacity from 600 to 850 cubic centimeters. The very primitive fossil man of Java, Pithecanthropus erectus, had average skull capacity of about 860 cc. (with range from 775 to 900 cc.) The Peking man, Sinanthropus, had a larger brain, the average of about forty specimens being 1,075 cc. Most of these estimates are based on fragmentary remains and may require revision. The skulls of existing chimpanzees have capacities of 350 to 400 cc., and the large gorillas have capacities of 400 to 600 cc. The average capacity of the skulls of American males now living is about 1,450 cc.

Man has the largest brain of all living animals except the whale and the elephant and the highest brain: body-weight ratio except for the very small marmoset, Hapale. But the human brain is so variable that mere size within the genus Homo seems to bear no relation to intelligence. There are reliable records which show that different people whose brains varied from 800 cc. to 2,200 cc. were regarded as normal. High intellectual ability does not require an unusually large brain, as shown by comparison of Anatole France with a brain of 1,100 cc. and Jonathan Swift with a brain of 2,200 cc. The size of the brain is exceedingly variable among all species of primates, and in mankind this variability is so great that few significant correlations have been established in a normal population between brain weight and racial differences or individual differences in mental capacity.

The human cortex

A vast amount of information about the gross and microscopic structure of the human cortex has been recorded, but our knowledge of how this complicated mechanism actually operates as the arbiter of human conduct and human cultural evolution is pitifully scanty. Summaries of present knowledge are given in the books by von Bonin ('50), Penfield and Rasmussen ('50), Jeffress ('51), and Eccles ('53).

Unquestionably, racial and individual differences in mental capacities and attitudes are correlated with corresponding differences in the bodily organization. It is only a question of learning how to find them. Most of these distinctive features are concealed in the internal histological texture of the body and its chemical properties and so are quite independent of the size and external shape of the brain. There is, however, some inconclusive evidence that brains of geniuses in music, mathematics, and other special skills do show characteristic enlargement of the parts of the cortex primarily concerned with these abilities. The left hemisphere is slightly larger in right-handed people and the right hemisphere in the left-handed, and there are corresponding differences in the surface markings of the two hemispheres.

It can, I think, be predicted that, when the brains of a sufficient number of men whose life histories show that they were unusually gifted in well-defined ways are adequately described, some recognizable structural features can be correlated with these distinctive mental capacities. This examination should include the surface configuration of the brain, the histological texture of the cortex, and the patterns of the related nervous connections.

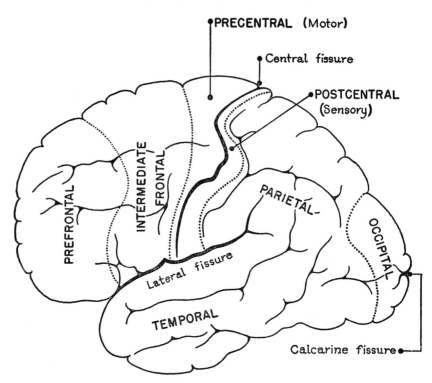

Fig. 9.—Lateral aspect of the left cerebral hemisphere of the human brain, showing a few of the fissures (full lines) and (dotted lines) the boundaries of the chief regions as defined by Bailey and von Bonin ('51).

The arrangement of the fissures and the convolutions which they separate is not the same in any two brains or on opposite sides of the same brain. There are, however, a few stable landmarks, of which the most obvious are the lateral fissure (of Sylvius) and the central fissure (of Rolando). The calcarine fissure, most of which is visible only on the medial surface of the hemisphere, is another useful landmark. Figure 9 shows the position of these three fissures and also of a few others that are less constant. The dotted lines of this diagram mark the approximate boundaries of the lobes of the cortex as defined by Bailey and von Bonin ('51). These lobes are characterized by distinctive patterns of internal cortical structure and of subcortical connections. The major regions here designated are given different names and somewhat different boundaries by other neurologists, depending on the criteria used.

Recorded measurements of the total superficial area of the cortex of both hemispheres vary from 1,877 to 2,895 square centimeters. Much of this variation is probably due to differences in methods of preparation and measurement. The average area of the human cortex is about four times that of an ape of the same size. About half of this cortex is concealed from view in the fissures, including the great median longitudinal fissure between the hemispheres. A large part of the precentral (motor) and the postcentral (sensory) projection areas is concealed within the central fissure. Most of the visual projection area is concealed in the calcarine fissure. The insula (island of Reil) is a large cortical area in the floor of the lateral fissure, with most of the auditory projection area concealed in the lower wall of the fissure. The large hippocampal formation is buried under the temporal lobe.

Great labor has been expended upon the effort to subdivide the cortex further according to distinctive patterns of arrangement of the nerve cells and fibers; but the various observers apply different criteria and their maps of the cortical areas are all different. Furthermore, these patterns of histological structure are extremely variable in normal brains, and most of the small cortical areas which have been named or numbered have no constant structural features or functional significance. There are some exceptions to this rule, to be mentioned immediately.

Brodmann published a series of maps of cortical areas based on the cellular structure of the cortex, one of which is here reproduced (Figure 10). Although the boundaries of most of these areas are arbitrary and probably meaningless, Brodmann's numbers are so often mentioned in the literature that his diagram may be used as a convenient chart of the cortical surface for descriptive purposes.

A few of Brodmann's areas have well-established functional significance, notably four of the projection centers. These are the somesthetic areas 1, 2, and 3; the visual area 17; the auditory area 41;

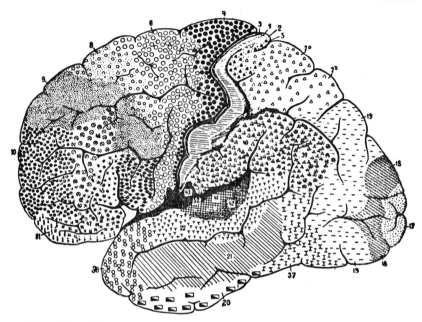

Fig. 10.—The same cerebral hemisphere as in Figure 9, showing the cortical areas which were mapped and numbered by Brodmann. Copied from one of his diagrams. From Bailey and von Bonin ('51).

and the motor area 4. The localization of other cortical functions presents problems of great difficulty which are discussed in Chapter 32.

The web of cortical tissue

The complexity of human cortical structure baffles analysis and the half of this complexity has not yet been seen, for presently available methods of study can reveal only its coarser features. Three of the methods of preparation in common use show details of the arrangement of cells, their various shapes, and the related nerve fibers as illustrated in Figure 11. These diagrams of the postcentral sensory area are much simplified and one of the complications not shown here is the fact that all the cell bodies pictured are embedded in a dense mat of neuropil composed of very thin naked fibers. This neuropil of the human cortex resembles that of the frog shown in Figure 2 (page 249). A small area of this neuropil in the precentral motor area is shown at B of Figure 12. The clear circles mark the

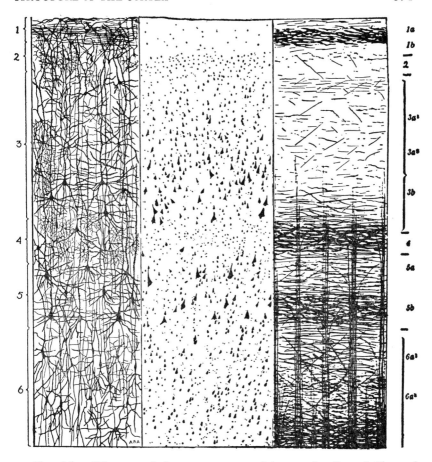

Fig. 11.—Diagram of the arrangement of layers of cells and fibers of the human postcentral cortex. At the left are cells as shown by the Golgi method; in the middle, cells shown by the Nissl method; at the right, nerve fibers shown by the Weigert method. From Bailey and von Bonin ('51).

positions of the unstained cell bodies. At the right of this area the two fibers, *a* and *b*, illustrate the way the incoming fibers branch to form the neuropil. Figure 13 is a detail drawn at higher magnification showing how the fibers of the neuropil are closely wrapped around the cortical cells. Every contact of a fiber with a cell is a synaptic junction (page 262). Some recent studies of the physiology of this structure are summarized by Eccles ('53, chap. 7).

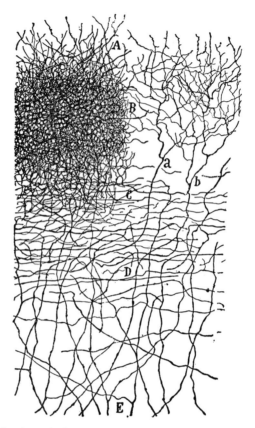

Fig. 12.—Section of the motor cortex, illustrating the free endings of incoming fibers (a and b). These fibers form a very dense neuropil, shown at B, which closely envelops the (unstained) cell bodies as illustrated in Figure 13. Golgi method. After Ramón y Cajal.

The cells are arranged in more or less well-defined layers, and in most parts of the cortex six layers are usually recognized and numbered as shown in Figure 11. There is no evidence that cortical nerve cells differ fundamentally from those of other parts of the brain physically, chemically, or physiologically. The distinctive features of the cerebral cortex are the patterns of arrangement of the cells and fibers and the momentarily changing patterns of functional connections among them.

It has been estimated that the human cortex contains more than

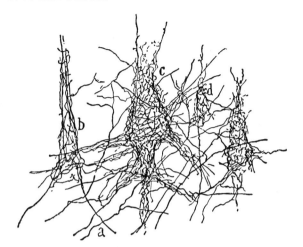

Fig. 13.—Section of the same area of cortex shown in Figure 12, drawn on a larger scale. The incoming fibers (a) form a closely woven feltwork around the cell bodies (unstained) of the pyramidal neurons (b, c, d). Golgi method. After Ramón y Cajal.

10,000,000,000 nerve cells. An estimate by Shariff ('53) gives a smaller number, about 7,000,000,000. Each of these cells is in functional connection with many others by branching nerve fibers, some of which may reach remote parts of both the same and the opposite cerebral hemisphere. A single cell may receive as many as a hundred terminals of these fibers from various sources, and the nervous activity excited by them may be discharged to many near and distant cortical areas or to subcortical regions extending through the brain stem and spinal cord.

In the attempt to get some conception of the number of possible functional connections among these millions of cortical cells, I asked several competent mathematicians to give me the answer to this simplified version of the problem: If one million cortical cells were connected with one another in groups of only two and each of these groups were connected with other similar groups in all possible ways, what would be the total number of such connections? The answers varied widely, for evidently these experts formulated the problem differently. The answers given were all very large numbers, expressed by 10 with an exponent of many thousands. In my published statement ('26, p. 5) I chose the largest of the numbers given by these computations, viz., $10^{2,783,000}$. If this number were written out in figures, it would take about two thousand pages of an ordinary book to print it. In view of the comments which this statement provoked, I now think that it is not expedient to publish any specific answer to the problem without a detailed explanation of the calculations employed.

These numbers, though inconceivably large, are probably smaller than the functional connections that are potentially available in the brain. The known structure of the retina confirms this supposition. McCulloch (Frank *et al.*, '48, p. 265) reports that the eye contains more than a hundred million photoreceptors, and that messages from these are transmitted from the retina to the lateral geniculate body of the brain by about one million fibers of the optic nerve. He says further that, in view of the complicated structure of the retina (which has been described in detail by Polyak, '41), this means that the eye can exist in $2^{100,000,000}$ states, each of which corresponds to a unique distribution of stimulation. The structure of the cerebral cortex is far more complicated than is that of the retina.

If these numbers are compared with those given by some astronomical calculations, they are vastly larger. It is, for example, estimated by competent authority (Shapley, '45) that the total weight of the sidereal universe is of the order of 10^{55} grams, a mass which comprises more than 10^{75} atoms, chiefly of hydrogen. These figures, of course, are approximations based on what is now visible.

Returning to the human cortex, we may safely say that its known structure provides for momentarily shifting patterns of nervous conduction in variety that is practically unlimited. Probably the majority of the cortical nerve cells are directly or indirectly connected with every cortical field. This is the structural apparatus of cortical associational processes. Of course, in any particular mental act only a very small proportion of these elements is actually involved, but as patterns of association change from moment to moment any particular cortical cell may be repeatedly activated in different combinations with others. The number of such patterns of intercellular connection that are activated during a brief mental process, such as deciding whether to spend a holiday in the country or in the office on urgent business, is so large that it is futile to try to express it in figures.

There is plenty of mechanism in the cortex, but no one has yet been able to offer even a plausible working hypothesis to explain just how this apparatus operates when consciousness emerges, or how the mechanical principles of conscious cerebration differ from those of the unconscious processes.

Summary

In both evolutionary and embryological development the cerebral cortex matures later than any other part of the brain. Its mass relative to the total mass of the brain increases progressively from lower to higher mammals and this increase is correlated with increase in learning capacity and intelligent behavior. The enlargement of the primate cortex was rapidly accelerated at the transition from ape to man, and this acceleration did not precede but followed the bodily changes associated with the erect posture.

Study of weights and measurements of the human brain and its parts reveals no features which can be safely correlated with racial differences. Racial and individual differences in mental capacity evidently depend more upon differences of internal texture and patterns of physiological connections among the nervous elements than upon the size and external configuration of the brain.

The internal texture of the cortex is inconceivably complicated, and methods of study now available reveal only the coarser features of this structure. This is why so little is known about the mechanical principles of both the unconscious and the conscious cortical functions.

CHAPTER THIRTY-ONE

Some General Functions of the Cortex

The cortex is a facilitating mechanism

The cerebral cortex never works independently of the more primitive structures from which it was derived. It is tied to all parts of the brain stem by elaborate systems of fibers, some of which transmit nervous impulses to the cortex and others from it, so that practically all lower centers are in reciprocal nervous connection with the cortex and are under more or less direct cortical control. This means that the cortex is not an autonomous field of operations, but rather a central integrating agency for all bodily functions. In short, it is a facilitating mechanism. This is an over-all function of the cortex as a whole, and probably it was the primary function at the beginning of its evolutionary history. This facilitation takes an amazing variety of forms in the higher animals, but always it is in evidence in one way or another.

In the human brain all parts of the cortex have enormous reserves of potential that may be released as needed, and apparently the large hippocampal formation is a reservoir of nonspecific potential energy that may be drawn upon for reinforcement and facilitation of a large variety of cortical functions, especially those of the visceral and emotional series. It is suggested by Arnot ('52) that the frontal lobes have a similar persistence or sustaining function for all voluntary actions. This facilitation mechanism is always in action through systems of circuits which include complicated feed-back apparatus

[396]

involving factors of both activation and inhibition. Mary Brazier ('48, '52) in concise summaries cites some of the relevant literature. The phylogenetic history of the hippocampus is instructive in this connection.

At the inception of cortical differentiation in fishes and amphibians the entire cerebral hemisphere was dominated by the olfactory system and the cortex emerged as a specialization within this field (page 376). The subsequent history of the evolution of the cortex shows an interesting series of changes in the olfactory connections of the cortex which I described in 1933. The salient features of this series are illustrated in Figure 4 (page 372). These diagrams show that in reptiles most of the cortex has olfactory connections and in primitive mammals far more than half of the cortex (piriform lobe and hippocampus) is under olfactory influence, directly or indirectly. In the human brain, on the contrary, the olfactory part of the piriform lobe (uncus) is reduced to insignificant size and the hippocampus, although large, has a scarcely recognizable olfactory component.

The explanation of these peculiar changes in the composition of the cortex is found in the fact that in all animals the sense of smell has two quite different functions. First, it is a specific modality of sense employed in feeding, mating, and the avoidance of enemies. Second, it exerts a nonspecific facilitating action upon other cerebral functions. All cortex has great reserves of potential energy, and these are massively developed in the hippocampus of the lower mammals. In primates the cortical reserves are enlarged and all cortex has increased facilitating efficiency. The hippocampus, which was originally an olfactory field, is here devoted to nonspecific facilitation of other activities, although some indirect olfactory connections are retained. The facilitation to which reference is made here includes both reinforcement and inhibition in reciprocal balanced relations. This hypothesis is supported by the experimental studies of Kaada ('51) and by much subsequent research.

In the course of evolution, as the facilitating mechanism of the cortex is enlarged, its analytic components are progressively more sharply localized in mosaic patterns (the projection centers), and the integrative functions are also more or less clearly segregated regionally, as explained in the next following chapter. During the course of this evolutionary development the amount of cortex is progressively increased, because the more complicated cortical functions require an increase in the number of nervous elements and in the intricacy of their interconnections. At the transition from ape to man this increase was very rapid. The earliest known fossil remains of Homo sapiens (as distinguished from other species of the genus Homo now extinct) have a skull capacity as great as that of modern man, and these primitive men probably had as many nerve cells in the brain as we do. Subsequent advance in mental efficiency involved changes in cortical texture rather than increase in its mass.

The weight of the average adult human brain is about 1,360 grams (48 ounces), and the range of variation extends from 200 to more than 2,000 grams. People with brains weighing less than 500 grams have lived to old age, though their intelligence was subnormal. Some of the most capable men the world has known had very small brains.

We know very little about the differences in internal texture which are correlated with specific types of mental capacity and why a small brain may provide mental competence far superior to a big one; but we do know that every normal human brain has great reserves of facilitating capacity and that the efficiency of one's behavior depends very largely upon the use that is made of these reserves. As William James pointed out long ago, much human failure is due to the fact that most people do not use half the brain power with which they are endowed. There is plenty of mechanism available and vast reserves that are never drawn upon except perhaps in explosive emotional outbursts without rational control. A graphic illustration of the availability of these reserves is the observation of Nicholson ('20), who found that a subject in complete muscular exhaustion, if hypnotized and given suggestion of muscular strength, could instantly recover his full muscular power.

The survival of our advanced cultures depends on more intelligent use of these reserves. For this we need skilled guidance, especially in the formative preadolescent years. Our present disorders and futilities can be permanently ameliorated only by educational programs that are more wisely administered than most of those now provided.

The history of civilization is a record of slow but dramatic enrichment of human life interspersed with episodes of wanton destruction of all the accumulated riches of property and spiritual values. These episodic reversions to bestiality seem to be increasing in virulence and in the magnitude of the resulting disasters until now we are threatened with the loss of everything that has been won in our struggle for the better life.

In view of this record it has been suggested that the enlargement of the human brain has gone so fast and so far that the result is actually pathological. Normal behavior depends upon the preservation of a balanced interplay between integrating and disintegrating factors and between the total pattern and local partial patterns. So, it is claimed, the human cortex is a sort of tumorous overgrowth that has got so big that its functions are out of normal control and "race" erratically like a steam engine that has lost its governor.

This ingenious theory was published by Morley Roberts and quoted with apparent approval by Wheeler ('28, p. 46). Their arguments seem to be plausible in view of the past history of wars, revolutions, and crumbled empires, and the present world-wide turmoil that threatens total destruction of civilization. But the theory is neurological nonsense. The evolution of brains—of all brains, human the same as the others—has gone on for a long time normally and on the whole progressively, if by progress we mean an increment of biological values. Our present crisis has not been thrust upon us by inexorable fate, by pathological deterioration of all the brains of the human race. There are plenty of healthy and vigorous brains that are competent to carry on constructive programs of industry, government, science, art, and literature. It is only a question of learning how to use what we have successfully.

There is no incurable organic defect in the mechanism of our culture, by which I mean the human brains that devise policies and the appropriate ways to carry them out. The defect is "functional" in the sense that the psychiatrist uses this term. A functional disease, of course, has an organic basis, and many "organic" things can be done to ameliorate social disorders. The people can be assured of adequate subsistence, housing, honest government, educational facilities, and so on. But these things do not constitute the core of our present distress.

The world is suffering from an endemic psychoneurosis, some symptoms of which are personal maladjustments, social disorder, race prejudice, political opportunism, and international conflict. Permanent cure cannot be effected by treatment of these symptoms. The basic cause lies in the minds of the individual people—a failure to strike a workable balance between personal profits of various sorts and the social responsibilities and obligations which must be met if any profit at all is to be realized. These clearly are moral issues, and public morals are contingent upon the morals of individual people. Our civilization is doomed unless there is an immediate revolutionary change in the moral standards and practices of our people, a determination to subordinate personal and national interests to the general welfare and to demand that our representatives in government observe the same code of social comity. These defects are curable. We know the remedy. It is simple and obtainable by everybody without price—simply an honest effort to do to others as we would have them do to us.

What if we fail, as we surely shall if present suicidal policies of personal and national self-seeking aggressiveness are continued? Will the human race then go the way of the dinosaurs and perish from off the face of the earth? This possibility I think can be ruled out. I have faith in humanity. If the present dominant powers fail to make good and destroy themselves because they cannot keep the peace with one another, there will still remain many other people who are endowed with just as good brains and whose culture is now retarded simply for lack of opportunity. Given the chance, these marginal populations may rise to the opportunity, develop a culture of different pattern, and perhaps do a better job of it. It is certain that many of the retarded people of our present population are capable of doing this, for some of them have already done it. It has taken only a few generations for some of the indigenous people of New Zealand and the Hawaiian and other Pacific islands to acquire abilities quite as good as those of their European neighbors. Negroes of central Africa have taken academic degrees on a par with the other students of European universities. Scores of other instances might be cited.

Signs, signals, codes, and symbols

All animals use specific external or internal events as signs which serve as triggers to activate the particular apparatus which gives the appropriate response. The prick of a thorn is immediately followed by an avoiding reaction. Such a sign may also excite a response which serves as a signal to other members of the group, that is, a means of communication.

A mother hen sees the shadow of a hawk drifting across her field of view and utters a warning call (a signal) that brings the brood to the shelter of her wings. The call may be repeated at every recurrence of the visible sign, and this implies that in both the hen and the chicks there is a stable configuration of some kind—a neurogram —which is attuned to respond to the appropriate sign. The use of the signal—the warning call—does not necessarily imply anything more than differential sensitivity to the sign, such as is seen in many artificial mechanisms, an automatic burglar alarm, for instance.

In subhuman animals the apparatus of these signs and signals is usually a genetically preformed structural arrangement which is common to all members of the species or race. Insects, birds, and mammals show a great variety of gestures and sounds of warning or allurement to communicate with others of the group. These signs and signals involve a simple sort of abstraction of particular items from mixed experience and this is always present experience. In higher animals some conditioned reflexes and other learned patterns of behavior may operate in a similar way, and this provides the organic substrate for the elaboration of symbols.

A symbol, as this word is used in the study of behavior, differs from the sign and signal in one important respect, namely, by the addition of a device for the preservation of a more or less enduring acquired neurogram of the sign or signal and the resulting behavior. This pattern is stored in some as yet unknown way and it is subject to recall when the appropriate trigger is pulled. It is, accordingly, an abstraction of higher order than the signal. This primitive type of organic memory is not bound to present experience but is preserved as such and so serves as a record of that experience. All this may go on below the level of awareness, or a conscious factor may also be present.

Symbols, like signs and signals, are coded in accordance with some system so that the nervous impulses are canalized in patterns adapted to activate the appropriate muscles in the proper sequence. In human psychoneural processes some of the symbols employed and codified are recognized subjectively as words, propositions, or mental images of other sorts. Others never emerge to the level of awareness. The bodily mechanisms employed have not been identified and described, but some of the successive steps in the development of this ability can be observed in behavior.

Symbols and the nervous apparatus employed are fabricated personally by every individual. There is no clear evidence that any symbolism is heritable, although the amazingly efficient system of communication among honeybees presents some interesting problems (Kroeber, '52). That symbols and codes can be used unconsciously is evidenced by the fact that they are so used in the electronic computing machines and the further fact that there is good evidence that symbols of some sort are used by subhuman animals. It is generally assumed that the ability to make and use symbols is a distinctively human capacity, but there is no room for doubt that symbols of more primitive type are used by some other animals.

A rat can generalize by abstracting similars from heterogeneous experience at a higher level than any bird is able to do. Under experimental conditions a rat can be taught to discriminate between squares and triangles, between any square and any triangle regardless of size, illumination, or arrangement of the objects. This is a learned behavior, and it is apparently a genuine abstraction of two geometric forms from the mixed experience of the training situation, not merely a response to a sign pointing to a particular feature of it. The forms presented by the trainer may differ in a variety of ways, and the rat learns to pick out from all of the objects seen one characteristic which is common to all squares, another which is common to all triangles, and to discriminate between the qualities so abstracted. After prolonged training, the rat learns to make this discrimination immediately. Some sort of a symbol must be employed, a symbol which

Hebb would call a concept; but I prefer to give the latter word a different connotation (page 360).

In this situation the rat acts as if he knows what he is doing, but we cannot discover just what he knows. There is no evidence that he has formed the concept of triangularity or has mental symbols for "triangle" and "square." He certainly makes no use of such symbols comparable with that so cleverly done by Euclid, and yet some simpler form of symbolism seems to be requisite for the behavior observed.

The adult man goes further and coins a word which may be written and so gives his mental symbol objectively recognizable corporeal form and endurance. Clearly the rat's learned behavior is a step toward the human kind of symbolic or semantic thinking, and it is probable that the rat does some thinking in terms of analysis of immediate sensorimotor experience and motor impulse with an emotional drive.

This behavior implies the presence of an enduring neurogram. The rat's neurogram differs from that of the bird in that it is not an inheritance common to all members of the species. It is an individual acquisition. It is made by the rat and it perishes with him. The rat's ability to generalize the difference between squares and triangles is a cortical function, and the hen cannot do this because no bird has sufficiently well-developed cerebral cortex to make the necessary analysis and generalization of the experiences had. The sorting mechanism is too simple to make the necessary discriminations.

In the process of formation of the rat's neurogram there is more or less enduring structural change which is colligated with a change in behavior. The behavioral change is not caused by the neurogram, nor is the neurogram caused by the behavior. The two changes are inseparably integrated in the causal situation, and if both are known either one may be taken as the symbol or token of the other. The electronic computing machine, to which reference is made below, may do a similar thing with radically different instrumentation, and here the engineer understands the process of sorting and generalization and the mechanical principles of the operation. The generalizations made by the artifical machine and the trained rat may be the same, but the engineering principles of the rat's operations are still unknown. The machine probably has no awareness of what it is doing. In the case of the rat, his sensations and emotions may introduce variables that are absent in the machine; but some basic similarities of the two operations are not affected by these variables. In fact, the machine too sometimes exhibits frustration tantrums that in a rat would be called neuroses.

A man can go further with the process of abstraction than can either the machine or the rat, but only at a higher level of integration where conscious control enters as an indispensable factor. An acquired abstraction which takes the form of an idea which can be symbolized in words, pictures, or other physical media has an endurance which may outlast the neurogram which originally embodied it. The verbal symbol may be used by the individual as a tool in all subsequent thinking processes, and it may also be spoken and written and so incorporated into the permanent structure of the culture of which the individual is a member. This is the most important distinction between human cultures and the social aggregates of other animals.

Because we do not yet know the details of the operation of the nervous mechanisms which generate ideas, it is not possible to give an objective description of the process. Accordingly, we cannot use the neurogram as the symbol of the idea; but, if the idea or concept is formulated in words, propositions, mathematical formulas, or in any other stable patterned form, then this expression becomes the symbol of the idea. As such it can be used without utterance by the thinker instrumentally in his own private mental exercises; and in addition to this it can be uttered and so publicized. In the latter case, the symbol becomes an object of regard which can have enduring objective existence as a medium of communication and social adjustment. The ability to generalize at the conceptual level is man's most distinctive attribute, though vague precursors of it have been recognized in the great apes. Mankind has this capacity because of the differentiation of a specifically human kind of cerebral cortex. For further consideration of the behavioral significance of signals and symbols see Dewey and Bentley ('49); for the so-called language of bees see Kroeber (52).

Summary

The cerebral cortex is primarily a facilitating apparatus with enormous reserves of potential energy which may be drawn upon as occasion demands for reinforcement and regulation of almost every kind of bodily activity. In the higher animals it is also a storehouse of a vast collection of records of past experience which are preserved in the form of some as yet unknown enduring change in the setup of the patterns of cortical activity. These hypothetical "engrams" or "neurograms" are the organic basis of memory.

The cortex as the supreme integrator of all bodily activities employs a type of integrating apparatus which is unique. It differs from that of the phylogenetically older brain stem in the use made of codes and symbols in successive hierarchies of increasing complexity. Some of the steps of this evolutionary development can be recognized behavioristically. At the culmination of this development in the human brain some of these symbols can be recognized subjectively as ideas that can be manipulated mentally. They can also be expressed overtly in words or otherwise and so communicated to other people. This ability to communicate with others through the medium of spoken or written words, pictures, and other objective symbols is the basic factor of man's superiority over all other living creatures.

CHAPTER THIRTY-TWO

Localization of Cerebral Functions

The nature of the problem

From the earliest times of which we have record search has been active for the organs of the body that do mental work. Solomon said that "wisdom resteth in the heart" and compassion resides in the bowels. The oldest extant Egyptian medical document assigned mental functions to the brain, as did Plato, but Aristotle thought that the brain was merely a refrigerating apparatus for cooling the blood and that intelligence was a function of the heart. In recent time T. H. Pear said, "Skill is muscular knowledge," and W. B. Cannon wrote a book about "the wisdom of the body."

There is a modicum of truth in these ancient and modern attempts to find the organs of mentation, but what these people really localized was physiological function that plays some part in the quite different kind of process that we experience consciously. Failure to take due account of the radical difference between these two kinds of vital processes is responsible for the disquieting confusion and controversy that have always prevailed and still persist today.

At the beginning of the nineteenth century it was the prevailing opinion in scientific circles that the brain is the organ of mind and that it operates as a whole with no local differences in the functions performed. The satisfying simplicity of this doctrine was rudely challenged by the publication in 1810 of Gall and Spurzheim's fantastic phrenological charts of the localization of mythical psychological "faculties." Although there was no adequate factual basis for these fantasies, their popular appeal had one good result—impressing the fact that there is a problem of cortical localization of mental processes. For fifty more years, little advance was made toward the solution of this problem. In 1865 Broca announced that injury to the third frontal convolution of the left cerebral hemisphere resulted in disordered speech (aphasia). Subsequent examination of Broca's specimens has shown that they are worthless as evidence for his conclusions, but his announcement immediately stimulated a program of intensive study of the problems of localization which has continued into the present.

This century of intensive research began with an acrimonious controversy between the advocates of localization of specific cerebral functions and those who defended the early view that the brain tissue is physiologically equipotential, at least for learning and other higher integrative functions—a controversy which is still active in a surprising variety of contexts.

We are now in a fair way to close this debate with no award of victory to either party but an equable division of the honors between them. The solution is simple in principle, although very complicated and insecure in its application. Many details remain obscure and radical revision of some generally accepted principles of biomechanics may be necessary.

The beginning of truly scientific study of cerebral localization is usually dated in 1870 when Fritsch and Hitzig observed that electrical stimulation of particular parts of the dog's cortex uniformly resulted in movement of specific muscles of the opposite side of the body. These observations were immediately verified and extended by experiments upon many kinds of animals and by clinicopathological studies of the symptoms which result from local injury or disease of the human brain.

These studies are still going on with improved technique and they are supplemented by other methods with the help of recently devised instruments of great precision. The results are spectacularly successful in some domains of cerebral physiology and this has made possible the triumphs of the current practice of brain surgery. But in other fields, particularly those of most significance for psychiatry, the search for localization of mental functions has resulted only in confusion and contention. This is due largely to the fact that there is no agreement about what it is that we are looking for.

The problem is of great practical importance. Before beginning medical treatment the physician should know what organs are affected, where they are located, their relations to other organs, and what clinical symptoms result from their impairment. This knowledge is available in the domain of clinical neurology; but the treatment of mental diseases is still for the most part empirical and too often futile because of lack of knowledge of the organic failures responsible for them. For a long time psychiatry was set apart from the rest of medical practice as an esoteric cult that treated the mind independently of the body which generates it. This fictitious entity was a survival from primitive mythology and more recent phrenology —a ghost that still walks in many of our mental hospitals. But that era is drawing to a close. The inspiring leadership of the late Adolf Meyer, who was generally acclaimed as the Dean of American Psychiatry, guided a movement in mental medicine that now points the way toward a truly scientific psychobiology.

This revolutionary change does not carry the implication that the old distinction between "organic" and "functional" mental disorders must be discarded. All mental disease is organic in the sense that it is disordered function of bodily processes; but the bodily functions involved in mentation are different in kind from all others and a different kind of treatment may be called for.

If the organ primarily responsible for mental distress—say an ulcerated tooth or a toxic goiter—can be identified, the dentist or the surgeon may effect a cure. But our most distressing cases of mental disease are as yet known only symptomatically, and treatment of symptoms is not good medical practice. What we want to find is causes, and, if the cause of a mental disorder is not disease of some particular organ but failure to integrate the partial patterns of the several organs normally, then the treatment must be directed to this failure.

Mentation as a vital function is an integrative process and, as we have seen, the laws of integration are biologically of different order from those of the analytic processes. These two types of process, however, always work hand in hand and faulty integration may be due to a variety of causes. One kind of mental imbalance can be cured by removal of a toxic goiter or correction of a vitamin deficiency; another kind may be alleviated by mental therapy alone. The latter treatment, indeed, is applied more or less skillfully in every department of medicine, not excepting surgery. Osler taught that mental therapy—he called it "faith"—is the most potent remedy in the pharmacopoeia. The psychiatrist, like every other physician, must treat his patient as a whole and not some disembodied complex of symptoms called a "mind," and he must have at his disposal all the various kinds of treatment that have proved to be useful whether they are called organic or functional.

Two kinds of localization

In recent years the controversies between the advocates of the equipotentiality of nervous tissues and those who assign specific functions to definite locations have concerned chiefly the cerebral cortex. In the peripheral nervous system, spinal cord, and brain stem, precise localization of many functional systems of nerve cells and fibers has made successful practice of clinical neurology and neurosurgery possible. No similarly useful localization of the mental functions has been successfully made, and the chief reason for this failure lies in the fact that two radically different kinds of function are performed in the cortex. Both are localized, but the principles of localization involved are different and failure to recognize these differences has led to confusion.

This difference between two types of localization of function is not confined to the cortex. It is everywhere apparent in the contrast between the analytic and the synthetic types of vital process. The analytic functions in general are performed by fixed and stable systems of tissues in spatial patterns that are hereditary and similar (with minor variations) in all members of each animal species. The integrative functions, on the contrary, are more labile. They are defined in terms of dynamic patterns of action that persist as patterns of function but are not inflexibly bound to any fixed structural pattern. These processes are localized in space *while they are in operation*, but they may operate without significant change of pattern, using any suitable tissue structures that may be available. Both the spatial factors and the temporal factors are differently organized in the two types of process. In all biological integration both types of organization are present in varying proportions.

This contrast between two types of localization pattern may be illustrated crudely by comparison of a river system and a waterspout. The river has a definable position on the map. It is relatively stable, although not absolutely so, for it is born, it grows, and finally dies a natural death as continents are elevated and eroded. The waterspout, or its analogue on land, the whirlwind, is an evanescent structure with a definable pattern of performance which always has a locus in space, although this locus may not be the same at any two moments. It is the pattern of performance which persists for longer or shorter time and may be repeated if similar conditions recur. Both the river and the waterspout are complicated integrated structures in which the spatial and the temporal factors are differently arranged. Neither of them is absolutely stable. The stabilizing factors of the river are chiefly topographic, those of the waterspout chiefly dynamic. In a whirlpool similar factors are present in a still different balance. The dynamic pattern persists in a location permanently fixed by the surrounding topography. Analogies of these types of integration—and many others—are found in the nervous system. The variety of patterns which they may assume is unlimited, but in all cases it is important that the difference between the two basic kinds of localization be recognized.

Evolution of localization

In the most primitive nervous systems known—the simplest polyps —the nerve-net is nearly, although not quite, equipotential. Integration is effected by mutual interplay among the parts in a dynamic field. There is no brain to serve as the center of integrative dominance. There is some stable localization defined by structure, but functional localization with no fixed position in space is predominant.

In the most primitive extant vertebrates, the lampreys, there is a well-developed brain in which a simple and efficient analytic apparatus is present. Since most of the activities to be controlled are mass-movements of the entire body musculature, no highly specialized integrative apparatus is necessary and most of the tissue of the brain is a relatively undifferentiated and a relatively equipotential neuropil. As the series of vertebrates from lower to higher is passed in review, it is possible to trace the steps in the progressive differentiation of this neuropil to the culminating stage of elaboration in the human cerebral cortex. It is evident that the evolutionary process started from a relatively equipotential nervous network within which the analytic apparatus was progressively differentiated in stable structural patterns which are different in each species of animals in adaptation to the way of life and the sensory and motor equipment. Parallel with this differentiation of the analyzers, the integrative apparatus was elaborated in accordance with quite different mechanical principles.

Twenty-five years ago in a brief survey of this history ('30a) I wrote: "We have, then, two kinds of localization: (1) a known localization of stable structural elements whose functions also are known, and (2) a localization of fields within which various recurring patterns of performance, or schemata, are known to be fabricated and within which inhibition, modification, or conditioning of these patterns takes place. The first is the traditional functional localization of neurological practice as applied particularly in clinical neurology. The second is the sort of thing that is usually implicit in current diagrams of cortical localization—with very unsatisfactory results. The failures are due largely to our ignorance of cortical functions, and particularly to the futile attempts to apply the criteria of localization of rigid structural elements to the second category of locations of patterns or schemata in fields."

The evidence for these statements drawn from comparative anatomy and physiology has been given in many publications and summarized in two of my own ('42, p. 291; '48, p. 82). The nature of this evidence will be illustrated by some examples.

One general characteristic of the mental functions should not for a moment be forgotten. Mentation is a total pattern, and as such it may use any or all of the organs of the body. We feel and think all over, just as a bird flies all over. But in the bird some parts of the body are more specifically related to flight than others, and similarly in the man some organs have specific and crucial parts to play in mentation and in particular kinds of mental activity.

For evidence that the whole body participates in the thinking process one has only to watch a small child struggling with the writing of a difficult theme. His facial grimaces and the all-over wriggling tell the story very clearly. In some adults this is equally evident in more organized form in facial expression and expansive gesture during conversation and in the antics of oratorical display exhibited by many public speakers. Even when these movements are suppressed and the person maintains poker-faced immobility the body is not passive, but there is active inhibition of the muscles. It has been shown experimentally that if one thinks intently about a particular muscular movement but refrains from making the movement the oscillographic record from these muscles shows an obvious change in their electrical potential.

Each kind of mental process—whether emotional, perceptive, rational, or volitional—has its own characteristic pattern of bodily function, and the nervous and other organs concerned can be localized, some with precision and clearly defined boundaries and others only as fields of preference for particular patterns of psychophysiological function that do not require any particular pre-established arrangement of the nervous elements activated.

It has been mentioned that localization of the nonmental analytical functions of the brain stem is now well advanced. Let us now inquire how these functions and those of integrative type are localized in spatial arrangement in the cortex.

Cortical localization

The first step in the attempt to localize the functions of the cortex was careful description of the surface configuration of the human and other brains to see if gross features of the convolutions and fissures can be correlated with specific physiological or mental functions. It was found that a few of the fissures are useful landmarks. The calcarine fissure passes through the middle of the visual projection area. The lateral fissure of Sylvius marks the upper border of the auditory area, and the central fissure of Rolando separates the area of cutaneous sensibility from the motor area. But most of the other fissures are so variable in length and position that they are not trustworthy guides to the adjoining structure or functions.

Microscopic examination of the cortex reveals two sorts of variables in the space relations of the nervous elements. One is marked by differences in structure of the different regions in an arrangement that can be mapped on the surface like the pattern of a mosaic. The other is marked by differences in the structure and arrangement of the layers of nervous elements in series from the surface inward. Both the mosaic patterns and the surface-interior patterns have been described in great detail in the brains of man and many other animals. The organization of the surface-interior patterns is probably of more fundamental significance physiologically than is that of the mosaic patterns.

The evolutionary history shows that from its inception the cortex has three primary subdivisions: the hippocampus (archipallium) medially, the piriform lobe (paleopallium) laterally, and a general cortex (neopallium) dorsally. These are the original projection centers and their boundaries are well defined anatomically and physiologically. The first two have olfactory connections and the neocortex has sensory and motor areas and other functional subdivisions. The olfactory areas reach their highest development in the most primitive mammals and further differentiation in the higher mammals takes place in the neocortex (Fig. 4, page 372).

In all mammals each of the three primary subdivisions of the cortex has easily recognizable distinctive histological texture. In the human brain the primitive hippocampal and piriform areas are termed allocortex in distinction from the neocortex or the isocortex of the neopallium. On the basis of histological structure the areas of neocortex are named after their most characteristic types of nerve cells. Thus we have: (1) granular cortex (koniocortex), with abundance of very small nerve cells, which is characteristic of the sensory projection areas; (2) agranular cortex in the motor areas; (3) homotypical cortex in the intervening associational areas.

Further subdivision of the human neocortex has been made by many workers using various criteria. On the basis of histological structure alone, more than a hundred areas have been mapped and named. But the descriptions of the various authors differ widely in the number of areas recognized and the criteria by which they are distinguished. The details of structure are extremely variable in brains from normal people of a homogeneous population, and these minute subdivisions of the cortex are meaningless without more precise definition of the criteria employed and more detailed knowledge of the connections and functions of the nervous elements.

Before the maps of mosaic localization of structurally defined areas of the human cortex now in current use can be physiologically interpreted we must have adequate information about the types of cells present in each layer of each area and the near and remote fibrous connections of each type of cell. In addition to this knowledge of structure, the functions of each type of cell and of all systems of related nerve fibers must be discovered by experiment or from examination of brains of persons whose medical history shows characteristic symptoms that can be correlated with local damage of brain tissue. Experiments upon animals, especially the primates most closely related to man, give invaluable information not otherwise obtainable.

These investigations are exacting and laborious, but enough knowledge has now been won to enable the surgeon to locate the boundaries of the sensory and motor projection centers with a fair degree of precision. The nervous pathways which connect these centers with the peripheral organs of sense and of movement are now well known, and this knowledge is of the utmost importance for the diagnosis and treatment of nervous diseases. The cortical projection centers are the highest members of the analytic apparatus of the nervous system, and the localization of the cortical apparatus of analysis is all to the good; but we must not lose sight of the fact that the cortex is primarily and fundamentally an integrator and that the synthetic functions pertain to the cortex as a whole. They cannot be localized in mosaic patterns like the projection centers. The elaborate differentiation of the apparatus of analysis in the projection centers is an essential prerequisite of the human capacities for unconscious and conscious integration as these are manifested in the higher mental processes, but the mechanical principles involved are different.

Localization of cortical integrative functions

As just mentioned, the projection areas play indispensable parts in cortical integration, the koniocortex in the sensory areas, and the agranular cortex in the motor areas. Some integration is effected in all of these areas, but the higher psychoneural functions which emerge in consciousness as perception, reasoning, and intelligently directed purposive conduct require the participation of more or less of the homotypical cortex of the so-called associational areas.

It is probable that some of the simpler sensorimotor, emotional, and conative sorts of consciousness can be experienced by animals which have no cerebral cortex, but there is no room for doubt that some kind of cortical activity is essential for normal efficiency of most human mental processes. Some of our primitive emotions, however, seem to be thalamic. This is especially clear in the case of pain.

Stimulation or injury of any part of the cortex is not painful to any important extent, but irritation or disease of the thalamus may give rise to very severe pain—just pain, with no localization or other quality. Penfield and Rasmussen ('50, p. 233) conclude that the pathway of pain conduction reaches the thalamus and consciousness without essential conduction to the cortex. The cortex also participates in the nervous process involved only if the pain is referred to a particular part of the body or is in any other way interpreted. This is the usual experience, but McCulloch ('49) reports that pain may sometimes be evoked by stimulation of the appropriate area of the cortex in patients with amputated limbs who have "phantom limbs." This cortically excited pain is explained by the fact that the "phantom limb" has no existence except as a cortical (imaginary) construction.

In the surgical operations known as prefrontal lobotomy more or less of the system of fibers that connect the cortex with the brain stem is interrupted. Such operations are sometimes performed for relief of intractable pain in patients who are otherwise mentally normal. In these cases the operation does not abolish the pain, but it may reduce or completely eliminate its distressing quality. After the operation the patient may be aware of the pain if he attends to it, but ordinarily it is so undemanding that it is disregarded.

The "psychosurgical" operations of the class just mentioned (including prefrontal lobotomy, topectomy, thalamotomy, and others) have been performed on thousands of patients in mental hospitals.

They may leave the analytic functions of the brain unimpaired but abolish or alleviate certain abnormal specific patterns of integrative type. These patients rarely regain completely normal mental capacity, but the most distressing symptoms may be relieved. The functions lost depend on many factors, including the location and nature of the injury. Critical psychological analysis of the postoperative history of these cases enables the observer to correlate various sorts of mental processes with more or less specific structural arrangements of the cerebral tissues. This extensive literature is summarized in several works, including Freeman and Watts ('50), Hill ('49), Fulton ('49), Mettler ('49), Greenblatt et al. ('50), Penfield and Rasmussen ('50), Mettler et al. ('54), and (in more colloquial style) Pfeiffer ('55).

The cortical areas destroyed or partially deactivated by these operations are not organs of specific mental functions, although they seem to contain structures which are essential for the assembly of certain dynamic patterns which are characteristic of particular kinds of mental processes. The boundaries of these areas of cortical "elaboration" are rather indefinite and inconstant, and in some (if not all) of the areas the structural patterns of the nervous elements may be regarded as provision for the usual or preferential location of the nervous "assemblies" (as described on page 433) employed in these several kinds of mentation. That these functions of elaboration, or mental synthesis, are not inflexibly bound to the tissue of any particular area is shown by the inconstancy of the symptoms which result from injury or total loss of large masses of brain tissue in these areas (see the discussion of cortical fields, page 263).

The arrangement in the human brain of the projection centers and the areas of elaboration of nervous assemblies of diverse types of mental functions, so far as these can be charted in mosaic patterns on the cerebral surface, is shown in Fig. 14. The areas connected with sensory and motor projection fibers are shaded and marked with Brodmann's numbers as shown in Figure 10. The boundaries of these areas can be mapped with a fair degree of precision, although there is considerable individual variation and these boundaries fluctuate from time to time, depending on various factors of physiological state. The boundaries and functions of the large zones of elaboration

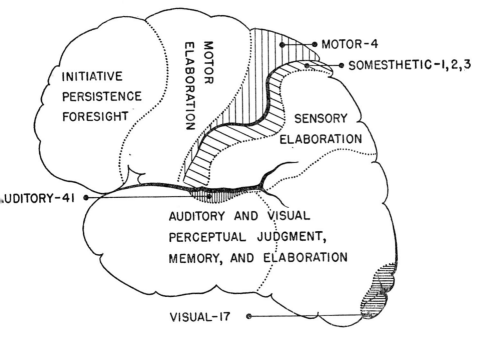

Fig. 14.—Lateral aspect of the left cerebral hemisphere drawn from the same specimen as Figures 9 and 10. The projection areas are shaded and marked with Brodmann's numbers. The areas of elaboration are designated after the descriptions of Bailey and von Bonin ('51) and Penfield and Rasmussen ('50).

cannot be so accurately given, for the functions of these areas are of different type and they are all interrelated in variable and momentarily changing ways.

Even in the motor cortex (Brodmann's area 4), mosaic localization of function is far less precise than is currently supposed. It has been shown, for example, by Glees and Cole ('50) that in the monkey the area for hand movements sends fibers of the pyramidal tract as far as the lumbar region of the spinal cord. Monkeys were trained to make specific skilled movements of the hand. After destruction of the appropriate cortical area this skill was lost. There was partial recovery of the skill, and the experiments indicate that this recovery was accomplished by use of adjoining areas of uninjured cortex.

The most convincing evidence for the conclusions expressed in
this chart is provided by oscillographic records of the changes in
electrical potential of nervous and other organs taken from living
subjects under normal and experimental conditions while the subjects are fully conscious. The surgical operations on the brain to
which reference has been made are performed under local anesthesia
which abolishes pain and yet allows the patient to tell the surgeon
what his mental experiences are during and after the operation.
These reports can then be correlated with the oscillographic records
taken from the site of the operation and simultaneously from other
parts of the brain and any other organs of the body as desired.
Since the operator can control the sensory stimulation of the subject
and the subject himself can control (to some extent) the course of
his own thoughts and feelings, a way is here opened for direct
correlation of subjective experience with bodily activity in process
and for precise localization of that activity. This is of advantage to
the patient because it gives the surgeon additional guidance during
the progress of the operation. It also gives invaluable data for scientific interpretation of the observed facts.

It is now apparent that the neurologist's maps of mosaic localization of the cerebral cortex, whether drawn in terms of recognizable
differences in cortical structure or of localization of particular functions, have value only as working tools in the search for the actual
operation of the integrative processes which the cortex performs.
These processes are circular (feed-back) reactions among the various
cortical areas and between the cortex and thalamic and other subcortical structures. Each cortical act must be viewed as part of a
larger operation considered as a dynamic equilibrated system which
is continuously active and continuously acted upon by intercurrent
influences originating outside or inside the body.

These observations on the structure and functions of the human
cortex in health and disease have been accompanied by extensive
programs of anatomical and experimental research upon the brains
of other corticated animals. Many puzzling features of the part
played by the cortex in the regulation of behavior are explained by
the evolutionary history. The course of cortical evolution and the
patterns of structure differentiated have been determined by two

physiological factors which in turn are correlated with the patterns of behavior exhibited. The first of these factors is the progressive enlargement and specialization of the systems of ascending and descending projection fibers which pass between the thalamus and hypothalamus on one hand and the pallial fields of the hemispheres on the other hand. The second factor is the correlated increase in the amount and complexity of the apparatus of correlation which is intrinsic to the cortex itself.

These two factors are so intimately related that at the earlier stages of the progressive structural differentiation of the cortex the mechanisms involved are not completely separated. There are, therefore, in these lower brains no areas which are exclusively projection centers or association centers. The projection systems and the associational systems seem to be represented in all parts of the reptilian cortex. In the generalized tortoise, Schepers ('48) recognizes about a score of more or less well-differentiated cortical areas, and their projection and associational connections are described. To this description he adds: "At the reptilian stage of evolution the telencephalon is as yet one functionally undivided whole whose component elements are integrated with one another in accordance with a simple functional pattern."

In the mammals also most of the cortex is connected with the brain stem by ascending (sensory) and descending (motor) systems of fibers. In both ascending and descending systems there are two types of conduction pathways which differ in structure and function.

The first and more primitive type of path is a chain of relatively short neurons linked together in series. The ascending path is interrupted by synapses in the reticular substance of the brain stem, and all along the way there are collateral connections for local reflexes. The descending path is a similar series of linked neurons which transmit motor impulses through the reticular substance with collateral connections there. Because of these interruptions transmission is relatively slow. The human cortex has both sensory and motor connections of this type, the motor systems having long been recognized as the so-called extrapyramidal fibers.

In addition to the primitive system of cortical connections just described, there are pathways of the second type composed of longer fibers with few synaptic interruptions and adapted for faster transmission. On the sensory side, these are the lemniscus systems, which may have only two synapses between the peripheral sense organ and the cortex. The motor side is represented by the pyramidal tract, which again may have only two or three synapses between the cortex and the muscles innervated.

The reticular substance is a continuous meshwork of nerve cells and fibers which extends from the corpus striatum throughout the brain stem and spinal cord. It serves as the central adjustor of local reflexes, and it also may be activated by terminal and collateral connections from the cortical pathways of the first type described above. Fibers of two kinds leave this reticulum. One of these descends to the lower motor centers for activation of reflexes. The other ascends to the cortex, where its fibers are widely distributed to both projection areas and association areas.

In all subhuman mammals that have been adequately studied it is seen that motor fibers descend to the reticular substance from almost all parts of the cortex. In the rat, Krieg ('47, p. 333) reports that "nearly every cortical area sends nonthalamic projection fibers to the cerebral peduncle or further." In the accompanying diagram (Figure 15), prepared by Dr. Elizabeth C. Crosby, it is shown that stimulation of many widely distributed areas of the cortex of the monkey may be followed by specific motor responses. More excitable areas are shown here than on earlier published diagrams because some of them respond only under very light anesthesia or none. The excitability of all the areas shown here has been personally verified by Dr. Crosby. The term "adversive movements" (*Adv. mov.* on the diagram) signifies generalized movements away from the side stimulated. If the motor cortex of area 4 is destroyed bilaterally, movements can still be evoked by stimulation of these cortical areas. The descending motor fibers from most of these areas have been followed to their endings in the brain stem, including many to the reticular substance.

The human cortex has not been so fully explored, but here too there is ample evidence that most of the cortex receives sensory fibers from the reticular substance and sends motor fibers into it. It follows from this that by far the larger part of the human cortex

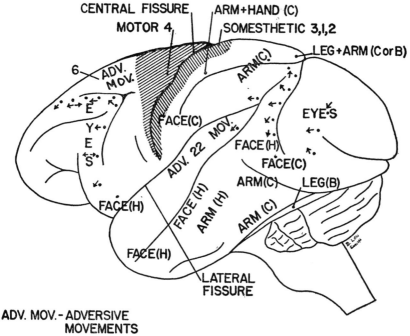

ADV. MOV.- ADVERSIVE
          MOVEMENTS

B- BILATERAL

C- CONTRALATERAL

H- HOMOLATERAL

Fig. 15.—Lateral view of the brain of the macaque monkey showing areas whose electrical excitation is followed by the bodily movements indicated. There are other excitable areas (not shown here) within the island of Reil and on the ventral and medial surfaces of the hemisphere. The Arabic numbers designate Brodmann's areas. Drawn by Dr. Elizabeth C. Crosby, to whom grateful acknowledgment is made.

has both sensory and motor functions and that all of these functions involve the interplay of widely dispersed cortical and subcortical activities. We may say that, with few exceptions, no distinctively cortical function is located exclusively in any particular place or "center." The visual projection area (number 17 of Brodmann, sometimes called the "area striata") is typical of the few exceptions. This peculiarity of the cortical associational apparatus explains many puzzling features of the aphasias and similar mental disorders. There can be no loss of sensory cortical functions without a related disturbance of motor functions.

From these facts we conclude that the cortical apparatus of motor response to sensory stimulation has two quite different parts which, however, never act independently of each other. The first part comprises the fast-acting lemniscus and pyramidal tracts and their clearly defined sensory and motor cortical projection areas. Each quality of sense is transmitted to its specific cortical projection center with a precise local sign. Here the quality, intensity, and location of the stimulus are recorded. The motor projection areas activate the lower motor apparatus for the appropriate response. But what is the proper response and how is it determined? This is the function of the associational areas, i.e., the homotypical cortex. Few fibers pass directly from sensory to motor projection areas. These pathways are interrupted in the intervening associational areas, and these areas receive large numbers of fibers from the subcortical reticular substance, where all presently acting sensory influences are correlated, integrated, and modulated with an affective or emotional quality before they reach the cortex. In the associational cortex this correlation goes further, including integration of present sensory data with memory vestiges of previous similar experiences. It is probable that the fast-acting pyramidal fibers first inhibit all lower reflex action. This provides time for the cortical associational apparatus to analyze the situation and establish the appropriate pattern of response. Just what mechanism is employed to determine which motor areas are to be activated and in what sequence is one of the still unsolved problems of cortical physiology.

The problem of the relations of analytic and integrative functions was thrust into the foreground of attention by Lashley's extended experimental investigations of the mechanisms of learning in rats, which were reported in a long series of papers, including an interim summary issued in 1929. His method was to train each of many animals in some particular way, that is, to set problems of different degrees of difficulty, and then in each case to discover how the ability to learn and remember was affected by surgical operations upon various parts of the brain.

I have published ('26, chaps. 8 to 11) a critical summary of the evidence then available about the structure and functions of the rat's cerebral cortex. Since that time much additional information has been contributed, including an important series of papers by Krieg ('46–'47) which give detailed descriptions of the structure and connections of this animal's cortex.

Lashley's findings validate with abundant experimental proof the general principle that learning is an over-all function of the cortex as a whole, together with various subcortical structures, and that this function is not localized in any particular area or areas of the brain. Learning is a total pattern in the Coghillian sense, not a partial pattern. From the experimental evidence (which is too extensive to summarize here) he concluded that the cortex is essentially equipotential functionally and that local structural differentiation has little relation to the mass-action of the cortex as a functional unit. "For learning of the mazes," he wrote ('29, p. 68), "no part of the cortex is more important than any other." And again (p. 142), "The more complex functions, divorced from purely sensory or motor processes, are largely carried out in independence of structural differentiation."

For the "purely sensory or motor processes" of the cortex to which Lashley refers, that is, those of the projection centers, the cortex is certainly not equipotential in rats or in men. Lashley himself has given one of the clearest demonstrations we have of very precise cortical localization of the visual sensory processes of the rat. For the more complex integrative processes he is right in denying the existence of any stable mosaic localization of particular "faculties" in the tradition of the now discredited maps of the phrenologists. But he is wrong in claiming that the so-called associational cortex is equipotential physiologically. The apparent equipotentiality of the rat's cortex in maze-learning cannot be accepted as valid without more exact analysis of the process.

The first careful survey of the rat's cortex was made by Droogleever Fortuyn ('14). His charts, which I have copied ('26, fig. 38), show twenty-five areas which are sufficiently different to merit separate designation. Krieg, after more critical study, distinguishes more than fifty structurally different areas of this cortex, and he describes the connections of each of them so far as revealed by his preparations. How many of these areas are really significant for behavior can be discovered, first, by describing more completely the nervous connections of each of them and then by investigating experimentally the specific functions of each area or group of areas of similar structure and connections. This very laborious program is well advanced for rats and several other species of animals.

Most of the cortex of the rat is included in the sensory and motor projection centers and there is extensive overlap of these areas. The so-called excitable motor cortex is coextensive with several sensory areas, and in addition to these fibers, the excitation of which causes specific muscular movements, there are other projection fibers which descend to subcortical regions from almost every area of the cortex. Most of the nervous elements of the associational systems are mingled with those of the projection systems, and such synthetic functions as maze-learning are performed by this dispersed and relatively nonspecific associational tissue. This accounts for the observed equipotentiality of the rat's cortex for this type of learning, which involves chiefly the somesthetic-motor systems. This cortex, however, is not equipotential in some other learning processes (for references see Halstead, '47, p. 138). In particular, cortical participation in the conditioning of visual habits is more definitely localized in the rat than is that of those acquired habits like maze-running that involve chiefly kinesthetic activities.

In animals with larger and more highly differentiated cortex, regional localization of some integrative processes becomes progressively more evident. As representatives of lower and higher mammals are passed in review, it is seen that mosaic localization of the analyzers is progressively more sharply defined in the higher species. For the integrative processes the primitive cortex seems to act as a whole, that is, relatively equipotentially, as a facilitating mechanism. But, as the associational tissue increases in amount in the higher mammals, this mass-action is more or less diversified, with local specialization of regions, each of which is the dominant field for some particular kind of synthesis, though this synthesis is not localized exclusively or invariably in the field in question.

Halstead ('47, chap. 16) reviews the evidence regarding local representation and mass action in learning from all experimental work upon many species of animals with this summary: "The significant fact would seem to be that nature has employed two basic principles: mass action with equipotentiality for some functions and regional-localization specialization for others. Any satisfactory general theory of cortical organization must take both principles into account."

There is ample evidence that in the human cortex there are many areas, each of which acts as the dominant integrating center for some distinctive kind of mental process. The cortical fields which lie between the sensory projection areas contain focal centers which play essential parts in perception of the sensory data received. Injuries in these fields may cause no sensory loss, but the patient may be unable to perceive the sensation, that is, to give any meaning to the things sensed. If the cortex of the visual projection areas (the "striate" areas) in the occipital lobes of both hemispheres is completely destroyed, the patient is totally blind ("psychically" blind), though many visual reflexes which are performed unconsciously by visual centers of the brain stem are not impaired. If the visual projection areas are uninjured and the adjacent visual association area ("parastriate area") is damaged, the patient may be able to see perfectly, but he has no understanding of what he sees. Visual sensation is unimpaired, but visual perception is lost. This is confirmed by the results of electrical stimulation of these areas. Von Bonin ('50, p. 76) writes: "Stimulation of the striate area in a conscious patient evokes rather shapeless sensations of light located in a definite part of the visual field. Stimulation of the parastriate area, however, evokes formed visual images with movements and with color."

If I see the printed letter *A*, the points of that object are registered neurologically in the visual projection area of the cortex, but the perception of the object as a letter is not located there. I recognize the object seen as the letter *A* regardless of its size, its shape, its color, the quadrant of the retina excited, or the part of the cortical projection area excited. The act of recognition, which is perception, is not directly dependent upon any particular pattern of arrangement of the nervous tissues. To quote the words of Adrian ('47, p. 52): "In this case what is significant is the particular spatial relation of excited and non-excited areas in the cortex, not the excitation of particular nervecells." What is localized is a relationship of cortical processes, not a structural organ. This change in the type of localization from a spatial to a dynamic pattern marks the transfer from the sensory level to the perceptual level of cortical processes. An interesting mathematical discussion of the mechanics of this transfer has been published by McCulloch and Pfeiffer ('49).

The problems related with localization of function in the nervous system are not simplified in the more primitive animals. They are, in fact, more baffling because in primitive vertebrates total patterns of behavior predominate and these do not require the refinements of localized tissue differention that are necessary in higher animals with capacity for a much larger variety of possible responses. It is to be expected, then, that localization of function is more obvious and more diversified in the human cerebral cortex than in that of any other animals; and this, in fact, is found to be true. The greatly enlarged associational areas of the human brain are by no means equipotential. This is true also of the corresponding areas in monkeys, as is clearly shown by many experimental studies. Four of these are mentioned here.

Klüver and Bucy, operating on monkeys, showed that surgical removal of the larger part of both temporal lobes resulted in symptoms that in a human patient would be classed as an experimental psychosis. This complex of characteristic symptoms was shown by eight monkeys, and it could not be obtained by removal of any other parts of the cortex. The functions the loss of which resulted in "psychic blindness," emotional changes, and other abnormalities are, of course, not localized exclusively in the area removed; but this area clearly includes an integrative center which in these monkeys is indispensable for their performance. For summaries and interpretations of these experiments see Klüver ('51 and '52). Bucy and Klüver ('55) have published a detailed description of the anatomical defects in one of these monkeys that lived under observation for two years after the operation described.

Harlow ('50) in a research extending over five years removed from several monkeys large areas of the frontal associational field and in other monkeys large areas of the posterior associational field. Comparison of the subsequent behavior of these two groups of monkeys with each other and with normal monkeys showed that both operations impaired ability to solve some complex learning tests. Large bilateral lesions of the frontal areas resulted in severe impairment (although not total loss) in tests of delayed reaction type. Similar lesions of the posterior areas showed severe impairment in tests of visual discrimination learning. He concludes that "delayed reaction behavior and visual discrimination behavior have foci and gradients of representation in different cortical areas. The quantitative nature of the deficits suggests that these intellectual functions are not represented exclusively in the frontal or posterior association areas."

Boland ('49), in a similar study of monkeys, removed small areas from different parts of the prefrontal cortex only. Removal of each subdivision of the frontal lobes produces different and characteristic changes in behavior, learning ability, emotive attitude, or other recognizable effects.

Blum, Chow, and Pribram ('50), also operating on monkeys, removed the whole or specific parts of the temporal, parietal, and preoccipital homotypical cortex. They conclude that this region, exclusive of sensory projection areas, "contains separate foci, concerned with facilitating discriminative learning in vision and somesthesis, and also acquisition of more complex habits; within this sector, it appears probable that there are also common neuronal pools which are capable of participation in a variety of functions."

The prefrontal area is much larger in man than in any other animals, and many neurologists believed that this cortex is the specific organ of our higher rational operations. This hypothesis has been definitely refuted by the so-called psychosurgical operations to which reference is made above. Injury to this area impairs the patient's initiative and ability to forecast the future, and this is due to loss of persistence or ability to sustain any course of thought or action (Arnot, '52).

The seat of consciousness

The eager search of the ancients for a seat of consciousness has never been given up. It continues with equal ardor in our time. But the enterprise is as futile as the search for the end of the rainbow. Consciousness is real and the rainbow is real; but there is no pot of gold at the end of the rainbow and there is no "little man" who operates like a train dispatcher in his tower and pulls the switches that control the traffic in the nervous pathways. One does not search for the seat of a cyclone. It is not the sort of thing that can sit down anywhere. So the search for a seat of consciousness can at best lead only to an empty chair awaiting the return of a fugitive ghost.

Descartes chose the pineal gland as the seat of the soul because its strategic position in the middle of the brain seemed to him an appropriate center for control of the flow of hypothetical animal spirits through the nerve fibers which were regarded as tubular structures. The more recent consensus that the cerebral cortex is the specific integrating apparatus of consciousness has been challenged. Paul Carus (*J. comp. Neurol.*, vol. 4) in 1894 and later Dandy ('46) suggested that in man the "center of consciousness" is located in the anterior part of the corpus striatum; and Alford ('48) argued that, because removal of all cortex from one cerebral hemisphere and extensive bilateral removal of both frontal or both occipital lobes results in no "obvious gross mental defects" and because no conscious process can be shown to be dependent upon the integrity of any particular cortical field, it follows that "the entire cortical area of both hemispheres and much of the immediately underlying structures have been systematically eliminated from the role of causing what is regarded as an essential defect of mental functioning." Accordingly, he said, "the main seat of mental activity" is located in a subcortical region, probably in the thalamus or hypothalamus. This argument is questionable on a factual basis, because adequate examination reveals that significant mental defects are obvious after the operations cited. A list of these defects is given by Halstead ('51, p. 264).

From his extensive clinical and experimental experience Penfield ('38) was led to a similar conclusion. This is expressed (Penfield and Rasmussen, '50, p. 235) in these words: "Within the diencephalon there are neurone circuits which may be considered the highest level of neuronal representation and re-representation. But much of the function at this level is made possible and is elaborated by the special areas of the cerebral cortex." This conclusion is supported by an impressive array of evidence, but it is presented frankly (on their p. 19) as hypothesis, not as fact. The hypothesis in my opinion rests on questionable evidence.

That the brain stem does play an important part in psychoneural activity is well established. But that Penfield's hypothetical "centrencephalic system" of the thalamus is the "highest level" of integration manifested in conscious experience he himself has recently questioned, for he says ('52, p. 30): "In a very real sense there is no 'higher' and no 'lower' in this system. The 'place of understanding' is not walled up in a cell nor in a center of gray matter. It is to be sought in the perfect functioning of all these converging circuits."

All hypotheses which purport to define a local center of consciousness in the cortex or anywhere else are suspect, because these psychoneurological processes are total patterns which cannot be split apart in this fashion. Vital processes of this type are patterned transactions within an equilibrated dynamic field which acts as a whole or not at all. The neurological and biochemical properties of such fields are described by Gerard ('55), with some interesting hypotheses about the mechanisms involved in normal and deranged mentation.

Total abolition of consciousness may result from a variety of causes —concussion, asphyxia (general or local), lowered blood pressure, etc. If, now, it is found that there is in the hypothalamus a "sleep center," the normal function of which is to suppress consciousness in slumber, it does not follow that this center is a seat of consciousness. It may act merely like the switch of an incandescent lamp;

and one does not say that the function of luminescence resides in the switch. It is the whole circuit which performs the function. The mechanism within the bulb of the lamp is, however, the critical part of the circuit that determines the quality of the light. So in the brain, although the occipital lobes play a critical part in vision and the temporal lobes in hearing, we do not say that the awareness of these processes is localized in these lobes or in any particular cortical or subcortical area where the signals involved are assembled and sorted.

A recent study of the mechanisms activated in the return of consciousness from deep anesthesia (Bernhaut, Gellhorn, and Rasmussen, '53) gives graphic illustration of this point. These authors find that the hypothalamus plays a distinctive and critical part in what they call the "awakening response" to normal sensory stimulation in the lightly anesthesized animal. The arousal involves an activation of the cortex from the hypothalamus. More than two dozen nervous pathways involved in this response are listed, and this list is far from complete. The experiments seem to show that the hypothalamus plays a critical role in the regulation of sleep and wakefulness, but it by no means follows that the consciousness aroused by hypothalamic activity is located in either the hypothalamus or the cortex.

The search for a seat of consciousness in general or of any particular kind of conscious experience is a pseudoproblem because the conscious act has properties that are not definable in terms of the spatial and temporal units which are employed in the measurement of the objects and events of our objective world. What we search for and find by objective inquiry is the apparatus which generates awareness. This mechanism has locus in space and time, but the awareness as such is not located in any particular part of the mechanism. This is not a new idea. More than sixty years ago my brother wrote (C. L. Herrick, '94): "Upon a dynamic theory of consciousness . . . there is no occasion for a special organ. The fact of coordination is the fact of consciousness. If the myriads of cortical cells are so interrelated that their reactions mutually modify each other that is all that is required. . . . Any attempt at the location of a physical centre becomes involved in absurdities." A judicious review of present knowledge about localization of consciousness is given by Percival Bailey ('56).

Summary

Solution of the problems of localization of functions in the cerebral cortex has been retarded by failure to recognize the fundamental difference between the analytic processes of the projection centers and the synthetic processes of the associational tissue. The former are localized in mosaic patterns, the latter in dynamic patterns involving fluctuating discharge of extensive and in some cases variable areas of cortical and subcortical nervous circuits.

The history of the evolution of the projection centers and the intervening areas of elaboration of sensorimotor experience shows that the former were localized in mosaic patterns from the beginning of cortical differentiation and that the integrative apparatus was progressively enlarged and structurally segregated in the areas between the projection centers. The functions of the association centers are not localized in stable patterns like those of the projection centers. There are, however, some ill-defined regions which are concerned usually and by preference with different types of mental functions.

No particular part of the brain can be designated as the seat of consciousness, because mental processes are field functions and the field involved is as wide as the entire domain of bodily activities and of the environmental influences to which the body responds.

Chapter Thirty-three

The Mechanics of Mentation

The apparatus of cortical synthesis

The analytic nervous functions are phasic responses to excitation and they are repeated in successive activations with great uniformity. The stable localization of most of these functions has been accurately determined. Integration of the higher nervous processes, on the contrary, is a continuous fluctuating process of different kind which is never exactly repeated and which may shift its location in space from moment to moment.

These fluctuating patterns of nervous transmission can, of course, use only such channels of communication as are available; but if there is a sufficient number of such channels a specific pattern of nervous interaction may use a different selection from among them at every repetition of the process. To cite a simple analogy, if a man in Philadelphia wishes to telephone to a person in Pittsburgh the usual connection would be by way of Harrisburg; but if the Harrisburg exchange should happen to be burned out he may still get his connection by way of Baltimore. The human cerebral cortex has a vast number of such interneuronic connections, far more than are available in the brains of any other animals, and this makes it possible for the man to perform feats of rational and artistic invention that no brute can ever approach.

Many attempts have been made to devise mechanical models of nervous connections that meet the requirements of the observed processes of reflex conditioning and higher forms of learning and reasoning. The earlier models based on a system of fixed stimulus-response circuits interconnected like those of an automatic telephone system failed to satisfy the requirements. Various "field" theories were then developed, taking as point of departure the electromagnetic field of physics.

The conflict between atomistic and field theories in the domain of physics, to which reference is made in Chapters 20 and 21, has been carried over into current psychology as the controversy between advocates of a structural psychology (like E. B. Titchner) and of a physiological stimulus-response process which requires a fixed system of connections of switchboard type (J. B. Watson), on one hand, and on the other hand the configurationists of the gestalt schools (Köhler, Lashley, et al.) who insist that the integrative nervous tissue is equipotential and that the performance of these synthetic operations may go on quite independently of any structural pattern of fixed nervous connections.

This is the same type of problem as that which was resolved in theoretical physics when the particulate theory of the Coulomb electromagnetic field was revised so as to give due recognition to both the individual particles and the "form of the relations of the motion of the parts" to the field as a whole. The functions of the parts are intelligible only as they are seen in this relation to the field as a whole, and the properties of the field are defined dynamically, not structurally.

The tissues concerned in these operations are not structurally homogeneous or physiologically equipotential. The problem is to find out what part these extremely diversified fixed structures actually play in the development of transient configurations of dynamic patterns, that is, to combine our knowledge of structural connections with a workable theory of field properties.

Just as the conflict between the particulate and field theories of physics was resolved by a relativistic formulation which selected some principles from each of the rival schools, so in psychology we now search for a psychoneural formulation that avoids the extremes of both the connectionist and the configurationist theories and selects some useful principles from both of them.

Hebb ('49) has devised a schema of an assembly of assemblies which presents a promising point of departure for further inquiry in the search for such a formulation. He applies some features of the field concept in an analysis of the known structure of cortical tissue in such a way as to arrive at a physiological formulation that is simple in principle and flexible enough to provide scope for unlimited complexity of nervous interaction in actual operation. His schema is consistent with the known structure of the cortex and avoids the rigidity of the conventional stimulus-response models of switchboard type. His principles are familiar and have often been stated in general terms. He goes further and applies them in the concrete form of hypothetical patterns of linkage of the nervous elements which comprise the mechanisms of perception, learning, reasoning, emotion, and volition.

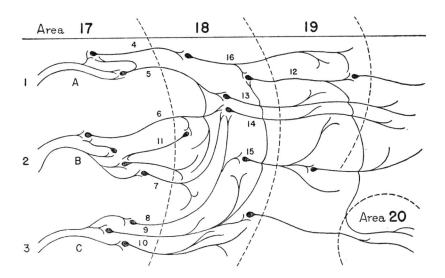

Fig. 16.—Simplified diagram of typical nervous connections of a visual cell-assembly as defined by Hebb ('49) and illustrated in his Figures 7, 8, and 9. The arrangement of the nervous elements is diagrammatic, but all types of connection shown have been observed. Boldface numbers 17, 18, 19, and 20 refer to Brodmann's areas of the cortex as shown in Figure 10. Letters A, B, and C designate parts of area 17 upon which three loci of the retina are projected (see the accompanying text).

Professor Hebb's book must be consulted for the details. In Figure 16 some of the types of nervous assembly in the visual area of the cortex are shown in oversimplified form. The boldface numbers, 17, 18, 19, and 20, designate cortical areas numbered according to Brodmann's map of the cortex. Area 17 is the visual projection center which receives fascicles of projection fibers, 1, 2, and 3, from the lateral geniculate body of the thalamus. Areas 18 and 19 are the neighboring zones of visual-sensory correlation or elaboration, and area 20 is a zone in the temporal lobe where visual-auditory elaboration is effected.

In area 17 the loci of the retina are projected in mosaic pattern, and A, B, and C designate three parts of this area, each of which is activated or "fired" from a specific retinal locus. The topological pattern of retinal stimulation is reproduced in area 17, but, as the diagram shows, conduction from area 17 is diffuse, the fibers 4 to 10, each of which comes from a specific locus of area 17, are dispersed, and there is no point-to-point correspondence between area 17 and area 18. In transmission from area 18 to other areas the excitation is diffused still farther. Nervous elements may be fired in remote parts of the same and the opposite hemisphere. Some of the cells of area 18 fire back into area 17 (cell no. 11), and others (nos. 12 and 14) may be fired by fibers from different parts of area 17 and also from other areas. Thus there is convergence as well as spread of excitation.

In the monkey the lateral geniculate body contains about one million nerve cells and the visual area 17 of the cortex has about 145 million cells (Chow, Blum, and Blum, '50). Every retinal locus of the geniculate body is connected by nerve fibers with a corresponding locus of cortical area 17 in a mosaic pattern, but each cell of the thalamus may fire 145 times as many cells in the cortex. Each of these cortical cells in its turn may fire a very large number of other cortical cells, so that there is a progressively expanding spread of the excitation through the cortex.

The assembly as illustrated is diagrammatic, but all types of connection shown (and countless others) are known to exist. We see here the mechanism of that distinction between the analytic and the integrative processes that has been repeatedly emphasized. The phasic analytic functions are performed by stable structure that can be mapped in mosaic patterns of localization, as in area 17; but as soon as the excitation passes beyond this area the topographical organization of the process ceases and no mosaic localization of it is possible.

The cortical areas represented in the diagram contain millions of nerve cells, only a very small proportion of which are fired as a result of any particular retinal stimulation. Only selected representative samples of those that are fired in some visual perception are drawn in the diagram. The selection of the cells which are fired in any assembly at any given moment is determined by many factors— the inherited pattern of structural arrangement of the nervous elements, habits formed during previous experience, transient changes in central excitatory state such as result from fatigue, and numerous others.

It is recognized in Hebb's scheme that, although the cortex is not homogeneous in structure or equipotential in function, the number of available nervous connections of part with part is so large and so all-pervasive that any local activity may excite activity in other near or remote areas in patterns of unlimited variety. The firing of any assembly may serve as a signal for the activation of one or more other assemblies that are in attunement with it.

In the growing child as experience is enlarged some experiences are repeated in substantially similar form. It is known that activation of any assembly of nervous elements leaves a "trace" (of unknown nature; see Eccles, '53, chap. 6) which facilitates the reactivation of that system upon repetition of the exciting cause. This is an organic memory. The theory postulates that the memory trace left by a frequently repeated stimulus takes the form of the slow development of a "cell-assembly," which is defined as a collection of nerve cells which may be widely scattered in space and which are so interconnected that they may act as a functional unit when the appropriate signal is given. In the adult brain there are innumerable such assemblies, and these are interconnected in a hierarchy of increasing complexity. A particular assembly may occupy a small area in one hemisphere, or it may include also cells in the opposite hemisphere, in the thalamus, or in other parts of the brain stem. Such an assembly is "capable of acting briefly as a closed system, delivering facilitation to other such systems and usually having a specific motor facilitation. A series of such events constitutes a 'phase sequence'—the thought process. Each assembly action may be aroused by a preceding assembly, by a sensory event, or—normally—by both. The central facilitation from one of these activities on the next is the prototype of 'attention' " (Hebb, p. xix). Hebb's figures 7, 8, and 9 and the accompanying text should be consulted for the details of the structure and operation of the assembly in various types of mental processes.

This sort of schematization of cerebral structure is frankly hypothetical but it is quite in harmony with what we know about the structure and physiology of the cortex. It defines fields of integrated activity of momentary duration, each of which has a specific pattern of performance and an enduring quality that facilitates its reactivation under appropriate conditions. Each assembly is attuned to respond to some specific kind of signal which may come from a peripheral sense organ or from some other assembly within the brain. The pattern exhibited at any moment is the resultant of firing of a large number of nerve cells in a specific arrangement. Upon repetition of the signal a similar pattern of performance may be activated in the assembly and the probability is that a slightly different selection of nerve cells will be fired, so that no two perceptions or memories are identical.

In all ordinary mental operations the number of such assemblies that are in action must be very large and the shifting patterns of their interplay are never exactly repeated. There is good evidence that certain types of assembly, notably those that are disordered in aphasia, are not permanently and irrevocably located in particular cortical areas. There is equally good evidence that many (perhaps most) assemblies are located by preference in rather vaguely defined cortical regions as pictured in Figure 14, page 417. The assemblies for vocal speech are usually in the third frontal convolution of the left hemisphere (in right-handed people), those for understanding spoken words are in the temporal lobe, and those for understanding written words are in the occipital lobes. But total destruction of these areas is not always followed by the expected type of aphasia, and aphasia may result from injury to parts of the cortex other than those mentioned.

Many other kinds of mental defect may result from local injuries distributed apparently at random over the cortex. Nevertheless there is a sufficient amount of well-controlled evidence to justify the opinion that the crucially important or dominant assemblies for the various kinds of mental processes are generally located in certain rather large and poorly defined regions.

The frequency with which this pattern of distribution is found justifies the inference that in the internal architecture of the cerebrum there is a stable arrangement of the chief pathways of nervous conduction that is similar, although not identical, in all persons. The cortical connections of these systems of fibers are much more variable so that the locations of the dominant assemblies may not be exactly the same in any two people. Furthermore, because all assemblies are defined in terms of the pattern of performance rather than in terms of the structural arrangement of the nervous elements, an assembly may shift with advancing age and experience from one location to another without loss of its distinctive physiological and psychological properties. In all cortical activity the assemblies are grouped in constellations with incessant shifting of their interrelations. If at any time some assembly is incapacitated by fatigue, a local vascular failure, or any other cause, some other assembly of similar type may be signaled to take its place. In this way the flow of cortical synthesis may go on with but negligible change in its character.

Although this is a speculative schematization of the physiology of cortical activity, it is supported by a large body of factual evidence. It may be confirmed and extended or modified by further research of various kinds—histological and biochemical study of the tissues involved, clinicopathological observations, animal experimentation, study of oscillographic records of local changes in electrical potential under normal and experimental conditions, and many others.

Hebb's analysis of the cortical mechanism is made from the standpoint of the sensory input. A different approach to the problem is suggested by Sperry ('52). As I mentioned on page 315, he finds the key factors in the motor output, that is, in the pattern of behavior to which cortical activity gives rise. It seems to me that there is no fundamental inconsistency here. We need adequate knowledge of both input and output before we can hope to solve the problem of the integrating mechanism that translates the one into the other. Both of these schemata are fruitful working hypotheses which can be examined further in many ways, most profitably perhaps by correlating physiological observations with subjective experiences as reported by human patients under a variety of experimental conditions.

Eccles' excellent summary ('53) of the chemical and electrical properties of the nervous tissues is followed by a chapter entitled "The Mind-brain Problem," in which he presents a series of models of neuronal networks designed to schematize the mind-brain relationships. His formulation of the problem is based on dualistic and interactional postulates, as expressed on page 261: "It is the way in which the brain achieves liaison with mind that is the essence of the problem." Stated in this way the problem, I repeat, is scientifically insoluble.

The problem with which science is properly concerned is not a search for liaison between brain as a physical instrument and some other entity which is mind. What we must do is to discover those characteristics of brain as living tissue which enable it to have as one of its own intrinsic physicalistic properties the awareness that we call mind. Eccles' elaborate and ingenious dialectic concerning the problem of "the way in which the spatio-temporal patterns of activity could be modified by a 'mind influence' or 'will' " (p. 271) leaves the problem in worse state than before. The invocation of a hypothetical "ghost" who operates the human machine (p. 285) presents some problems (which Eccles lists) that can probably be approached more fruitfully by a search for the as yet unknown physicalistic principles of mentation. What we need here is more knowledge of the actual structure and operation of the nervous mechanisms that do the thinking.

The field of mental processes

If we regard the assembly as a dynamic field, its basic properties are determined by the structural arrangement of the nervous elements which at any given moment are in action. The experiments of Burr ('47), Köhler ('40), and many others suggest that other properties can be formulated in terms of now current principles of electrodynamics. And there are still other properties which are accessible to us now only introspectively that cannot be measured in the numerical units of conventional mechanics. For these some other type of formulation must be found.

The assembly field is not a vague abstraction like the hypothetical equipotential ground within which equally hypothetical configurations are developed, as postulated in gestalt psychology. This field is never equipotential, and it has recognizable structure which is different in its various parts. Nevertheless the dynamic pattern is not inflexibly bound to that structure or to any particular segment of it. The pattern may be reproduced wherever suitable structure is present, and it may change its locus within limits set by the properties of this structure.

Attention has been called (page 265) to the fact that the fields with which we are concerned in psychophysics must be treated as unitary wholes and not split apart by particulate analysis. There is a polarization of subject and object (page 294); and in the process of perception the spatial and temporal factors are projected outward into the objective field. In the integrative process as this is experienced subjectively these factors are blended in relationships that are relativistic and not necessarily measurable in numerical units. Furthermore, in the higher processes of mental integration and abstraction, spatial and temporal factors may not appear at all in the subjective aspect of the process. The mechanisms of this field of subjective experience are not confined inside the skin of the perceiving person.

If at night I am looking at the sky, recognize one of the stars as our nearest neighbor, Alpha Centauri, and am steering a boat by the light of that celestial beacon, then the bodily organs involved in this mental act include eye and brain and muscle, all acting in reciprocal interplay. Indeed, the dynamic system operating is more far-reaching than this, for the star is also an essential component. It follows that the causal complex of which my conscious control of the course of the boat is one component embraces not only an intricately linked series of very diversified bodily activities but also events which took place twenty-five million million miles away and nearly five years ago, for Alpha Centauri is distant 4.35 light-years from the earth.

If we attempt to view this causal situation in its entirety, we recognize a number of things and events which are localized in space and time and which are locally segregated as bodily organs with specific functions, such as sense organs, groups of co-operating muscles, reflex arcs, and so on, and also a selection of relevant objects in the near and remote surroundings. In this transaction the distant star, its image on the retina, and the nervous and muscular processes activated by the signal all lie in the field of assemblies concerned. This field embraces also innumerable assemblies which have been established by past experience, the patterns of which are preserved and stored as "neurograms," or memory "traces," and which are inactive until quickened by receipt of the appropriate signal. This is the objective picture as viewed by a spectator; but to the behaving subject these temporo-spatial relations are irrelevant except as means to an end, and in practice most of the necessary adjustments are made quite unconsciously. The mental process as subjectively experienced has an integrity which cannot be analyzed in terms of objective units of measurement.

It is clear, moreover, that the cortex as a thinking machine does not work independently as a self-contained mechanism. Most cortical activities are circular in pattern and many of these circuits extend beyond the cortex itself. These functions are influenced by the physiological activities of many nonnervous organs and by the general physiological state of the body as a whole. Many of these influences reach the cortex through the blood stream and its contained respiratory gases, nutriments, and endocrine products. The pattern of cortical functions may be determined by all of these internal processes in combinations of practically unlimited variety and also by what is going on in the surroundings as these events are sensed and projected inward to register their specific qualities in appropriately sensitized cortical areas.

The field of cortical activity, accordingly, includes the entire body and everything around it to which the body responds in any way and which is acted upon by the body. In cortical integration relevant data may be sorted out from the whole range of present and previous experience. At this highest level of integration common features of mixed sensory and motor experience are abstracted and organized as generalizations, ideas, and concepts. Symbols are devised for these generalizations, and these are used as tools of thought at all stages of the rational processes. The mechanisms employed in these operations are not well understood. Grinker ('53, chap. 10) discusses field theory as applied in psychosomatic medicine.

In the preceding pages the properties of cortical fields have been regarded as manifestations of an irradiation of nervous discharges through existing pathways of nervous conduction which form an intricate meshwork that can transmit nervous impulses in an unlimited variety of patterns determined by momentarily changing conditions of sensory stimulation and internal excitatory state. The observed histological structure of the brain provides the requisite mechanism for such fluctuating patterns of nervous discharge and there is ample physiological evidence that this is the way cortical nervous tissue does perform its functions. There is, moreover, rapidly increasing evidence that other physical principles also may be involved (for summaries see Gerard, '49 and '55). The field functions may include such factors as the "continuous field action" of Köhler ('51), which involves electrical transmission through the tissue fluids as "volume conductors" in addition to the nervous elements.

Efforts to discover by experiment what these nonnervous factors are and the laws of their operation are now in process, with promise of important results. None of the field theories now current meet the requirements of the observed facts. This is probably because the very complex problem is oversimplified by omission of essential factors. This can be corrected only by further search, taking into account the properties of the nervous fabric and also the possibility that different factors of field physics (still incompletely understood) participate in the process.

Cortical use of signals and symbols

The analytic apparatus of the body is a sorting mechanism of various grades of complexity. The sorting machines now in use in industry and research present a similar series, ranging from a simple sieve to the intricate electronic computing machines of recent design. A comparison of the two series is instructive. Some engineering principles which are common to both series are illustrated more clearly in one, some in the other.

In most sorting mechanisms some sort of a sign is used for selection of particular items from a mixed assemblage—it may be a punched hole in a card or any one of many others. It has been shown (page 401) that in animal evolution there is a progressive elaboration of the apparatus of sorting and communication from one sorting device to another that is manifest in behavior as a series of more complicated patterns. These patterns range from responses to simple signs and the use of signals for communication to inconceivable complexity in the elaboration of symbols in the cortical processes of emotive and rational thinking and the resulting conduct.

The symbols serve as codes or simplified signals, each of which may transmit the result of a very complicated operation of an assembly to one or more other assemblies that are attuned to respond to it. In the course of these transformations space factors and time factors are mutually interchangeable in a variety of ways. This reciprocal interplay between the spatial and temporal relations within the operating mechanism is especially characteristic of cortical nervous processes and the colligated mental experiences. This has been discussed in Le Gros Clark's Robert Boyle Lecture ('47), Adrian's Waynflete Lectures ('47), Gerard's Gregory Lecture ('49), and many similar studies. Particular features of the neurophysiological complex have been selected for mathematical analysis by exports in biophysics, and the engineers have succeeded in applying some of these principles in the construction of electronic computing machines which duplicate some complicated mental processes with remarkable fidelity.

The signals and codes to which reference is made here are strictly physiological processes. It is emphasized by Sperry ('52) that these neurological processes are neither isomorphic copies nor codal representations of the corresponding subjective processes. They are instruments employed in the process of thinking as this is inspected objectively. The thinking process as experienced subjectively uses codes and symbols of a different order, and the exact relation between the two systems of codes is just the problem that has not yet been solved. (In regard to verbal symbols see page 290.)

In this connection Lashley ('42, p. 318) says: "The transition from the visual perceptual to the motor level thus appears to be, primitively, the translation of one system of space coordinates into another." To this he adds, on page 320: "In the light of experimental evidence concerning the nature of nervous activity it seems most probable that the various patterns of integrated activity in successive levels of the nervous system have the form of tuned resonating circuits."

These patterns reverberate throughout extensive cortical areas. They are evanescent and constantly changing, but some of them leave residual traces which endure and can be repeated again and again in memory. Because the destruction of large areas of the cortex, variously distributed in different experiments, does not destroy specific memories of learned behavior, it is evident that it is the pattern of the tuned resonating circuits that persists as the memory trace and that this more or less stable dynamic pattern can be reduplicated anywhere in the cortex provided the cortical loss does not exceed a certain proportion of the whole cortex. These experiments were performed on rats, whose cortex is far simpler and more nearly homogeneous than the human cortex. The experiments of Penfield ('52) indicate that in the human brain the more elaborate memory patterns which involve mental symbols are registered locally, chiefly in the temporal lobe. Gerard ('55) cites experiments which reveal some details of the physiological process involved in the formation of enduring memories.

It is of interest that the computing machine also has a memory of similar kind. Complicated patterns of activity can be retained in the form of enduring changes in the apparatus (analogous with the neurograms in the brain), and these patterns can be re-evoked when the time comes for the appropriate circuit to act and relate them to succeeding events in the process of calculation. To quote Hoagland ('49):

"Thus, information can be stored until ready for use, and the machine quite literally possesses a functional memory in the form of patterns of dynamic electrical configurations or of molecular patterns which may be called upon to furnish information by appropriate stimuli arriving as timed pulses from other circuits in the apparatus. It is important to realize that this memory need not be lodged in any one locus in the machine, but belongs to its function as a whole. To ignore this is to commit the fallacy of Descartes in locating the action of mind on matter in the pineal gland."

Organic memory is an integrative total pattern, and the memory of the computing machine has similar properties. Its location in the apparatus is of the same type as that found by Lashley in the brain of the rat—an enduring dynamic pattern that may be embodied in any suitably organized structure. In both cases a particular pattern of resonating circuits may be reactivated by incoming signals which fit or are in attunement with the functional pattern in question, and this pattern is not inflexibly bound with any particular structural arrangement. These processes are known experimentally to involve reciprocal interchange between temporal and spatial factors; and they may involve also transition from three-dimensional space to four-dimensional space-time, or conceivably to a dimension not yet defined. These possibilities are being explored.

In Lashley's paper quoted above he wrote ('42, p. 302): "There is some reason for believing that generalization is one of the primitive, basic functions of organized nervous tissue." This generalization is not a mere aggregation of more elementary processes. Like other integrative functions, it is not reducible to an additive assemblage of stimulus-response units. From insects to primates, generalizations are exhibited in differential responses. His conclusion, previously quoted, that "the various patterns of integrated activity in successive levels of the nervous system have the form of tuned resonating circuits" has been confirmed by abundant evidence in neurological and engineering research. Lashley ('49) has more recently illustrated and discussed the nervous mechanisms (which he calls "neural schemata") available for these dynamic systems.

On the basis of known histological structure of the brain, Pitts and McCulloch ('47) have constructed diagrams of the auditory and visual nervous circuits, including a number of feed-back mechanisms, and they have subjected these to mathematical analysis. The results of this and their previous studies are startling. Regarding the hypothetical mechanisms discussed, they say, "If mistaken, they still present the possible kinds of hypothetical mechanisms and the general character of circuits which recognize universals, and give practical methods for their design." The universals to which reference is made here are characterized as "abstracted universals of a kind," and they have nothing in common with the absolute universals of metaphysics. Generalizations can be mechanically abstracted from particulars by a sorting machine. The brain is a glorified sorting machine and the "universals" which it abstracts are more appropriately called generalizations.

The mechanisms employed in the mechanical calculator and the mechanical brain are different, but both processes involve some common principles that may serve as guides for further inquiry into the mechanics of cerebral activity. This promise has already been fulfilled. For the science concerned with control and communication in general, Norbert Wiener has suggested the name "cybernetics," and he has written a book about it ('48). He explains that by copying the human brain (not its mechanism but its operations) the engineers have designed their calculating machines, and the more we learn about calculators the better we understand the brain.

Marvelously intricate as the artifical computing machines are, their complexity is trifling as compared with the known structure of the human brain, and they are far less efficient from the standpoint of energy requirements. It has been estimated that the human cortex contains about 10,000,000,000 nerve cells, and the nervous system as a whole has a vastly larger number. Each of these cells has its own built-in power supply. As previously described, these cells are interconnected by nervous conductors in such complicated ways that the number of patterns of intercellular connection is practically unlimited. Each contact of one nervous element with another (a synapse) may be compared with a relay in a system of electrical conductors. Measured in electrical engineering terms, the nervous relays are only one-thousandth as fast as vacuum tube relays, but they are much smaller and much less power is required to operate them.

We are told on competent authority (McCulloch and Pfeiffer, '49) that "a computer with as many vacuum tubes as a man has neurons in his head would require the Pentagon to house it, Niagara's power to run it, and Niagara's water to cool it." The vacuum tubes can be replaced by transistors with great saving of space and power, but even if this is done the human brain is about a million times more efficient in terms of energy requirements. Presently available machines work more than ten thousand times faster than the human brain can operate in the solution of the same problem (Kemeny, '55). But, even so, the brain when in good working order has abilities with which the artificial machines cannot compete.

The late models of electronic computing machines abstract from the sorted data some common factors as generalizations which are retained in usable form stored in a sort of mechanical memory. These may be recalled for use at an appropriate stage of the process of computation and synthesized with others to form generalizations of a next higher order. The electronic calculators perform feats of computation involving solution of arithmetical problems, differential equations, and integrations that resemble in results achieved the output of the most proficient mathematical minds. Errors are automatically detected and in some situations automatically corrected. The activities are goal-directed. They have elaborate scanning mechanisms that are not at all similar to those available in the human cortex and yet accomplish similar results.

Although these machines cannot think, they can solve in a few minutes complicated mathematical problems that would require many months of arduous computation by an expert mathematician. Indeed, they can find the answers to some types of problems that are insoluble by the mathematicians. A problem is formulated in accordance with a pre-established code, the relevant data are fed into the machine, and these are so manipulated by the mechanism that complicated mathematical problems are solved with the speed of lightning and the results filed for future reference. The operation is so flexible that the procedure at every step is determined by the result obtained at the preceding step. One cannot but be impressed by the amazing resemblance of this process to what goes on in a human brain while engaged in similar calculations.

The mechanisms employed in these machines were designed in accordance with known principles of mechanics; but the generalizations employed in reasoning and recognized subjectively as ideas have no counterparts in objective experience. They are unique products of a different kind of mechanism which works at a higher level of integration. It is nevertheless possible to find precursors of them and of their symbols in physiological processes and also in the computing machines.

The electronic computing machines are complicated refinements of a class termed servomechanisms, in which some of the output of energy is returned to the source to control the further output. Familiar examples are the governor of a steam engine and the thermostat of a house-heating system. This return of energy to the source is a "feed-back," which may reinforce the existing pattern of operation or it may change the pattern of performance during its course. The latter case is illustrated by a missile the course of which is directed by radar. Signals received from a moving target guide the missile and change its direction in accordance with the movements of the target. A similar sort of "negative feed-back" is seen in the pursuit of prey by an animal. It occurs also in the nervous circuits within the brain.

Most nervous functions are circular in pattern, a characteristic example being the thalamocortical circulation, a circulation not of blood but of nervous impulses in two-way traffic. Within the cerebral cortex there are innumerable similar circular processes, all of which are servomechanisms.

All servomechanisms are goal-directed by nature. In the artificial machines there is a purpose in the mind of the designer, an end to be achieved. And there is a purposive quality which is intrinsic to the mechanism as such. Its activities are goal-directed, and the action ceases when the goal has been reached. The controlling factor in the process is the degree to which the act has not been completed. We observe the same thing in all goal-directed animal behavior and in human perception. The purposive quality that everybody recognizes in human voluntary action differs from that exhibited by other servomechanisms in only one fundamental respect: the purpose is consciously recognized as such and this awareness of ends and means is of enormous advantage as a controlling factor in the effort to reach the objective.

The current literature dealing with the mechanics of cerebration is extensive and rapidly increasing. Only a few examples are cited here. A good nontechnical description is given by Pfeiffer ('55, chaps. 17, 18). Summaries and additional references are given by Frank *et al.* ('48), Jasper ('48), Gerard ('49), Jeffress ('51), Kemeny ('55), and Eccles ('53), among others. Mary Brazier ('48, '51, '52) has explained with brilliant clarity the significance of these recent findings for neurology, psychology, and psychiatry, and Northrop ('48) has discussed their psychological and philosophical significance. Reiser ('55) explains why the digital computing machines, which solve so efficiently complicated problems involving only two-valued deductive logic, cannot perform the creative inductions of human imaginative thinking. The inorganic machine can solve a problem only if the requisite data are given in appropriately coded form. It takes a human brain to invent the problem and the proper code.

The marvelously efficient electronic calculators are not thinking machines. They have great heuristic value for neurology because they furnish unique opportunity for study of some mechanical principles of wide import. But let it not be overlooked that these principles may find expression in a great variety of mechanical structures, and no dead mechanism which has been made or conceived can serve as an adequate model of the incomparably more elaborate apparatus of living cortical tissue. The only way to find out how the brain works is to study the brain itself.

Summary

The brain is a glorified sorting machine and the projection centers of the cortex make the final refinements of this analysis of the data of experience. In the remainder of the cortex the raw data are rearranged in patterns which are in large measure determined by the use made of them, that is, by experience. This is an integrative process which employs mechanisms and mechanical principles of different order from those of the analytic systems.

Relatively stable patterns of nervous discharge are established during the learning process. These are integrated dynamic systems that habitually employ the same arrangements of nervous elements. Such an arrangement is called by Hebb a "cell-assembly." There are innumerable assemblies which are tuned resonating circuits, each of which may be widely extended within the cortex and beyond it to the brain stem. They are so interconnected as to provide for integrations at successively higher levels. These dynamic systems are not inflexibly bound to their cell-assemblies. This flexibility is so great that a particular physiological or mental process may be repeated with only minor variations by the use of a great variety of structural elements, and this explains the puzzling inconstancy of the clinical symptoms which result from local cortical injuries.

Our knowledge of the mechanics of cortical action is rapidly expanding in fields of inquiry that hitherto were inaccessible or sterile. Mechanical calculating machines have been devised which evidently have some factors that are common to the machine and the living brain. But the calculator, which does not think, is designed and operated by thinking brains, and the only way to find out how thinking is done is to study the living mechanism that does it.

CHAPTER THIRTY-FOUR

The Dimensions of Mind

Facts and theories

About forty years ago an eminent psychologist who was director of one of our most progressive schools of education asked me to prepare for his classes a little book that would explain in simple language exactly what goes on in the brain during a train of thought. That book has not yet been written. If ever it is produced, it will sell in carload lots and the author will win enduring fame.

The trouble is, we do not know where to look for the crucial facts or what kind of facts we are looking for. This basic problem of psychobiology has not been solved. I offer no solution, but now we are able to see more clearly some hitherto neglected factors and the directions of inquiry that give promise of more fruitful results.

The preceding chapters are concerned with general principles and no attempt has been made to fill in the details of evidence from which the principles have been derived. These principles are theories, not facts, but there is factual basis for all of them and this foundation of validated fact is more firmly laid for some of them than for others. We know a great deal about the physical conditions which are requisite for the various kinds of conscious processes and about the laws of mental operations as these are experienced subjectively; but scientifically acceptable principles of the mechanics of thinking have not been found. In the search for these principles theory plays an indispensable part; but we must not allow theory to take control over facts, something that has happened all too often with disastrous consequences.

Thoughtful people have always been interested in this problem, but from the beginning progress was retarded (and it still is) by primitive mythologies which set a world of spirits apart from the natural world. The mind (or soul) is regarded as an independent entity released from the limitations set by the natural order of the world in which we live. Minds which are thus isolated from reality are unhampered by the hard facts of life and cannot successfully adjust to them. The most pernicious expression of this failure is the construction of fantastic codes of conduct and standards of probity which run counter to the natural laws of successful personal and social adjustment. The inevitable results of this common practice are bigotry, intolerance, persecutions, ideological, religious, political, and industrial conflicts, wars, and disintegration of the social fabric. Many of the major crimes and disasters which blemish the record of past and present human conduct are the results of this artificial and un-natural separation of man's spiritual nature from the physical world which embodies it and sustains it.

When the leadership of the people passes into the hands of men with distorted minds, general approval of the distortion may become a compulsive neurosis of a vast population, as illustrated by Hitler's Germany. Similar perversions of the natural order of successful social adjustment are prevalent in every community, not excepting our own, and if unchecked the inevitable disasters will follow. The only remedy for these personal and social maladies is a re-education of the people along the lines of a scientifically acceptable psychobiology which will keep our mental constructions in more true and efficient working relations with the natural world and human nature in its social relationships. All of man's ambitions and ideals of richer and more satisfying life can be realized only by keeping the mind-body relationship in harmonious working order. The more we know about this relationship the larger the measure of success in this quest.

Pioneers of psychobiology

Practically all of our scientific knowledge about mind-body rela-

tionships has been acquired during the last two centuries. Toward the
end of the nineteenth century a beginning was made to bring together the data accumulated in various unrelated fields of inquiry,
and the science of psychobiology was born. At that time there were
a few men of unusual acumen and prescience who were able to draw
from the available fragmentary evidence some general principles of
wide import which could serve as promising working hypotheses to
point the way toward further advance.

It was my good fortune to be intimately associated with two of
the most inspiring leaders of that movement, namely, my older
brother, Clarence L. Herrick, and his pupil, George E. Coghill.
These two men so profoundly influenced my own life and the development of psychobiology that I have written a biographical
memoir of each of them ('49, '55). My brother formulated the basic
principles of psychobiology with remarkable insight. Although stated
in general terms and without the quantitative precision of those now
current, their import is clear. Coghill and I got these principles by
word of mouth with a wealth of detail and a vital quality that cannot
be transferred to the printed page, and this teaching was the seedbed of all our subsequent growth.

The conception that mind or something psychoid is a common
property of all living things and a property that differs in definable
ways from the physicochemical processes of conventional physiology
has been elaborated by many people in a great variety of ways. It
is sometimes carried still further into the inorganic realm, and something psychoid or premental is ascribed to every natural thing and
to nature as a whole. Many of these discussions invoke mystical
factors which are scientifically inadmissible, but there is a solid core
of factual evidence here which should not be ignored. I have mentioned only a few of these excursions beyond the frontiers of verifiable knowledge. In the final section of my biography of Coghill I
assembled some of his philosophical fragments in the form of an
imaginary dialogue. As I review that episode now, I feel that we
were both groping in the dark for principles whose exact significance
eluded us. In this book I have tried to clarify and systematize some
of those germinal ideas. The reader will no doubt agree that current
psychobiological theory at its best is still in a fetal stage of develop-

ment. But I am sure that the youngster is viable and has an excellent life expectancy.

Coghill's program of research led to the conclusion that mentation is a total pattern of integrative type, and some of the properties of mentation, as we experience it subjectively, he was able to recognize behavioristically in all other animals. He sharply distinguished the integrative processes from the analytic functions (which he called "organismic"). I go further and maintain that this distinction is manifest in all natural processes, both inorganic and vital, and that we recognize various levels of integration which are defined in terms of the patterns of performance. The distinctive characteristics of integration as I describe them (Chapter 8) reach their highest development in human rational thinking. All integrative processes are directive. At every step from lower to higher levels something new is added. The higher patterns are not made by simple additive assembly of the properties of the lower, and the laws of their operation are not identical with those of the lower. This is as true of a chemical reaction as of the creative imagination of a philosopher or a poet.

The patterns of integration are of infinite variety and they all have some features in common. These common features include those which are called mind or mind-stuff in the various systems of panpsychism. They are distinctive processes, some of which have dimensions of different order from those of the Euclidean and Newtonian systems.

Theory of dimensions

My brother's hunch that the solution of the mind-body problem may involve dimensions as yet unrecognized is now receiving serious attention. Coghill took some first steps in that direction. He pointed out that in both biological and psychological integration the relations of spatial and temporal factors are different from those of the analytic systems. These differences are mentioned here in various contexts (Chapters 19, 23, 25, 27), and in Chapter 21 a few of Coghill's statements are quoted. Let us now recapitulate the interpretations which have been made here.

The analytic functions of stimulus-response type are necessarily

oriented in behavioristic space and time, but the integrative processes are as a rule oriented in space-time without separate individuation of spatial and temporal dimensions. When vital processes are
stepped up from the biophysiological to the biopsychic level the
individuation of space and time is preserved in our perceptual awareness of the things and events sensed. The perceptions, accordingly,
are necessarily oriented in three-dimensional space and linear dimensional time with the percipient as a fixed point of reference. The cognitive and emotional components of mentation, however, stem directly from a four-dimensional field of space-time, and many of our
conceptions and sentiments have no temporal or spatial components
at all.

It may be conjectured that all conscious experience goes on at
levels higher than four-dimensional space-time with parameters
which have not yet been defined. In Chapters 21, 25, 27, and 33
some facts which support this hypothesis are mentioned in various
contexts. These higher dimensions are not like those of current
physics, which are (or may be) expressed numerically. They may be
manifest only in terms of patterns which cannot be defined quantitatively. Mathematics and symbolic logic are now developing methods
of handling dimensions devoid of any quantitative factors. I have
cited (Chapter 5) the unitary principle of Whyte ('49), which he
says "provides a nonquantitative *theory of tendency* applicable to a
wide class of one-way processes. It leads, for example, to a theory of
organism using terms which are equally relevant to 'physical' and
'mental' processes, and do not imply any fundamental dualism." He
recognizes a formative property of all natural processes which is the
creative factor of integration in my terminology.

The conception of a hierarchy of dimensions at successive levels
has been elaborated by Økland ('49, '50) in two stimulating papers.
He extends the four-dimensional concept of space-time to include the
mind as a fifth dimension. In his theory, "mental and non-mental
events are united with each other as physical time is united with
physical space." This is an observed relationship, and he insists that
no metaphysical concepts are implicit in it.

These five dimensions, he says, may be symbolized by a rectangu-
lar co-ordinate system where the X-axis represents the three dimen-

sions of Euclidean space, the Y-axis the physical time, and the Z-axis the psychical contents of experience. These dimensions are defined as the primary contents of experience, and they are regarded as the universal elements of everything in nature. "In my terminology," he says, "every living thing has a fifth dimension, forming a unity together with its physical appearance, the individuals being more or less complicated in psychological as well as in physical respects. . . . The theory vindicates a modern and critical panpsychism, according to which all nature has a fifth dimension, at first appearing as inorganic forces, later on as unconscious and conscious minds."

This analysis, it should be emphasized, is of nature *as known to man*, for these dimensions are the primary contents *of experience*. As I have repeatedly mentioned, what we are dealing with in natural science and naturalistic philosophy is human experience of nature. It follows that the psychic factor, the "Z-axis," is necessarily inherent in the act of knowing. There is always a transactional relation between the knower and the known, and "indeed the act of knowing has an important effect upon the known" (Margenau; see the comments on page 266 above). But it does not necessarily follow that the "Z-factor" is present in the thing known in its own right and apart from the knower.

In the experience which we objectify, the "Z-factor" is eliminated, and in objective science we aim to reduce this factor to zero. In introspective psychology, on the contrary, the "Z-factor" is the primary object of regard. It is the province of psychobiology to bridge the gap between these two fields of inquiry.

In view of the fact that mind as experienced subjectively is evidently at a different level of integration from that of any unconscious behavior whatever, I maintain that a new dimension is added when awareness emerges. The issues are confused rather than clarified if this difference between the conscious and the unconscious is neglected and both are assigned to the same dimension. What we observe is processes at different levels of integration, with corresponding differences in the parameters of their dimensions. We must not read a "Z-factor" of human type back into a human ovum, an ameba, a plant, or any inorganic thing without more evidence than is now available, and our dimensions should be defined and named accordingly. If now we grant that this is the proper procedure, it is none the less true that there is adequate evidence that the "Z-factor" of human experience is a member of a class of integrative processes that has distinctive properties, and this should be recognized.

The biologist must be a practical realist; that is, he must believe in the real existence of a natural world to which the organism must adjust in order to survive. He has evidence that the existence of this world is not conditioned by his knowledge about it; that is, it is a world the reality of which is not dependent upon the "Z-factor" of human perception of it. Pursuing the inquiry on this assumption, he finds objective evidence of a series of integrative levels of increasing complexity and efficiency which are distinguished by the patterns of their organization and the resulting behavior. At the higher levels of this series he finds a pattern of organization which has as one of its properties subjective awareness. The hypothetical precursors of this mysterious capacity to have conscious experience have been variously named—"mind," "mentation," "mind-stuff," "formative property," and so on. However these primordia of mind are named, they have this in common: they are all patterns of integration at various levels of complexity, and the property of awareness is a step-up of integration to a dimension which is different from that of any of the others. To this I would add that the unique quality of human rational thinking suggests that this reasoning process goes on at a level which is again higher than those which are adequate for simpler kinds of mentation. The dimension which is added here is apparently the use of symbols which are consciously fabricated at successively higher levels of abstraction.

It is probable that the operations at these high levels of integration can best be described in terms of a field theory which takes into account the known diversities of the structure and functions of the several parts of the field and integrates these so as to preserve the unity of the dynamic process as a whole. The field of these operations includes the entire body and everything in the environment with which the body has transactional relations. No scientifically acceptable field theory which satisfies these requirements has yet been formulated. There are many unexplained variables, the interrelations of which have not been clarified. The search now is for principles of dynamics which will close this gap and reveal the distinctive properties of those higher dimensions of psychobiological integration that characterize the various types of mentation.

Some of the most disconcerting unexplained experiences are those characterized as telepathy, clairvoyance, extrasensory perception, and others which are grouped in the class of so-called psi phenomena. It must be recognized that many unprejudiced people have recorded experiences that have not been satisfactorily explained by chance or coincidence or any known principles of mechanics. The only way to solve these problems is to extend the current programs of adequately controlled experimental research by well-trained scientists with minds unhampered by preconceptions and metaphysical postulates. The problems of so-called parapsychology, comprising the psi phenomena, do not differ in principles from those presented by every mental and intentionally controlled act of whatever sort. Unconscious factors evidently play a critical role in psi phenomena, just as they do in all conscious behavior, and the search for explanation of both classes of events may lead to the discovery of principles that cannot be defined in terms of either Newtonian or quantum mechanics.

In both psychology and parapsychology progress has been obstructed by the presumption that the observed events are expressions of an adventitious interplay between two independent and disparate domains—the natural and the spiritual—or between a mystic "ideological reality" and "physical reality." This dualistic hypothesis explains nothing and closes the door to further scientific inquiry. Our world of experience is one world, not two; and if this integrated continuum is artificially dismembered no scientific treatment of the fragmented data of experience is possible.

Several prominent students of parapsychology take their stand on dualism and claim to have proved experimentally that psi phenomena (and all mental acts also) are nonphysical processes. As I have elsewhere shown ('55a), this claim is preposterous. These excursions into mysticism and the spiritistic theories derived from them have reinforced a strong prejudice on the part of most scientists against the whole program of parapsychology, a prejudice originally fostered by the charlatanry and delusions prevalent at the beginning of serious study of the alleged phenomena of "spiritualism."

This attitude of skepticism has again obstructed progress. Because some of the psi phenomena do not seem to be explicable by any presently available scientific principles, they are regarded as spurious. But we do not regard gravity as a spurious phenomenon because we do not know how to explain it. What we try to do is to find out how it works, and if no current theories fit the facts we search for other principles that satisfy the requirements. And we try to eliminate any preconceptions or prejudices that may distort the picture. It does not help us to understand psi phenomena to vilify the investigators by accusation of fraud without supporting evidence. In view of the fact that it has been one of the major concerns of students of these phenomena for more than seventy-five years to discover and expose fraud, it is as unscientific as it is unethical to favor the presumption that their findings "are dependent on deliberate fraud or mildly abnormal mental conditions" (Price, '55). Even though we grant that the author just cited has shown that so-called extrasensory perception "is incompatible with current scientific theory," it by no means follows that the recorded data must be rejected as "supernatural" or "nonphysical." It may be that the difficulty arises from the limitations and imperfections of current theory.

The way to learn the true facts about psi phenomena is to explore them by carefully controlled observation and experiment, with every safeguard against error, delusion, and fraud that ingenuity can devise and with a mind receptive to the possibility that the explanations sought may be found only after revision of current physicalistic theory of space, time, and causality.

The open door

These are some of the directions of inquiry which seem to me to offer promise of significant results in psychobiology. We have gained much information about the development, the structure, and the physiological properties of the cortical integrative apparatus. And now, with the presently available methods of oscillographic recording of cortical and other bodily activities and the application of improved clinical and psychological methods, it is possible to make direct correlation of the mental experiences of conscious persons with the organs involved in these vital processes.

This is all to the good, but just what is distinctive about the vital processes from which awareness emerges is still obscure. We have not yet found the answer, but many pieces of it are known, and these must be patiently fitted together as our knowledge is extended.

This much has been gained: we have placed conscious experience in a frame of reference which is congruous with that of all other natural things. This opens the door for thoroughgoing reconstruction of prevailing codes of personal and social conduct that will keep man's spiritual life in more harmonious and efficient adjustment with his physical surroundings. He lives in a natural world, and because he himself is also natural this adjustment in all its relationships can be successfully accomplished by natural means. Furthermore, because man is an intelligent agent he plays the decisive part in determining the course of his own evolutionary future.

The Unknown God

This survey has led to some basic scientific principles, some provisional working hypotheses, and a larger number of unanswered questions. It is obviously incomplete, but it has not reached a dead end. The way is open for further inquiry, and some directions of research that promise fruitful results have been suggested. The critical problems related to the mechanics of mentation are complicated by the fact that many of them as usually stated involve metaphysical conceptions of the supernatural that are inaccessible to natural science. The naturalists are inclined to shy away from these topics because they are irrelevant to their fields of research.

It must be admitted, however, that the visions of the mystics are real events that influence their conduct and that the supernaturalism indoctrinated by the metaphysicians and theologians motivates the behavior of multitudes of people. A comprehensive science of psychobiology cannot neglect these spiritistic beliefs and the resulting practice, because in actual operation they obviously are controlling factors of much personal behavior and of massive social movements.

In our own culture the cleavage of the "spiritual" from the "natural," which is a survival from the most ancient mythologies, has fostered popular ideologies of religious fanaticism, class rivalries, and political antagonisms that are biologically unfit and even suicidal because they result in social disintegration. Our ultimate survival is endangered as long as ideological fantasies that are incompatible with

things as they are control individual and national patterns of behavior. We must somehow manage to heal this artificial dismember-
ment of the human personality before we can hope for a permanent
cure of the present disorder.

Spiritistic ideologies that are irreconcilable with our scientific knowledge must be rejected. Some of them are unmitigated evils, and
as such they must not be ignored. But this does not mean that all
metaphysics and all supernaturalism are evil, for there are many
cherished beliefs for which we have no acceptable scientific evidence
that have great behavioristic value if intelligently applied for the
relief of tensions arising from distress and frustration.

Let us look at the question of the naturalist's attitude toward
the supernatural from this point of view. If we examine it dispas-
sionately and with the mind receptive to all the evidence, we may
find that rigorously mechanistic science may keep the peace with
supernaturalism on the basis of mutual understanding and tolerance.

The operations of natural science are limited by definition to the
domain of nature. We cannot talk rationally about the supernatural
without first explaining what we mean by nature. All science is a
human construction based on human experience, and it can go no
further than the range of possible experience. This sets a logical and
an actual operational limit to nature as envisaged scientifically and
practically.

We have, accordingly, accepted (on page 39) Santayana's definition: "Nature is the sum total of things potentially observable, some
observed actually, others interpolated hypothetically." What may lie
beyond the range of possible human experience is none of the
naturalist's business. Manifestly, then, we cannot expect to find any
evidence for or against a faith in the supernatural by scientific inquiry. If such a faith or hypothesis is entertained, it must be on other
than scientific grounds.

Science as conventionally defined does not comprise all of human
experience, but science, philosophy, esthetics, religion, and all the
other domains of experience should co-operate harmoniously for a
common objective—the enrichment of life. Faiths of various qualities
play a much larger part in all human affairs than is generally recog-

nized. I believe the sun will rise tomorrow morning, but this is a faith, not a fact. A faith is more than a belief based on factual evidence. There is always an extension into the unknown and usually a more or less vivid factor of expectancy and desire or aversion, a factor which gives the faith its motivating efficiency.

Whether any particular faith is justified depends basically on two considerations: first, its consistency with all available knowledge and, second, the consequences which follow from its exercise. In the faiths actually cherished by people, both of these factors vary within the widest possible limits. In common practice the validity of a faith is evaluated by the amount and quality of the supporting evidence. But a faith that can be supported by very little scientifically acceptable evidence or none at all may be justifiable on other grounds. We may ask, how does it work? Does it contribute to personal health of body and mind and to social betterment, or does it foster personal and social disorder? A faith or working hypothesis of any kind that cannot be shown to be erroneous factually must nevertheless be rejected if in practice it results in personal conduct and social movements that are harmful. It is equally true that a faith for which there is little factual evidence may justifiably be entertained if it promotes moral culture and social welfare. On these grounds the justification of a faith is a factual matter to be decided on evidence.

If, now, a naturalist or anybody else wishes to speculate about what may lie beyond the range of possible human experience, that is his privilege. The scientist cannot object to it provided these excursions into transcendentalism do not invade his own domain. It is legitimate to extrapolate from the known facts into the unknown but not to reverse the procedure. Our metaphysics must not be divorced from our physics and from veridical knowledge.

Those of us who prefer to keep our speculations about the unknown within the domain of the natural without any appeal to the supernatural should recognize that within our own field of experience there are many things for which we have as yet no natural explanation. We still have much to learn about the nature of the elementary particles of physics, the radiations of energy into which they are convertible, and the field of operation of the radiations. At the other extreme of magnitude the properties of metagalactic space are still obscure. And between these limits our knowledge is incomplete about the mechanics of the vital processes, of heredity, of muscular contraction, of voluntary action, of hypnotism, of alternating personality, and of the so-called psi phenomena.

In his youth Santayana wrote at the beginning of his *Reason in Science*, "Religion and art have had their day." Science, he then thought, had come at last to displace religion. Fifty years later he said: "Of course we were wrong. . . . Always bear in mind that my naturalism does not exclude religion; on the contrary it allows for it. I mean that religion is the natural reaction of the imagination when confronted by the difficulties of a truculent world" (Cory, '53).

Human imagination is the source of the greatest triumphs of science, technology, art, and philosophy. We must be careful not to cripple its exercise by arbitrary restrictions. It gives us our preeminence over the brutes. But it does not follow that this capacity for constructive thinking is something unique in our cosmos. It is a legitimate hypothesis that this or perhaps some quite different kind of mentality may now be in operation on some other planets of our stellar systems, and there may be patterns of mind far more efficient than ours. Some philosophers go further and admit the possibility of a cosmic mind of higher order than those embodied anywhere locally.

These and the various other theories of panpsychism can claim no scientific support other than by analogy with the only kind of mentation that we know anything about—our own. But in view of these considerations there are, in my opinion, no scientific or philosophic grounds for denying the possibility of an "All Knower," the regulating agency of the natural cosmos which is knowable by man and we know not what besides. Faith in divine power, wisdom, and guidance is for many people their strongest motivation for moral conduct and sustenance of spiritual values. This is for them literally a saving faith in times of distress and affliction. As such it has biological value which the naturalist should frankly recognize, however much he may deplore the irrational dogmatism and fanaticism of some of its advocates. This belief in a personal God conceived as the apotheosis of all the most noble qualities of mankind inspires multitudes of people to resist evil and cherish the finest ideals of which men are capable. For these people this faith is a more efficient motivation for stability of character and good behavior than any other resources that are available to them. Belief in such a God cannot be based on any available scientific evidence. It is frankly an act of faith, a faith that satisfies natural cravings and gives comfort and moral fortitude to millions of people. It is unseemly for any man of science or any philosopher to contemn that faith, even though he himself may not entertain it.

If this faith is clothed in the garb of religion, we should not fail to heed A. Eustace Haydon's warning that by too much faith in gods and other worlds and too little faith in man a practical program of vital religion has been all too long delayed. Here the sciences of man provide us with our most useful implements of cultural development.

We may render to God the things that are God's and to science only the things that are nature's.

We already know enough about our natural cosmos to be humbled by the stupendous magnitude and splendor of it and to be inspired by the realization that the human population of it plays a part in cosmic evolution that is by no means insignificant. For the mind of man, with its capacity for intelligent control of his own cultural development and of the natural resources which are available for his use, is nature's noblest product so far as we know.

The personal worth and dignity of a man is his natural birthright. It is essential that this be everywhere recognized, for this is the cardinal factor of all previous human achievements and our only hope of further evolutionary progress. What this future has in store we cannot forecast, because we do not know what lies beyond the present horizons of the known or the limits of the knowable.

Dogmatism has no place in science, and dogmatism about the unknown is especially reprehensible. We live by faith, faith in the order of nature, faith in ourselves, and faith in our fellow men. This faith is our most prevalent motivation, and it is a reliable guide for behavior just in so far as it is founded on knowledge. Where knowledge is lacking we may extrapolate with due regard for the uncertainties arising from the incompleteness of our knowledge. The mystics too often neglect this caution. The naturalists must not, and they find within the bounties of nature ample scope for their best endeavors and for the satisfaction of their highest aspirations.

We are citizens of the universe. This universe is dynamic and intrinsically creative at all levels of organization. This native creativity is amplified in the domain of organic evolution and glorified when aware of itself in human purposive planning. The sublimity of this conception of man's place in nature commands our reverence and our utmost effort to meet the demands imposed upon us by that nature which is our alma mater.

Bibliography

Adrian, Edgar Douglas. 1947. The physical background of perception. Oxford: Clarendon Press.

Agar, W. E. 1953. A contribution to the theory of the living organism. 2d ed. New York: Cambridge University Press.

Alexander, Irving E., and Thomas F. O'Brien. 1954. High-tone stimulation and hearing loss. Proc. nat. Acad. Sci., Wash., *40*:848–52.

Alexander, Jerome. 1948. Life, its nature and origin. New York: Reinhold.

Alford, Leland B. 1948. Cerebral localization: outline of a revision. New York: Nerv. ment. Dis. Monogr. Ser. 77.

Allee, W. C. 1947. Animal behaviour. Encyclopaedia Britannica, 1947 ed.

———. 1947a. Animal sociology. Encyclopaedia Britannica, 1947 ed.

———. 1951. Cooperation among animals, with human implications. New York: Schuman.

———, A. E. Emerson, O. Park, T. Park, and K. P. Schmidt. 1949. Principles of animal ecology. Philadelphia: Saunders.

Allport, Floyd H. 1955. Theories of perception and the concept of structure. New York: Wiley.

Ames, Adelbert. 1951. Visual perception and the rotating trapezoidal window. Psychol. Monogr., *65*(7):1–32.

Anderson, O. D., and R. Parmenter. 1941. A long-term study of the experimental neurosis in the sheep and dog. (Washington: National Research Council) Psychosom. Monogr., *2*(3, 4).

Ariëns Kappers, C. U. 1929. The evolution of the nervous system. Haarlem: E. F. Bohn.

———, G. Carl Huber, and Elizabeth Caroline Crosby. 1936. The comparative anatomy of the nervous system of vertebrates, including man. New York: Macmillan.

Arnot, Robert. 1952. A theory of frontal lobe function. Arch. Neurol. Psychiat., Chicago, 67:487–95.

Ashby, W. Ross. 1952. Design for a brain. New York: Wiley.

Bagehot, Walter. 1873. Physics and politics. New York: Appleton.

Bailey, Percival. 1956. Concerning the localization of consciousness. Trans. Amer. Neurol. Ass. 1955, pp. 1–12.

————, and Gerhardt von Bonin. 1951. The isocortex of man. Urbana: University of Illinois Press.

Baitsell, G. A. 1955. The cell as a structural unit. Amer. Scientist, 43:133–41, 147. Based on a paper in Amer. Nat., 74:5–24 (1940).

Baldwin, J. M. 1902. Development and evolution. New York: Macmillan.

Barber, Bernard. 1952. Science and the social order. Glencoe, Ill.: The Free Press.

Barker, Roger G., Jacob S. Kounin, and Herbert F. Wright (eds.). 1943. Child behavior and development. New York: McGraw-Hill.

Barron, D. H. 1954. The histogenesis of the spinal cord and the early development of behavior. Proc. Ass. Res. nerv. ment. Dis., 33:155–73.

Bartley, S. Howard. 1942. Visual sensation and its dependence on the neurophysiology of the optic pathway. (Lancaster, Pa.) Biol. Symposia, 7:87–106.

————, and Eloise Chute. 1947. Fatigue and impairment in man. New York: McGraw-Hill.

Bath, Cyril J. 1948. Europe in the modern age. New York: American Association for the United Nations.

Beach, Frank Ambrose. 1947. Payday for primates. Nat. Hist., 56:448–51.

Beck, Lewis White. 1949. The "natural science ideal" in the social sciences. Sci. Mon, 68:386–94.

Beebe, William. 1921. Edge of the jungle. New York: Holt.

Benedict, F. G., and C. G. Benedict. 1930. The energy requirements of intense mental effort. Proc. nat. Acad. Sci., Wash., 16:438–43.

Bentley, Arthur F. 1941. The factual space and time of behavior. J. Phil., 38:477–85.

————. 1950. Kennetic inquiry. Science, 112:775–83.

Berger, Hans. 1921. Psychophysiologie. Jena: Fischer.

Bernhaut, M., E. Gellhorn, and A. T. Rasmussen. 1953. Experimental contributions to problem of consciousness. J. Neurophysiol., 16:21–35.

Bertalanffy, Ludwig von. 1950. The theory of open systems in physics and biology. Science, 111:23–29.

Birkhoff, George D. 1933. Aesthetic measure. Cambridge, Mass.: Harvard University Press.

Bishop, George H. 1948. The skin as an organ of senses with special reference to the itching sensation. J. invest. Dermatology, *11*:143–54.

Blake, Robert R., and Glenn V. Ramsey (eds.). 1951. Perception: an approach to personality. New York: Ronald.

Blum, Josephine Semmes, Kao Liang Chow, and Karl H. Pribram. 1950. A behavioral analysis of the organization of the parieto-temporo-pre-occipital cortex. J. comp. Neurol., *93*:53–100.

Boland, Grant L. 1949. Partial lesions of the prefrontal lobes of the macaque. (abstr.) Anat. Rec., *103*:426–27.

Bonin, Gerhardt von. 1950. Essay on the cerebral cortex. Springfield, Ill.: Thomas.

Boodin, John Elof. 1943. Cosmic attributes. Phil. Sci. *10*:1–12.

Boring, Edwin G. 1950. A history of experimental psychology. 2d ed. New York: Appleton-Century.

———. 1955. Dual role of the Zeitgeist in scientific creativity. Sci. Mon., *80*:101–106.

Bouglé, C. 1926. The evolution of values. Trans. Helen Stalker Sellars. New York: Holt.

Boulding, Kenneth E. 1949. Is economics necessary? Sci. Mon., *68*:235–40.

Boyajian, A. 1944. A. A. Michelson visits Immanuel Kant. Sci. Mon., *59*:438–50.

Brazier, Mary A. B. 1948. Neural nets and integration of behaviour. An essay in perspectives in neuropsychiatry. London: H. K. Lewis.

———. 1951. The electrical activity of the nervous system. New York: Macmillan.

———. 1952. Expanding concepts in neurophysiology. Arch. Neurol. Psychiat., Chicago, *67*:545–49.

Bridgman, P. W. 1954. Science and common sense. Sci. Mon., *79*:32–39.

———. 1956. Probability, logic and ESP. Science, *123*:15–17.

Brillouin, L. 1949. Life, thermodynamics, and cybernetics. Amer. Scientist, *37*:554–68.

Bronowski, Jacob. 1953. The common sense of science. Cambridge, Mass.: Harvard University Press.

Bucy, Paul C., and Heinrich Klüver. 1955. An anatomical investigation of the temporal lobe in the monkey (Macaca mulatta). J. comp. Neurol., *103*:151–251.

Bull, Nina. 1951. The attitude theory of emotion. New York: Nerv. ment. Dis. Monogr. Ser. 81.

Buros, Oscar Krisen (ed.). 1953. The fourth mental measurements yearbook. Highland Park, N.J.: Gryphon Press.

Burr, H. S. 1947. Field theory in biology. Sci. Mon., *64*:217–25.

————, and F. S. C. Northrop. 1935. The electro-dynamic theory of life. Quart. Rev. Biol., *10*:322–33.

Burrow, Trigant. 1953. Science and man's behavior. New York: Philosophical Library.

Byrd, Richard E. 1938. Alone. New York: Putnam.

Cameron, D. Ewen. 1948. The current transition in the conception of science. Science, *107*:553–58.

Cannon, Walter, B. 1939. The wisdom of the body. 2d ed. New York: Norton.

Cantril, Hadley. 1947. The place of personality in social psychology. J. Psychol., *24*:19–56.

————. 1947a. Understanding man's social behavior. Preliminary notes. Princeton, N.J.: privately printed.

————. 1949. Toward a scientific morality. J. Psychol., *27*:363–76.

————. 1949a. Psychology working for peace. Amer. Psychologist, *4*:69–73.

————, A. Ames, A. H. Hastorf, and W. H. Ittelson. 1949. Psychology and scientific research. Science, *110*:461–64, 491–97, 517–22.

Carmichael, Leonard (ed). 1954. Manual of child psychology. 2d ed. New York: Wiley.

Carpenter, C. R. 1934. A field study of the behavior and social relations of howling monkeys (Alouatta palliata). Comp. Psychol. Monogr., *10*(2):1–168.

————. 1940. A field study in Siam of the behavior and social relations of the gibbon (Hylobates lar). Comp. Psychol. Monogr., *16*(5):1–212.

————. 1942. Sexual behavior of free ranging rhesus monkeys. J. comp. Psychol., *33*:113–62.

————, and N. M. Locke. 1937. Notes on symbolic behavior in a cebus monkey (Capucinus appella). J. genet. Psychol., *55*:267–78.

Carr, Harvey A. 1925. Psychology. New York: Longmans.

Chauncey, Henry. 1952. The use of the selective service college qualification test in the deferment of college students. Science, *116*:73–79.

Child, C. M. 1924. Physiological foundations of behavior. New York: Holt.

————. 1941. Patterns and problems of development. Chicago: University of Chicago Press.

Chisholm, George Brock. 1949. Social responsibility. Science, *109*:27–30.

Chow, Kao Liang, Josephine Semmes Blum, and Robert A. Blum. 1950. Cell ratios in the thalamo-cortical visual system of Macaca mulatta. J. comp. Neurol., *92*:227–39.

Clark, W. E. Le Gros. 1947. Anatomical pattern as the essential basis of sensory discrimination. Springfield, Ill.: Thomas.

————. 1947a. Observations on the anatomy of the fossil Austral-opithecinae. J. Anat., *81*:300–33.

————. 1950. History of the primates. 2d ed. London: British Museum.

————. 1955. The fossil evidence for human evolution. Chicago: University of Chicago Press.

Coghill, G. E. 1929. Anatomy and the problem of behavior. London: Cambridge University Press.

————. 1930. The structural basis of the integration of behavior. Proc. nat. Acad. Sci., Wash., *16*:637–43.

————. 1930a. The genetic interrelation of instinctive behavior and reflexes. Psychol. Rev., *37*:264–66.

————. 1933. The biologic basis of conflict in behavior. Psychoanal. Rev., *20*:1–4. Also in Trans. Amer. neurol. Ass., 58th meeting, 1932, pp. 629–32.

————. 1938. Space-time as a pattern of psycho-organismal mentation. Amer. J. Psychol., *51*:759–63.

————. 1941. The educational methods of F. Matthias Alexander. An appreciation. An essay on pages xxi–xxviii of The universal constant in living, by Mr. Alexander. New York: Dutton.

Cohen, Morris R. 1931. Reason and nature. New York: Harcourt, Brace.

Condon, E. U. 1948. Science and security. Science, *107*:659–65.

Conklin, Edwin Grant. 1930. Heredity and environment in the development of men. 6th ed. Princeton, N.J.: Princeton University Press.

————. 1943. Man, real and ideal. New York: Scribner.

Connolly, Cornelius Joseph. 1950. External morphology of the primate brain. Springfield, Ill.: Thomas.

Cory, Daniel. 1953. Santayana's last year. Atlantic Monthly, *191*(4): 66–69.

Cowles, John T. 1937. Food-tokens as incentives for learning by chimpanzees. Comp. Psychol. Monogr., *14*(5):1–96.

Cushen, W. Edward. 1955. Operations research and philosophy. Science, *121*:584–86.

Dandy, W. 1946. The location of the conscious center in the brain—the corpus striatum. Johns Hopk. Hosp. Bull., *79*:34–58.

Darling, F. Fraser. 1951. The ecological approach to the social sciences. Amer. Scientist, *39*:244–54.

Dart, R. A. 1947. The attainment of poise. S. Afr. J. med. Sci., *21*(3):74–91.

Detwiler, S. R. 1945. The results of unilateral and bilateral extirpation of the forebrain of Amblystoma. J. exp. Zool., *100*:103–17.

Dewey, John. 1917. The need for a recovery of philosophy. In Creative intelligence, New York: Holt, pp. 3–69.

———. 1925. Experience and nature. Chicago: Open Court Pub. Co.

———. 1938. Logic, the theory of inquiry. New York: Holt.

———. 1939. Freedom and culture. New York: Putnam.

———. 1948. Common sense and science. J. Phil., *45*:197–208.

———, and Arthur F. Bentley. 1949. Knowing and the known. Boston: Beacon Press.

Dobzhansky, Th. 1950. Heredity, environment, and evolution. Science, *111*:161–66.

———. 1951. Genetics and the origin of species. 3d ed. New York: Columbia University Press.

Dreiman, David B. 1955. How to get better schools. New York: Harper.

Droogleever Fortuyn, A. E. B. 1914. Cortical cell-lamination of the hemispheres of some rodents. Arch. Neurol. Psychiat., Chicago, *6*:221–354.

Dusser de Barenne, J. G. 1934. Central levels of sensory integration. Proc. Ass. Res. nerv. ment. Dis., *15*:274–88. Condensed under same title in Arch. Neurol. Psychiat., Chicago, *34*:768–76 (1935).

Dyson, Freeman J. 1953. Field theory. Sci. Amer., *188*(4):57–64.

Eby, Kermit. 1951. Life is my laboratory. Univ. of Chicago Mag., *45*(5):14–17.

Eccles, John Carew. 1953. The neurophysiological basis of mind: the principles of neurophysiology. New York: Oxford University Press.

Edinger, Tilly. 1949. Paleoneurology versus comparative brain anatomy. Confinia Neurologica, *9*:5–24.

Eells, Kenneth, Allison Davis, Robert J. Havighurst, Virgil E. Herrick, and Ralph Tyler. 1951. Intelligence and cultural differences. Chicago: University of Chicago Press.

Emerson, Alfred E. 1939. Social coordination and the superorganism. Amer. Midland Naturalist, *21*:182–209.

———. 1954. Dynamic homeostasis: a unifying principle in organic, social, and ethical evolution. Sci. Mon., *78*:67–85.

Engel, Leonard. 1955. What Einstein was up to. Harper's Magazine, *211*(1267):69–74.

Frank, Lawrence K. 1948. Society as the patient: essays on culture and personality. New Brunswick, N.J.: Rutgers University Press.

———. 1951. Nature and human nature—man's new image of himself. New Brunswick, N.J.: Rutgers University Press.

———, Norbert Wiener, G. Evelyn Hutchinson, W. K. Livingston, and Warren S. McCulloch. 1948. Teleological mechanisms. Ann. N.Y. Acad. Sci., *50*:187–277.

Freeman, Walter, and James W. Watts. 1950. Psychosurgery. 2d ed. Springfield, Ill.: Thomas.

Fulton, John Farquhar. 1943. Physiology of the nervous system. 2d ed. New York: Oxford University Press.

———. 1949. Functional localization in relation to frontal lobotomy. New York: Oxford University Press.

Garnett, A. Campbell. 1942. Scientific method and the concept of emergence. J. Phil., 39:477–86.

Geldard, Frank A. 1953. The human senses. New York: Wiley.

Gerard, R. W. 1940. Organism, society and science. Sci. Mon., 50:340–50, 403–12, 530–35.

———. 1942. Higher levels of integration. Biol. Symposia, 8:67–87.

———. 1949. Physiology and psychiatry. Amer. J. Psychiat., 106:161–73.

———. 1955. Biological roots of psychiatry. Science, 122:225–30.

———, and A. E. Emerson. 1945. Extrapolation from the biological to the social. Science, 101:582–85.

Gesell, Arnold. 1945. The embryology of behavior: the beginnings of the human mind. New York: Harper.

Gibbs, Frederic Andrews. 1951. The most important thing. Amer. J. Publ. Hlth, 41:1503–1508.

Ginzberg, Eli. 1948. Social science and the established order. Science, 107:607–11.

Glass, Bentley. 1951. A biologic view of human history. Sci. Mon., 73:363–68.

Glees, P., and J. Cole. 1950. Recovery of skilled motor functions after small repeated lesions of motor cortex in macaque. J. Neurophysiol., 13:137–48.

Goldstein, Kurt. 1940. Human nature in the light of psycholopathology. Cambridge, Mass.: Harvard University Press.

Granit, Ragnar. 1955. Receptors and sensory perception. A discussion of aims, means, and results of electrophysiological research into the process of reception. New Haven, Conn.: Yale University Press.

Gray, George W. 1955. The Yerkes laboratories. Sci. Amer., 192(2):67–77.

Greenblatt, Milton, Robert Arnot, and Harry C. Solomon (eds.). 1950. Studies in lobotomy. New York: Grune & Stratton.

Greenman, E. F. 1948. The extraorganic. Amer. Anthrop., 50:181–99.

Griffin, Donald R. 1953. Sensory physiology and the orientation of animals. Amer. Scientist, 41:208–44.

Grinker, Roy R. 1953. Psychosomatic research. New York: Norton.

Grünbaum, Adolf. 1952. Causality and the science of human behavior. Amer. Scientist, *40*:665–76.

———. 1955. Time and entropy. Amer. Scientist, *43*:550–72.

Guggenheim, Louis Kaufman. 1948. Phylogenesis of the ear. Culver City, Calif.: Murray and Gee.

Guilford, J. P. 1955. Structure of human intellect. Science, *122*:875.

Hadamard, Jacques. 1945. An essay on the psychology of invention in the mathematical field. Princeton, N.J.: Princeton University Press.

Haldane, J. B. S. 1949. Interaction of physics, chemistry and biology. In Sellars *et al.*, 1949, pp. 202–21.

Halstead, Ward C. 1947. Brain and intelligence; a quantitative study of the frontal lobes. Chicago: University of Chicago Press.

———. 1951. Brain and intelligence. In Jeffress, 1951, pp. 244–88.

Hamilton, G. V. 1948. A research in marriage. New York: Lear.

Haring, Douglas C. 1947. Science and social phenomena. Amer. Scientist, *35*:351–63.

———. 1950. The social sciences and biology. Beiträge zur Gesellungs- und Völkerwissenschaft. Berlin: Gebr. Mann, pp. 125–35.

Harlow, Harry F. 1950. The effect of large cortical lesions on learned behavior in monkeys. (abstr.) Science, *112*:428.

Hartung, Frank E. 1945. The social function of positivism. Phil. Sci., *12*:120–33.

———. 1948. On the contribution of sociology to the physical sciences. Phil. Sci., *15*:109–15.

Haskins, Caryl P. 1939. Of ants and men. New York: Prentice-Hall.

———. 1951. Of societies and men. New York: Norton.

Hayek, F. A. 1952. The sensory order. An inquiry into the foundations of theoretical psychology. Chicago: University of Chicago Press.

Hayes, Cathy. 1951. The ape in our house. New York: Harper.

Hebb, Donald O. 1949. The organization of behavior. A neuropsychological theory. New York: Wiley.

Helson, Harry. 1930. The tau effect—an example of psychological relativity. Science, *71*:536–37.

———, and Samuel M. King. 1931. The *tau* effect: an example of psychological relativity. J. exp. Psychol., *14*:202–17.

Henderson, Lawrence J. 1913. The fitness of the environment. New York: Macmillan.

Henle, Paul. 1942. The status of emergence. J. Phil., *39*:486–93.

Herrick, C. Judson. 1894. The evolution of Huxley. Denison Collegian, *27*:60–62.

———. 1905. A functional view of nature as seen by a biologist. J. Phil., *2*:428–38.

———. 1915. Introspection as a biological method. J. Phil., *12*:543–51.

———. 1921. A sketch of the origin of the cerebral hemispheres. J. comp. Neurol., *32*:429–54.

———. 1924. Neurological foundations of animal behavior. New York: Holt.

———. 1925. Some relationships of the visceral nervous system. Int. Clinics, 35th Ser. *1*:36–45. Philadelphia: Lippincott.

———. 1926. Brains of rats and men. Chicago: University of Chicago Press.

———. 1926a. Biological determinism and human freedom. Int. J. Ethics, *37*:36–52.

———. 1926b. Fatalism or freedom. A biologist's answer. New York: Norton.

———. 1927. The amphibian forebrain. IV. The cerebral hemispheres of Amblystoma. J. comp. Neurol., *43*:231–325.

———. 1928. The spiritual life. J. Relig., *8*:505–23.

———. 1929. Mechanism and organism. J. Phil., *26*:589–97.

———. 1930. The order of nature. The Monist, *40*:182–92.

———. 1930a. Localization of function in the nervous system. Proc. nat. Acad. Sci., Wash., *16*:643–50.

———. 1931. An introduction to neurology. 5th ed. Philadelphia: Saunders.

———. 1932. The thinking machine. 2d ed. Chicago: University of Chicago Press.

———. 1933. The functions of the olfactory parts of the cerebral cortex. Proc. nat. Acad. Sci., Wash., *19*:7–14.

———. 1933a. Morphogenesis of the brain. J. Morph., *54*:233–58.

———. 1933b. The amphibian forebrain. VI. Necturus. J. comp. Neurol., *58*:1–288.

———. 1933c. *Idem.* VIII. Cerebral hemispheres and pallial primordia. J. comp. Neurol., *58*:737–59.

———. 1934. *Idem.* IX. Neuropil and other interstitial nervous tissue. J. comp. Neurol., *59*:93–116.

———. 1934a. *Idem.* X. Localized functions and integrating functions. J. comp. Neurol., *59*:239–66.

———. 1936. Neurobiological foundations of modern humanism. Proc. Inst. Med. Chicago, *11*:86–99.

———. 1936a. Is truth a value? J. Phil., *33*:169–75.

———. 1938. A biologist looks at the profit motive. Social Forces, *16*:320–27.

———. 1938a. A biological survey of learning. Educational Trends, *6*:5–13.

———. 1939. A neurologist makes up his mind. Sci. Mon., *49*:99–110.

————. 1941. Optic and postoptic systems of fibers in the brain of Necturus. J. comp. Neurol., *75*:487–544.

————. 1941a. Development of the optic nerve of Amblystoma. J. comp. Neurol., *74*:473–534.

————. 1941b. Naturalistic ethics. The Humanist, *1*:73–79.

————. 1942. Optic and postoptic systems in the brain of Amblystoma tigrinum. J. comp. Neurol., *77*:191–353.

————. 1944. The incentives of science. Sci. Mon., *58*:462–66.

————. 1944a. Apparatus of optic and visceral correlation in the brain of Amblystoma. J. comp. Psychol., *37*:97–105.

————. 1945. The natural history of experience. Phil. Sci., *12*:57–71.

————. 1946. Scientific method and human values. Amer. Scientist, *34*:239–45.

————. 1947. The proprioceptive nervous system. J. nerv. ment. Dis., *106*:355–58.

————. 1947a. Seeing and believing. Sci. Mon., *64*:253–60.

————. 1948. The brain of the tiger salamander, Ambystoma tigrinum. Chicago: University of Chicago Press.

————. 1949. George Ellett Coghill, naturalist and philosopher. Chicago: University of Chicago Press.

————. 1949a. A biological survey of integrative levels. In Sellars *et al.*, 1949, pp. 222–42.

————. 1954. One hundred volumes of the Journal of Comparative Neurology. J. comp. Neurol., *100*:717–56.

————. 1955. Clarence Luther Herrick, pioneer naturalist, teacher, and psychobiologist. Trans. Amer. Phil. Soc., *45*(1):1–85.

————. 1955a. Psychology from a biologist's point of view. Psychol. Rev., *62*:333–40.

————, and O. Larsell. 1948. The proprius system. (abstr.) Anat. Rec., *100*:673.

Herrick, C. L. 1894. The seat of consciousness. J. comp. Neurol., *4*:221–26.

————. 1896. Is the decorticated dog conscious? J. comp. Neurol., *6*:xxi–xxiii.

————. 1904. The beginnings of social reaction in man and lower animals. J. comp. Neurol., *14*:118–23.

————. 1910. The metaphysics of a naturalist (philosophical and psychological fragments compiled by H. Heath Bawden). Bull. Sci. Lab. Denison Univ. *15*:1–99.

Hill, Denis (ed). 1949. Anglo-American symposium on psychosurgery, neurophysiology, and physical treatments in psychiatry. Proc. roy. Soc. Med., *42* (Suppl.):1–95.

Himwich, H. E. 1952. The functional organization of the central nervous system, an experimental analysis. Proc. Inst. Med. Chicago, 19:115–27.

Hoagland, Hudson. 1949. Rhythmic behavior of the nervous system. Science, 109:157–64.

Hockett, Charles F. 1948. Biophysics, linguistics, and the unity of science. Amer. Scientist, 36:558–72.

Holmes, S. J. 1944. Life, morals, and Huxley's "Evolution and Ethics." Science in the University. Berkeley, Calif.: University of California Press, pp. 319–32.

———. 1948. Organic form and related biological problems. Berkeley, Calif.: University of California Press.

———. 1948a. What is natural selection? Sci. Mon., 67:324–30.

———. 1948b. Life and morals. New York: Macmillan.

Hook, Sidney. 1949. John Dewey at ninety. The man and his philosophy. The New Leader, 32(43):1–3.

Hooker, Davenport. 1936. Early fetal activity in mammals. Yale J. Biol. Med., 8:579–602.

———. 1939. A preliminary atlas of early human fetal activity. Pittsburgh: privately printed.

———. 1939a. Fetal behavior. Proc. Ass. Res. nerv. ment. Dis., 19:237–43.

———. 1942. Fetal reflexes and instinctual processes. Psychosom. Med., 4:199–205.

———. 1943. Reflex activities in the human fetus. In Barker, Kounin, and Wright, 1943, chap. 2 (pp. 17–28).

———. 1952. The prenatal origin of behavior. Lawrence, Kan.: University of Kansas Press.

Horst, C. J. van der. 1947. The limitations of classification. S. Afr. Museums Ass. Bull., 4(3):56–62.

Howells, William. 1954. Back of history. The story of our own origins. Garden City, N.Y.: Doubleday.

Hunt, J. McV. (ed). 1944. Personality and the behavior disorders. New York: Ronald. See especially the chapters Conditioned reflex method and experimental neurosis, by H. S. Liddell; Experimental behavior disorders in the rat, by Frank W. Finger; and Experimental studies of conflict, by Neal E. Miller.

Huxley, Julian. 1943. Evolution, the modern synthesis. New York: Harper.

———. 1944. On living in a revolution. New York: Harper.

———. 1953. Evolution in action. New York: Harper.

Huxley, T. H., and Julian Huxley. 1947. Evolution and ethics: 1893–1943. London: Pilot Press. See also T. H. Huxley, Collected essays, vol. 9. New York: Appleton, 1902.

Irvine, W. 1955. Apes, angels and victorians. New York: McGraw-Hill.
Ittelson, W. 1952. The Ames demonstrations in perception. New Brunswick, N.J.: Princeton University Press.

James, William. 1890. The principles of psychology. New York: Holt.
————. 1904. A world of pure experience. J. Phil., *1*:533–43.
Jasper, Herbert H. 1948. Charting the sea of brain waves. Science, *108*:343–47.
Jeans, James. 1943. Physics and philosophy. New York: Macmillan.
Jeffress, Lloyd A. (ed.). 1951. Cerebral mechanisms in behavior. New York: Wiley.
Jenkins, Iredell. 1948. What is a normative science? J. Phil., *45*:309–32.
Jennings, H. S. 1906. Behavior of the lower organisms. New York: Columbia University Press.
Jensen, Howard E. 1941. Science and human values. Sci. Mon., *53*:258–66.
————. 1953. Mental health: a local public-health responsibility. Men. Hyg., N.Y., *37*:530–44.
Johnson, H. M. 1936. Pseudo-mathematics in the mental and social sciences. Amer. J. Psychol., *48*:342–51.
————. 1945. Are psychophysical problems genuine or spurious? Amer. J. Psychol., *58*:189–211.

Kaada, Birger R. 1951. Somato-motor, autonomic and electrocorticographic responses to electrical stimulation of "rhinencephalic" and other structures in primates, cat and dog. Acta Physiologica Scandinavica, *23* (Suppl. 83):1–285.
Katz, Bernhard. 1952. The nerve impulse. Sci. Amer., *187*(5):55–64.
Katz, David. 1937. Animals and men: studies in comparative psychology. New York: Longmans.
Keeton, Morris T. 1950. Edmund Montgomery. A definitive study of a pioneer in philosophy. Dallas, Texas: University Press in Dallas.
Keith, Arthur. 1949. A new theory of human evolution. New York: Philosophical Library.
Kellogg, Winthrop Niles, and Luella A. Kellogg. 1933. The ape and the child. New York: McGraw-Hill.
Kemeny, John G. 1955. Man viewed as a machine. Sci. Amer., *192*(4):58–67.
Klüver, Heinrich, 1949. Psychology at the beginning of World War II. J. Psychol., *28*:383–410.
————. 1951. Functional differences between the occipital and temporal lobes with special reference to the interrelations of behavior and extracerebral mechanisms. In Jeffress, 1951, pp. 147–99.

————. 1952. Brain mechanisms and behavior with special reference to the rhinencephalon. Journal-Lancet, *72*:567–74.

Köhler, Wolfgang. 1918. The mentality of apes. New York: Harcourt, Brace.

————. 1938. The place of value in a world of facts. New York: Liveright.

————. 1940. Dynamics in psychology. New York: Liveright.

————. 1944. Value and fact. J. Phil., *41*:197–212.

————. 1951. Relational determination in perception. In Jeffress, 1951, pp. 200–43.

Krechevsky, I. 1932. "Hypothesis" versus "chance" in the pre-solution period in sensory discrimination-learning. Univ. Calif. Publ. Psychol., *6*:27–44. The genesis of "hypothesis" in rats. *Ibid.*, pp. 45–64.

Krieg, Wendell J. S. 1946. Connections of the cerebral cortex. I. The albino rat. A. Topography of the cortical areas. J. comp. Neurol., *84*:221–75. B. Structure of the cortical areas. *Ibid.*, *84*:277–383.

————. 1947. *Idem.* C. Extrinsic connections. J. comp. Neurol., *86*:267–394.

Kroeber, A. L. 1948. White's view of culture. Amer. Anthrop., *50*:405–15.

————. 1949. Values as a subject of natural science inquiry. Proc. nat. Acad. Sci., *35*:261–64.

————. 1949a. The concept of culture in science. J. gen. Educ., *3*:182–96.

————. 1952. Sign and symbol in bee communications. Proc. nat. Acad. Sci., *38*:753–57.

La Barre, Weston. 1954. The human animal. Chicago: University of Chicago Press.

Langfeld, Herbert S. 1931. A response interpretation of consciousness. Psychol. Rev., *38*:87–108.

Lapan, Arthur. 1937. The causal situation. J. Phil., *34*:179–86.

Larsell, O. 1934. The differentiation of the peripheral and central acoustic apparatus in the frog. J. comp. Neurol., *60*:473–527.

Lashley, K. S. 1929. Brain mechanisms and intelligence. Chicago: University of Chicago Press.

————. 1942. The problem of cerebral organization in vision. (Lancaster, Pa.) Biol. Symposia, *7*:301–22.

————. 1947. Structural variation in the nervous system in relation to behavior. Psychol. Rev., *54*:325–34.

————. 1949. Persistent problems in the evolution of mind. Quart. Rev. Biol., *24*:28–42.

————. 1951. The problem of serial order in behavior. In Jeffress, 1951, pp. 112–46.

Lawrence, M. 1949. Studies in human behavior. Princeton, N.J.: Princeton University Press.

Leake, Chauncey D., and Patrick P. Romanell. 1950. Can we agree? A scientist and a philosopher argue about ethics. Austin, Texas: University of Texas Press.

Lewin, Kurt. 1951. Field theory in social science. New York: Harper.

Lief, Alfred. 1948. The commonsense psychiatry of Dr. Adolf Meyer. New York: McGraw-Hill.

Lillie, Ralph S. 1945. General biology and philosophy of organism. Chicago: University of Chicago Press.

————. 1948. Some aspects of theoretical biology. Phil. Sci., 15:118–34.

————. 1948a. Philosophy of organism: a rejoinder to Professor Werkmeister. Phil. Phenom. Res., 8:706–11.

————. 1948b. Randomness and directiveness in the evolution and activity of living organisms. Amer. Nat., 82:5–25.

————. 1951. Biology and unitary principle. Phil. Sci., 18:193–207.

Loeb, Leo. 1945. The biological basis of individuality. Springfield, Ill.: Thomas.

Lundberg, George A. 1947. Can science save us? New York: Longmans.

————. 1950. Alleged obstacles to social science. Sci. Mon., 70:299–305.

————. 1950a. Can science validate ethics? Bull. Amer. Ass. Univer. Professors, 36:262–75.

Luneburg, Rudolf Karl. 1947. Mathematical analysis of binocular vision. Princeton, N.J.: Princeton University Press.

McCulloch, Warren S. 1949. Physiological processes underlying psychoneuroses. In Hill, 1949, pp. 71–84.

————, and John Pfeiffer. 1949. Of digital computers called brains. Sci. Mon., 69:368–76.

Maier, Norman R. F. 1929. Reasoning in white rats. Comp. Psychol. Monogr., 6(3):1–93.

————. 1937. Reasoning in rats and human beings. Psychol. Rev., 44:365–78.

————. 1938. A further analysis of reasoning in rats. Comp. Psychol. Monogr., 15(1):1–85.

————. 1939. The specific processes constituting the learning function. Psychol. Rev., 46:241–52.

————. 1940. The behavior mechanisms concerned with problem solving. Psychol. Rev., 47:43–58.

————. 1948. Experimentally induced abnormal behavior. Sci. Mon., 67:210–16.

————. 1949. Frustration: the study of behavior without a goal. New York: McGraw-Hill.

————, and T. C. Schneirla. 1935. Principles of animal psychology. New York: McGraw-Hill.

Margenau, Henry. 1950. The nature of physical reality: a philosophy of modern physics. New York: McGraw-Hill.

————. 1954. On interpretations and misinterpretations of operationalism. Sci. Mon., 79:209–10.

Marrazzi, Amedeo S. 1953. Some indications of cerebral humoral mechanisms. Science, 118:367–70.

Masserman, Jules H. 1943. Behavior and neurosis. Chicago: University of Chicago Press.

————. 1950. Experimental neuroses. Sci. Amer., 182(3):38–43.

Mead, George Herbert. 1934. Mind, self and society. Chicago: University of Chicago Press.

————. 1936. Movements of thought in the nineteenth century. Chicago: University of Chicago Press.

Mead, Leonard C., and Joseph Wulfeck. 1952. Human engineering: the study of the human factor in machine design. Sci. Mon., 75:372–79.

Mead, Margaret. 1939. Coming of age in Samoa, 1928. Included in From the south seas, compl. 1939. New York: Morrow.

Mettler, Fred A. (ed.). 1949. Selective partial ablation of the frontal cortex. New York: Hoeber.

————, Archie Crandell, J. R. Wittenborn, Kathleen Litten, Emanuel H. Feiring, and Malcomb B. Carpenter. 1954. Factors, in the preoperative situation of schizophrenics, considered to be of significance in influencing outcome following psychosurgery. Psychiat. Quart., 28:549–606.

Meyer, Adolf. See Lief, 1948.

Meyer, Agnes E. 1955. Voluntary action in a democracy. Bull. Amer. Ass. Univer. Professors, 41:42–61.

Montgomery, Edmund. 1907. Philosophical problems in the light of vital organization. New York: Putnam.

————. 1910. The revelation of present experience. Boston: Sherman, French.

Moog, Florence. 1947. Huxley on progress. Amer. Scientist, 35:540–42.

Morgan, C. Lloyd. 1908. Animal behaviour. 2d ed. New York: Longmans.

————. 1926. Emergent evolution. New York: Holt.

————. 1943. Animal behaviour. Encyclopaedia Britannica, 1943 ed.

Morris, Charles, and Lyle V. Jones. 1955. Value scales and dimensions. J. Abnorm. soc. Psychol., *51*:523–25. Condensed from Varieties of human value. Chicago: University of Chicago Press. In press, 1956.

Moulton, J. F. 1924. Law and manners. Atlantic Monthly, *134*:1–5.

Moulyn, Adrian C. 1950. The limitations of mechanistic methods in the biological sciences. Sci. Mon., *71*:44–49.

Mountford, Charles P. 1951. Brown men and red sand. Journeyings in wild Australia. New York: Praeger.

Muller, Herbert J. 1943. Science and criticism. New Haven, Conn.: Yale University Press.

Muller, Hermann J. 1955. Life. Science, *121*:1–9. Condensed in The Humanist, *15*:249–61.

Murdock, George Peter. 1949. The science of human learning, society, culture, and personality. Sci. Mon., *69*:377–81.

Murphy, A. E. 1943. The uses of reason. New York: Macmillan.

Nachmansohn, D. (ed.) 1951. Nerve impulse. Trans. 2d conference. New York: Josiah Macy, Jr., Found. See also 3d conference, 1952, and the symposium on the neuron, Cold Spr. Harb. Sympos., vol. 17, 1952.

Needham, Joseph. 1943. Time, the refreshing river. New York: Macmillan.

———. 1945. A note on Dr. Novikoff's article. Science, *101*:582.

———. 1946. On science and social change. Sci. Soc., *10*:225–51.

Neumann, John von. 1951. The general and logical theory of automata. In Jeffress, 1951, pp. 1–41.

Nicholson, N. C. 1920. Notes on muscular work during hypnosis. Johns Hopk. Hosp. Bull., *31*:89–91.

Nissen, Henry W. 1946. Primate psychology. In Encyclopedia of psychology. New York: Philosophical Library, pp. 546–70.

Northrop, F. S. C. 1947. The logic of the sciences and the humanities. New York: Macmillan.

———. 1948. The neurological and behavioristic psychological basis of the ordering of society by means of ideas. Science, *107*:411–17.

Novikoff, Alex B. 1945. The concept of integrative levels and biology. Science, *101*:209–15.

———. 1945a. Continuity and discontinuity in evolution. Science, *102*:405–406.

Ogden, Robert Morris. 1925. Crossing "the Rubicon between mechanism and life." J. Phil., *22*:281–93.

Økland, F. 1949. Er tilvaerelsen femdimensjonal? (with English summary). Oslo: Cammermeyers Boghandel.

————. 1950. The structure of nature. Norske Videnskapsakedemi i Oslo, I. Mat.-Naturv. Klasse, 1950, no. 5, pp. 1–11.

Osborn, Henry Fairfield. 1917. The origin and evolution of life. New York: Scribner.

Pannekoek, A. 1953. Anthropogenesis. A study of the origin of man. Amsterdam: North-Holland Publishing Co.

Parker, G. H. 1908. The origin of the lateral eyes of vertebrates. Amer. Nat., 42:601–609.

————. 1919. The elementary nervous system. Philadelphia: Lippincott.

Patrick, G. T. W. 1929. What is the mind? New York: Macmillan.

Penfield, Wilder. 1938. The cerebral cortex and consciousness. Arch. Neurol. Psychiat., Chicago, 40:417–42.

————. 1952. Memory mechanisms. Trans. Amer. neur. Ass. for 1951, pp. 15–31, 38, 39.

————, and Theodore Rasmussen. 1950. The cerebral cortex of man. New York: Macmillan.

Perry, Ralph Barton. 1926. General theory of value. New York: Longmans.

Pfeiffer, John. 1955. The human brain. New York: Harper.

Pitts, W., and W. S. McCulloch. 1947. How we know universals: the perception of auditory and visual forms. Bull. Math. Biophysics, 9:127–47.

Planck, Max. 1949. The meaning and limits of exact science. Science, 110:319–27.

Polyak, S. L. 1941. The retina. Chicago: University of Chicago Press.

Price, George R. 1955. Science and the supernatural. Science, 122:359–67. For critical comments on this essay, see Science, 123:9–10 (Jan. 6, 1956).

Rapoport, Anatol. 1950. Science and the goals of man. New York: Harper.

————. 1953. Operational philosophy, integrating knowledge and action. New York: Harper.

Rashevsky, Nicholas. 1948. Mathematical biophysics. Rev. ed. Chicago: University of Chicago Press.

————. 1951. Mathematical biology of social behavior. Chicago: University of Chicago Press.

Redfield, Robert (ed.). 1942. Levels of integration in biological and social systems. Lancaster, Pa.: Biol. Symposia, 8:1–240.

Reiser, Oliver L. 1955. Logic, cybernetics, and general semantics. Gen. Semantics Bull., nos. 16, 17, pp. 57-62. Reprinted from Synthese, 9(3–5):306–18 (1953).

Riese, Walther. 1942. The principle of integration, its history and its nature. J. nerv. ment. Dis., *96*:296–312.

Riesen, Austin H. 1947. The development of visual perception in man and chimpanzee. Science, *106*:107–108.

———. 1950. Arrested vision. Sci. Amer., *183*(1):16–19.

———, and Elaine F. Kinder. 1952. Postural development of infant chimpanzees. New Haven, Conn.: Yale University Press.

Romanell, Patrick. 1950. See Leake and Romanell, 1950.

———. 1955. Does biology afford a sufficient basis for ethics? Sci. Mon., *81*:138–46.

Romano, J. (ed.). 1949. Adaptation. (sympos.) Ithaca, N.Y.: Cornell University Press.

Romer, Alfred Sherwood. 1949. Time series and trends in animal evolution. In Genetics, paleontology and evolution. Princeton, N.J.: Princeton University Press, pp. 103–20.

Roofe, Paul G. 1948. A biological criterion of progress. Amer. Scientist, *36*:151–53.

Rosenblueth, A., N. Wiener, and J. Bigelow. 1943. Behavior, purpose and teleology. Phil. Sci. *10*:18–24.

Royce, Josiah. 1903. Outlines of psychology. New York: Macmillan.

Rudebeck, Birger. 1945. Contributions to forebrain morphology in Dipnoi. Acta Zoologica, *26*:9–156.

Russell, Bertrand. 1927. Philosophy. New York: Norton.

Santayana, George. 1905. Reason and common sense. New York: Scribner.

Sargent, Stephen S. 1950. Social psychology, an integrative interpretation. New York: Ronald.

Scharrer, Ernst. 1932. Experiments on the function of the lateral-line organs in the larvae of Amblystoma punctatum. J. exp. Zool., *61*:109–14.

Schepers, G. W. H. 1948. Evolution of the forebrain. Cape Town, S.A.: Maskew Miller.

Schneirla, T. C. 1948. Psychology, comparative. Encyclopaedia Britannica, 1948 ed.

———. 1949. Levels in the psychological capacities of animals. In Sellars *et al.*, 1949, pp. 243–86.

———, and Gerard Piel. 1948. The army ant. Sci. Amer., *178*(6): 17–23.

Schrödinger, Erwin. 1944. What is life? London: Cambridge University Press.

Scott, J. P. (ed.). 1950. Methodology and techniques for the study of animal societies. Ann. N.Y. Acad. Sci., *51*(6):1001–1122.

Seidenberg, Roderick. 1950. Posthistoric man. Chapel Hill, N.C.: University of North Carolina Press.

Sellars, Roy Wood. 1938. An analytic approach to the mind-body problem. Phil. Rev., *47*:461–87.

———. 1943. Causality and substance. Phil. Rev., *52*:1–27.

———. 1944. Reformed materialism and intrinsic endurance. Phil. Rev., *53*:359–82.

———, V. J. McGill, and Marvin Farber (eds). 1949. Philosophy for the future. New York: Macmillan.

Shapley, Harlow. 1945. On the astronomical dating of the earth's crust. Amer. J. Sci., *243*A:508–22.

———. 1948. Time and change in the metagalaxy. Sci. Mon., *67*:243–53.

Shariff, Ghouse Ahmed. 1953. Cell counts in the primate cerebral cortex. J. comp. Neurol., *98*:381–400.

Sheldon, W. H. 1941. On the nature of mind. J. Phil., *38*:197–207.

Sherrington, Charles S. 1948. The integrative action of the nervous system. 2d ed. (revision of 1906 ed.). New Haven, Conn.: Yale University Press.

———. 1952. Man on his nature. 2d ed. London: Cambridge University Press.

Simpson, George Gaylord. 1947. The problem of plan and purpose in nature. Sci. Mon., *64*:481–95.

———. 1949. The meaning of evolution. New Haven, Conn.: Yale University Press.

———. 1953. The major features of evolution. New York: Columbia University Press.

Sinnot, Edmund W. 1945. The biological basis of democracy. Yale Rev., *35*:61–73.

———. 1950. Cell and psyche: the biology of purpose. Chapel Hill, N. C.: University of North Carolina Press.

Snyder, L. H. 1949. The genetic approach to human individuality. Sci. Mon., *68*:165–71.

Sonneborn, T. M. 1949. Beyond the gene. Amer. Scientist, *37*:33–59.

———. 1950. Partner of the genes. Sci. Amer., *183*(5):30–39.

Sperry, Roger W. 1950. Neuronal specificity. In Weiss, 1950, pp. 232–39.

———. 1951. Mechanisms of neural maturation. In Stevens, 1951, chap. 7, pp. 236–80.

———. 1951a. Regulative factors in the orderly growth of neural circuits (sympos.). Growth, *10*:63–87.

———. 1952. Neurology and the mind-brain problem. Amer. Scientist, *40*:291–312.

Stephenson, William. 1953. The study of behavior. Q-technique and its methodology. Chicago: University of Chicago Press.

Stern, Curt. 1949. Principles of human genetics. San Francisco: W. H. Freeman.

Stevens, Stanley Smith (ed.). 1951. Handbook of experimental psychology. New York: Wiley.

Swann, W. F. G. 1939. What has become of reality in modern physics? Sigma Xi Quart., 27:19–35.

Thompson, D'Arcy W. 1942. On growth and form. New York: Macmillan.

Thompson, Laura. 1950. Science and the study of mankind. Science, 111:559–63.

Thorndike, Edward L. 1936. Science and values. Science, 83:1–8.

Thrapp, Dan Lincoln. 1950. Early "missing links" from Africa. Nat. Hist., 59(7):304–309, 333–34.

Thurstone, L. L. 1947. Multiple factor analysis. Chicago: University of Chicago Press.

————. 1948. Psychological implications of factor analysis. Amer. Psychol., 3:402–408.

Tinbergen, N. 1953. Social behaviour in animals with special reference to vertebrates. New York: Wiley.

Troland, Leonard T. 1928. The fundamentals of human motivation. New York: Van Nostrand.

Tryon, Roger Choate. 1929. The genetics of learning ability in rats. Univer. Calif. Publ. Psychol., 4:71–89.

Tunturi, Archie R. 1944. Audio frequency localization in the acoustic cortex of the dog. Amer. J. Physiol., 141:397–403.

————. 1945. Further afferent connections to the acoustic cortex of the dog. Amer. J. Physiol., 144:389–94.

Turck, Fenton B. 1952. The American explosion. Sci. Mon., 75:187–91.

Tute, Richard. 1946. Science and world community. Sci. Mon., 63:321–23.

Vinacke, W. Edgar. 1948. The basic postulates of psychology. Sci. Mon., 67:110–14.

Walls, Gordon Lynn. 1942. The vertebrate eye and its adaptive radiation. Bloomfield Hills, Mich.: Cranbrook Institute of Science, Bull. 19.

Warden, Carl J. 1931. Animal motivation: experimental studies on the albino rat. New York: Columbia University Press.

———, Thomas N. Jenkins, and Lucien H. Warner. 1934–40. Comparative psychology. 3 vols. New York: Ronald.

Washburn, Margaret Floy. 1936. The animal mind. 4th ed. New York: Macmillan.

Watson, D. M. S. 1953. Africa and the origin of man. Amer. Scientist, 41:427–38.

Weiss, Albert Paul. 1929. A theoretical basis of human behavior. 2d ed. Columbus, Ohio: R. G. Adams & Co.

Weiss, Paul. 1947. The place of physiology in the biological sciences. Federation Proc., 6:523–25.

——— (ed.). 1950. Genetic neurology. Chicago: University of Chicago Press.

———, and Helen B. Hiscoe. 1948. Experiments on the mechanism of nerve growth. J. exp. Zool., 107:315–95.

Werner, Heinz. 1945. Motion and motion perception: a study on vicarious functioning. J. Psychol., 19:317–27.

———, and Seymour Wapner. 1949. Sensory-tonic field theory of perception. J. Person., 18:88–107.

———. 1952. Toward a general theory of perception. Psychol. Rev., 59:324–38.

Wever, E. G. 1949. Theory of hearing. New York: Wiley.

Wheeler, William Morton. 1913. Ants, their structure, development, and behavior. New York: Columbia University Press.

———. 1923. Social life among the insects. New York: Harcourt, Brace.

———. 1928. Emergent evolution. New York: Norton.

White, Leslie A. 1940. The symbol: the origin and basis of human behavior. Phil. Sci., 7:451–63.

———. 1948. Man's control over civilization: an anthropocentric illusion. Sci. Mon., 66:235–47.

———. 1949. Ethnological theory. In Sellars et al., 1949, pp. 357–84.

———. 1949a. The science of culture. New York: Farrar, Straus.

Whitehead, Alfred North. 1926. Science and the modern world. New York: Macmillan.

———. 1929. Process and reality. New York: Macmillan.

Whitman, C. O. 1888. The seat of formative and regenerative energy. J. Morph., 2:27–49.

———. 1892. The metamerism of Clepsine. Festschr. f. Rudolf Leuckarts, pp. 384–95. Leipzig: Englemann.

Whittaker, E. T. 1943. Aristotle, Newton, Einstein. Science, 98:249–54, 267–70.

Whyte, Lancelot Law. 1948. Scientific thought in the coming decades. Harper's Magazine, 197(1182):44–48.

———. 1948a. The next development in man. New York: Holt. Also Mentor Books, 1950.

———. 1949. The unitary principle in physics and biology. New York: Holt.

———. 1954. Accent on form. New York: Harper.

Wiener, Norbert. 1948. Cybernetics, or control and communication in the animal and the machine. New York: Wiley.

Williams, Robert R. 1948. Natural science and social problems. Amer. Scientist, 36:116–26.

Williams, Roger J. 1946. The human frontier. New York: Harcourt, Brace.

———. 1953. Free and unequal. Austin, Texas: University of Texas Press.

———. 1955. Implications of humanics for law and science. J. Publ. Law, 3(2):328–44.

Willier, Benjamin H., Paul Weiss, and Viktor Hamburger (eds.). 1955. Analysis of development. Philadelphia: Saunders.

Wolfe, John B. 1936. Effectiveness of token-rewards for chimpanzees. Comp. Psychol. Monogr., 12(5):2–72.

Wright, Quincy. 1948. Social tensions. The Humanist, 8:21–22.

Yakovlev, Paul I. 1948. Motility, behavior and the brain. J. nerv. ment. Dis., 107:313–35.

Yerkes, Robert M. 1943. Chimpanzees, a laboratory colony. New Haven, Conn: Yale University Press.

———, and Ada W. Yerkes. 1929. The great apes. New Haven, Conn.: Yale University Press.

———, and ———. 1935. Social behavior in infrahuman primates. In A handbook of social psychology. Worcester, Mass.: Clark University Press, pp. 973–1035.

———, and Henry W. Nissen, 1939. Pre-linguistic sign behavior in chimpanzees. Science, 89:585–87.

Zuckerman, S. 1932. The social life of monkeys and apes. London: Kegan Paul.

———. 1933. Functional affinities of man, monkeys, and apes. New York: Harcourt, Brace.

Index

Accumulative knowledge: 8, 30

Acquired patterns of behavior: 70, 77, 84
  established in prenatal period, 116–17
  and genetic traits, 117–19
  and learning, 360–62
  and neurological development, 241–44, 254
  and perception, 347–49
  in social structure, 177–78, 181–83

Adaptation: 8, 128–35
  as basis of biological rank, 122–23

Adrian, Edgar D.: 333–34, 425, 442

Affect: see Emotion

Agar, W. E.: 94, 96, 291

Alexander, Irving E.: 343

Alexander, Jerome: 53

Alexander, S.: 146

Alford, Leland B.: 427–28

Allee, W. C.: 24, 107, 170, 175, 176, 189–90, 215

Allport, Floyd H.: 340

Altruism: 17, 180, 186, 214–15
  as solution to world disorder, 221–23

Amblystoma: see Salamander, brain structure of

Ameba:
  analytic apparatus of, 87
  and values of, 140

Ames, Adelbert: 26, 348–49, 351

Amphibians:
  brain structure of, 81, 244–52, 371–73, 376–81
  evolutionary origin of, 242
  individualistic traits of, 175
  sensitivity of vibrations in, 335–36

Amphioxus: 337

Analogous patterns of behavior: 106–107
  between human beings and other animals, 215
  in social organization, 177–78

Analogous structures in evolution: 106

Analytic experience:
  sensorimotor behavior as, 164–65
  and synthetic experience, 163

Analytic factors of behavior, defined: 14

Analytic processes: 86–89, 101–102
  brain apparatus for, 241, 243–48
  and cortical localization, 409–12, 431, 434–35
  factors of, 88–89
  and integrative processes, 91–98
  levels of organization of, 103–104
  as sorting mechanism, 441–48

Analytic sciences:
  methodology of, 28–30
  universals in, 44–45

Anderson, O. D.: 99

Animals:
  analytic and integrative apparatus of, 87–89, 243–52

[489]

Animals (*continued*):
  behavior of, literature on, 24
  classification and biological rank of,
    14, 119–23
  cortical evolution in, 371–83,
    419–20
  cortical functions of, 324–26,
    396–99, 401–404
  cortical structure, comparative
    anatomy and physiology of,
    371–87
  experience of, 160–61, 163–66
  experimental neurosis in, 99–100
  human control of, 16
  mentality of, 290, 320–29
  progressive evolution of, 123–27,
    239–43, 397
  sensory responses of, 330–31
    auditory and tactile, 334–36
    visual, 336–37
  social groups of, 170–71
    familial, integrative, and associa-
      tive, 171–72
    individualistic patterns of,
      175–76, 180
    totalitarian patterns of, 172–75
  values of, 139–40
Animism: 19, 235, 285–86
Antisocial behavior: *see* Social disorders
Ants, social organization of: 172–74
  see also Insects
Ape men: 317, 388
Apes: *see* Primates
Aphasia: 350, 425, 436
Aptitude tests: 364
Ariëns Kappers, C. U.: 248, 261
Aristotelian mechanics: 270
Aristotle:
  on origin of thought, 141
  theory of brain function of, 406
Army ants, social organization of: 173
Arnot, Robert: 396, 427
Artistic values: 143
Ashby, W. Ross: 130
Assembly of nervous elements (Hebb):
  433–37
Associative type of animal society: 172
Atomic bombs, manufacture of: 70
Atomistic theory of nature: 94, 264–65

Attitudes:
  measurement of, 31, 152
  in scientific method, 31
Attitude theory of emotion: 315
Auditory organs: 334–36, 342–43,
  417, 444
Australian aborigines, social structure
  of: 183–84
Automata, mechanisms as: 57–58
Awareness: *see* Mind

Bagehot, Walter: 189, 195
Bailey, Percival: 388–89, 430
Bain, Alexander: 315–16
Baitsell, G. A.: 54
Baldwin, J. M.: 118
Baldwin's *Dictionary of Philosophy and
  Psychology:* 18, 300
Barber, Bernard: 190
Barker, Roger G.: 82, 310
Barron, D. H.: 84
Bartley, S. Howard: 281, 332, 344
Bath, Cyril J.: 126
Bats, hearing of: 331
Beach, Frank A.: 324
Beck, Lewis W.: 49
Beebe, William: 173
Bees, communication among: 402
Behavior:
  abnormal, 90–101
  acquired and inherited, 116–19,
    177–78
  animal, literature on, 24
  classification of, 76
  conscious and unconscious, 19–20,
    285
  control of, 16–17
  definition of, 13–15
  development of, 80–85, 310
  factors of, summary, 25
  goal-directed quality of, 15, 20–21
  good and bad, criteria of, 3–5
  human, biology of, 5–9
  mental factors in, 22–23, 35–36
  motivations of, 15, 18–21, 23
  patterns of, 15, 76–85
  as product of human mechanism,
    68–71
  psychobiology of, 24

as science, methods of study of, 26–38
total patterns and partial patterns of Coghill, 14, 80, 273
values as motivating agents, 23
see also Mental disorders; Social disorders

Behaviorism: 8
American school of, 253–54
exclusion of consciousness from field of study, 19–23
and functionalism, 26–27

Benedict, C. G.: 280

Benedict, F. G.: 280

Bentley, Arthur F.: 15, 267, 271, 348, 404

Berger, Hans: 281

Bernard, Claude: 58

Bernhaut, M.: 429

Bertalanffy, Ludwig von: 46, 50–51

Bichat, M. F. X.: 92

Binet, Alfred: 365

Biology, human: *see* Human biology

Birds:
brains of, 368, 382, 403
development of behavior patterns of, 84
individualistic traits of, 175
instinctive behavior patterns of, 84–85
vision of, 242, 330

Birkhoff, George D.: 151

Bishop, George H.: 261

Blake, Robert R.: 351

Blum, Josephine S.: 426

Body-mind relationship: 42–43, 233–37, 284–98, 368, 411–12, 438, 450–51, 461
biological analysis of, 299–305
see also Psychobiology

Boland, Grant L.: 426

Bonin, Gerhardt von: 387–89, 425

Boodin, John E.: 289

Boring, Edwin G.: 272, 288

Bouglé, C.: 141–42

Boulding, Kenneth E.: 190, 199

Boyajian, A: 58–59

Brain:
analytic apparatus of, 243–48, 409–12
comparative anatomy and physiology of, 370–87, 422–24
cortex, *see* Cortex, cerebellar; Cortex cerebral
and cybernetics, 443–47
development of, 239, 241, 315, 370–83, 410
integrative apparatus of, 243–44, 248–52, 409–12, 414–27, 436
levels of integration, 251–52
nonnervous field functions, 267–68
of primates, 309, 323–27, 386–87, 398, 420
size related to intelligence, 385–87, 398
surgery of, 415–18, 426–27
weights of, 398
see also Nervous system; Localization of nervous functions
see also parts of the brain

Brain, and mind: *see* Body-mind relationship

Brazier, Mary A. B.: 259, 345, 397, 448

Bridgman, P. W.: 30, 63, 348

Brillouin, L.: 51

Broca, Paul: 407

Brodmann, K., cortical areas of: 389–90, 416–17

Bronowski, Jacob: 32, 37

Bucy, Paul C.: 426

Bull, Nina: 99, 315–16

Burke, Edmund: 143

Buros, Oscar K.: 367

Burr, H. S.: 264–65, 439

Burrow, Trigant: 181–82, 189

Byrd, Admiral Richard E.: 137–38

Cameron, D. Ewen: 213

Cannon, Walter B.: 17, 215, 315, 359, 406

Cantril, Hadley: 26, 32, 145, 153, 189, 194, 203, 340, 345–46

Carmichael, Leonard: 81, 189, 310, 356

Carpenter, C. R.: 189, 324

Carr, Harvey A.: 18, 146

Carus, Paul: 427

Catalysis in emergent evolution: 53–54

Cattell, J. McKeen: 302

Causality: 71–74, 213
  circular, 72
  and freedom of choice, 211–13
  immanent, 72, 105, 134–35, 212
  and quantum physics, 61–64
  teleological, 131–35

Cephalization, in animals: 91

Cerebellum: 369–70
  see also Cortex, cerebellar

Cerebral cortex: see Cortex, cerebral

Chance, and mechanisms: 61–64

Change, laws of: 43–44, 110, 112–13

Chauncey, Henry: 364

Chickens, pecking rank of: 174

Child, C. M.: 91, 356

Chimpanzee:
  brain of, 323–24
  experiments on development of, 309
  mental capacity of, 324–25
  social structure of, 180
  see also Primates

Chisholm, George B.: 203

Chow, Kao Liang: 434

Chute, Eloise: 281

Circular causation: 72
  see also Feed-back mechanism

Clark, W. E. Le Gros: 317, 328, 343, 386, 442

"Classical field" in electrodynamics: 263–64

Classical mechanics, causal relations in: 72

Classification, biological: 119–23

Classification of facts in scientific method, 30–31

Codes, 401–402

Code script: 59

Coghill, G. E.: 14, 20, 25, 27, 59, 80–84, 86–88, 94, 98, 142, 166, 254, 272–76, 312–13, 316, 356, 452–53

Cognition, elements of: 299–302
  see also Mind

Cohen, Morris R.: 151

Cole, J.: 417

Communication system of body: 258–60
  cortical assemblies, 431–37
  cortical use of signals and symbols, 441–48

Communistic insect society: 172–74

Competence of individual, as trend of evolution: 114

Computing machine, electronic: 403–404, 442–48

Comte, Auguste: 195

Conation: see Volition

Concepts: 301, 403

Conceptual knowledge: 30, 162, 301–302
  nonspatial, nontemporal frame of, 165, 272–75, 279
  see also Mind

Conditioning of reflexes: 253–54, 355–58

Condon, E. U.: 201

Confucius, golden rule of: 223

Conklin, E. G.: 207, 212, 214

Connolly, Cornelius J.: 386

Consciousness: see Mind

Continuity, and homogeneity: 90

Coral reefs, formation of: 79

Corpus striatum: 251, 370, 382, 427

Cortex, cerebellar: 251, 252, 316–17

Cortex, cerebral:
  analytic functions of, 243–44, 409–12, 422
  areas of Brodmann, 389–92, 416–17
  assembly of assemblies, 433–37
  association and elaboration, see Cortex, cerebral, integrative functions
  auditory functions of, 342–43, 417
  development of, 173, 383
  evolution of, 370–87, 397–99
  facilitating functions of, 396–400
  general properties of, 368–70, 384–87
  integrative functions of, 243–44, 422, 424–27, 431–38
  olfactory functions of, 372, 376–77, 379–81, 397
  projection areas and fibers of, 375, 379–80, 389, 416–17, 419–22
  reserves of energy of, 396–98
  signs, signals, codes, and symbols of, 326, 401–404, 441–48

structure of, 370–75, 384–95
variability of, 385, 388–89
visual functions of, 341, 420, 424–26, 433–35
see also Brain; Localization of nervous functions; Mind; Nervous system

Cortical learning: 358, 360–62

Cory, Daniel: 464

Coulomb field of electrodynamics: 263–64, 432

Creative property of mechanisms: 47, 57–61, 213

Crosby, Elizabeth C.: 248, 420–21

Cultural factors in human social organizations: 195–98

Cultural values in human social organizations, 199–204

Culture patterns, origin of: 5–6

Cushen, W. Edward: 151

Cybernetics: 445

Dandy, W.: 427

Darling, F. Fraser: 190

Dart, R. A.: 317

Dartmouth Eye Institute: 348

Darwin, Charles: 112, 114–15, 129

Data: *see* Facts

Davis-Hess "culture-fair" tests: 364

Decentralization of democratic structure: 185–86

Democracy:
as social pattern: 176, 183–87, 191–92, 202
as answer to world tensions, 221
education for, 223–26

Descartes, René: 40, 427

Determinism: 53
and freedom of choice, 211–13
and quantum physics, 61–64

Detwiler, S. R.: 335

Dewey, John: 15, 28–29, 32–33, 64, 72–73, 145–46, 158–60, 162, 189, 314, 404

Dictatorial social organizations: 174–75, 185

Directive quality:
of evolution, 72, 112–16, 130–31

of mechanisms, 50, 71–73
of perception, 351–52
see also Goal-directed behavior

Disintegration: 98–101

Diversification of species: 113–14

Dobzhansky, Th.: 115, 118

Dogs, senses of: 242, 330–31

Domain of manners: 84, 192

Dreiman, David B.: 225

Droogleever Fortuyn, A. E. B.: 423

Drosophila: *see* Fruit flies, breeding experiments with

Dualism: *see* Body-mind relationship

Dusser de Barenne, J. G.: 252

Dynamic realism of C. L. Herrick: 42, 286

Dyson, Freeman J.: 264

Ears: *see* Auditory organs

Earthworm, response to stimulation: 129

Eby, Kermit: 225–26

Eccles, John C.: 259, 360, 387, 391, 435, 438, 448

Ecological system, concept of: 190, 194

Eddington, Sir Arthur: 30

Edinger, Tilly: 121

Education:
and culture, 195–96
for democracy, 223–26
mass, 192–93
in mental hygiene, 202
purpose of, 84
in United States, 223–26

Eells, Kenneth: 364

Eggs: *see* Ova

Einstein, Albert: 62, 90, 167, 267, 277–78, 290
conversion formula of, 55
theory of relativity of, 264

Elections in United States: 224

Electromagnetic field, theory of: 263–65

Emergence: 53–54

Emergent view of consciousness: 279, 307

Emerson, A. E.: 72, 107, 189–90, 215

Emotion: 200, 313, 315–16, 318–19

Empirical sciences: *see* Natural sciences

Encyclopaedia Britannica: 24, 132

Endocrine systems: 90–91

Energy:
  concept of, 55, 280–82
  patterns, transformation of, 46, 104

Engel, Leonard: 62, 267

Entropy: 50–53

Environment:
  adaptation to, *see* Adaptation
  control of, 208–209
    as criteria of biological success, 14, 125
    physical features of terrain changed by, 113
  as factor in human values, 142–43
  and heredity, 116–19

Equalitarian communities: 185

Eskimos, education of: 186

Ethical standards of behavior: 147–57
  and freedom of will, 213–17
  need for, 186–87, 191–92, 220–30

Euclidean geometry, principles of: 44

Europe, democratic monarchies of: 185
  ideological dualism in, 182

Evaluation: *see* Values

Evolution:
  biological, limit of, 5
  cortical, 371–83, 410–12
  emergent, 53–54
  of experience, 158–68
  factors of, 114–19
  general principles of, 112–14
  human, 2, 5, 118–19, 175–76
  of human culture, 5–6
  levels of, 108–10
  of mind, 320–29
  organic, classification and biological rank of animals, 119–23
  phylogenetic tree of, 105–106
  progressive, 115, 123–27, 152
  social factors in, 169–88
  of value, 136–57

Expenditures in United States: 228–29

Experience:
  definition of, 158
  extraspective and introspective, 1, 162
  growth of, 165–67
  natural history of, 158–60

nature of, 40, 160–65
  and social conduct, 70, 128–29
  and scientific data, 31, 167, 288
  unconscious and conscious, 161, 322–23
  see also Mind

Experimental embryology: 48, 81

Experimental genetics: 48

Extrapyramidal fibers: 378, 419

Extrasensory perception: *see* Psi phenomena

Extraspective and introspective experience: 1, 162

Eyes: *see* Visual organs

Facts, meaning and value of: 31–36

Faith: 409, 462–65

Family groups: 170–72

Fantasies, nonspatial and nontemporal frame of: 165

Fasciculus solitarius: 246

Fascist governments: 174–75, 185

Fatigue, studies of: 281

Feed-back mechanism: 133–34
  in cortical processes, 418, 444
  in servomechanisms, 447

Feeling: 299, 313, 318–19, 338
  see also Emotion

Fields, polarized: 263–69
  electromagnetic, theories of, 263–65, 432
  of mental processes, 432, 438–41
  as pattern of human behavior, 263, 265–69, 294–95

Fishes:
  cortical apparatus of, 376
  cutaneous sense organs of, 321
  ganoid, brain of, 248
  individualistic traits of, 175
  sensitivity to vibrations of, 335
  transition of, to land animals, 242

Fit, survival of: 2–4

Fitness, criteria of: 2, 4, 149, 187, 214, 220–21

Florez, Admiral de: 73–74

Frank, Lawrence K.: 30, 72, 133, 189, 193–94, 254, 394, 448

Freedom of choice: 211–17
  dangers of, 3–4

Freeman, Walter: 416
Fritsch, G.: 407
Frog, brain of: 250, 376, 380
Fruit flies (Drosophila), breeding experiments with: 117
Frustration, behavior resulting from: 21, 99–100
Fulton, John F.: 99, 416

Gall, Franz J.: 406
Garnett, A. Campbell: 307
Geldard, Frank A.: 334
Generalizations:
  in scientific method, 30–31
  verified, as universals, 44–45
Genes, recombinations of: 115
  see also Mutations
Genetic patterns of behavior: see Heredity; Innate behavior patterns
Geotropism: 336
Gerard, R. W.: 107, 189, 351, 428, 441, 442–43, 448
German campaigns of conquest: 183, 204, 451
Gesell, Arnold: 82, 189, 197, 310, 316–17, 356
Gestalt school of psychology: 267, 432, 439
Gibbs, Frederic Andrews: 237
Ginzberg, Eli: 199
Glass, Bentley: 53
Glees, P.: 417
Goal-directed behavior: 15, 20–21, 47
  frustration of, 99–100
  means and ends in, 131–35
Goldstein, Kurt: 164
Golgi method: 391
  of servomechanisms, 446–47
Good and evil:
  criteria of, 3–4
  scientific guidance toward, 200–201
  in social conduct, 66–68
  socially imposed secondary norms of, 181–83
  in values, 147–50
Granit, Ragnar: 340, 347
Gray, George W.: 309, 325
Greenblatt, Milton: 416

Greenman, E. F.: 119, 176
Griffin, Donald R.: 331
Grinker, Roy R.: 441
Groups:
  human, democratic, 179–87
  individualistic, 175–76
  social, 79, 169–72
  totalitarian, 172–75
  see also Social organization
Grünbaum, Adolf: 53, 72, 288
Guggenheim, Louis K.: 336
Guilford, J. P.: 365

Hadamard, Jacques: 290
Haeckel, E. H.: 196
Haldane, J. B. S.: 54
Halstead, Ward C.: 29, 355, 363, 366, 424, 428
Hamilton, G. V.: 23
Hanover Institute: 348–49
Haring, Douglas C.: 189–90, 196
Harlow, Harry F.: 426
Hartung, Frank E.: 189, 195
Haskins, Caryl P.: 171–72, 176, 189–90
Hastorf, A. H.: 26
Haydon, A. Eustace: 465
Hayek, F. A.: 287–88, 332, 352
Hayes, Cathy: 309
Head dominance in animals: 90–91
Hearing: see Auditory organs
Hebb, Donald O.: 20, 24, 286–87, 340, 342, 360–63, 403, 433–38, 448
Hedonism: 152–53
Heisenberg, Werner: 62, 266
Heliotropism: 336
Helmholtz, H. L. F. von: 346
Helson, Harry: 344
Henderson, Lawrence J.: 303
Henle, Paul: 307
Heredity:
  behavior patterns established by, 70, 77, 177
  human, biological process of, 115
  interference with, 88–89
  Lamarckian principle of, 116–18
  and learning, 360–62

Heredity (*continued*):
  and natural selection, 105, 112,
    114–16, 118–19
  and neurological development,
    241–42, 254
    analytic and integrative apparatus,
      243–53
  and patterns established during pre-
    natal period, 116–19
  and perception, 347–49
  social, *see* Social heredity
  and social organization, 177–78,
    181–83
Herrick, C. Judson: 25, 27, 34, 56, 81,
  91, 125, 149, 152, 154, 158–59,
  213–14, 234, 239, 242, 244–45,
  249, 252, 254, 274, 288, 295,
  302–303, 317, 333, 336, 337, 343–
  44, 356–57, 394, 411, 423, 452, 457
Herrick, Clarence L.: 25, 42, 55, 125,
  190, 346, 429, 452, 453
Hill, Denis: 416
Himwich, H. E.: 253
Hippocampus: 371–72, 375, 378, 380,
  389, 397, 413
Hiscoe, Helen B.: 259
Hitzig, E.: 407
Hoagland, Hudson: 259, 443–44
Hockett, Charles F.: 50
Holmes, S. J.: 115, 189, 214
Holtfreter, J.: 261
Homeostasis: 46
  and moral behavior, 215–17
  and perception, 347
Homogeneity, and continuity: 90
Homologous patterns of behavior:
  106–107
  between humans and other animals,
    215
  in social organizations, 177–78
Homologous structures in evolution:
  106
Hook, Sidney: 158–59
Hooker, Davenport: 82–84, 310
Hopi Indians, study of: 190
Howells, William: 119, 176, 189, 324,
  386
Huber, G. Carl: 248
Human biology: 3–9

Human development:
  postnatal, 308–10
  prenatal, 116–17, 310–12
Humanism, and science: 36
Human mechanism: 66–75
Human nature: 1–3, 70, 74
  changing, 84
Human race:
  progress of, 126–27, 398–400
  psychoneurosis of: 181–82
Hunt, J. McV.: 99
Huxley, Julian: 34, 115, 120, 125,
  130, 189, 214, 222
Huxley, Thomas H.: 3, 34, 115, 174,
  189, 213–14
Hydrotropism: 336
Hypnotic suggestion: 282, 398
Hysteresis, as property of mechanisms:
  54

Idealism: 285
Ideas: *see* Concepts; Conceptual
  knowledge
"Immanent causality": 72, 105,
  134–35, 212
Indeterminism of Heisenberg: 61–63,
  266
Individual: *see* Self
Individual diversity as trend of evolution: 114
Individualistic social patterns: 172,
  175–76
  in democracy, 176, 183–87
  human, 179–83, 191, 204
  personal factors in maintaining,
    192–95
Individuality of mechanisms: 78–80
Industrial machines, and human
    machines, 73–74
  see also Computing machine,
    electronic
Inhibition and reflex actions: 254
  and conscious actions, 314
Innate behavior patterns, established
    during prenatal period: 117
  see also Heredity
Inorganic matter:
  and experience, 161
  integration of, 63, 89
  and mind-stuff, 160, 291

Insects:
  eyes of, 336
  mentality of, 321–22
  social organization of, 172–74
Insight in animals: 325–26
Instinct: 76, 82–85
Institute for Associated Research: 348
Integrative factors of behavior:
  defined, 14
  in perception, 349–51
Integrative processes: 63, 86–87,
    89–98, 101–102, 453
  and analytic processes, 91–98
  brain apparatus for, 243–44, 248–52
  and conceptual experience, 163–65,
    301–302
  and cortical assemblies, 431–38
  and cortical localization, 409–12,
    414–27
  dimensions of, 275–79, 453–54
  disintegration, 98–102
  levels of organization of, 103–10
  mental acts as, 322–23
  normative conception of integration,
    89–90
Integrative type of animal society: 172
Integrity of organism: 78–80
Intelligence: 359–60
  and cortical structure, 384–87
  factor analysis of, 365
  growth of, 306–19
  "lapsed," 322
  measurement of, 272, 362–67
  mechanisms of, 360–62
  principles of, 299–302
  psychometric, 363, 366
  in subhuman primates, 324–27
  see also Mind
International tensions: 181, 201
Introspective and extraspective
  experience: 1, 162
Irvine, W.: 214
Isolated systems in nature: 52
Isolationism: 225–26
Ittelson, W.: 26

Jackson, Hughlings: 251
James, William: 97, 207, 315–16, 398
Jasper, Herbert H.: 448
Java man (Pithecanthropus erectus),
  skull capacity of: 386

Jeans, Sir James: 30, 61, 135
Jeffress, Lloyd A.: 387, 448
Jellyfish, nervous system of: 241, 250
Jenkins, Iredell: 24, 29
Jennings, H. S.: 24, 189
Jensen, Howard E.: 153, 202
Johnson, H. M.: 151, 293
Jones, Lyle V.: 152
Jungle, law of: 192

Kaada, Birger R.: 397
Kansas, University of, Coghill material
  in Department of Anatomy: 81
Katz, David: 24, 259
Keeton, Morris T.: 25
Keith, Arthur: 115, 189, 229
Kellogg, Luella A.: 309
Kellogg, Winthrop N.: 309
Kemeny, John G.: 446, 448
Kinder, Elaine F.: 317, 364
King, Samuel M.: 344
Klüver, Heinrich: 281, 302, 347, 426
Knowledge:
  nature of, 40–41, 359–60, 453
  conceptual, 30, 162, 301–302
  objective and conceptual, 162, 279,
    301–302
  perceptual, 162, 301
  and statistical methods, 62–63
Köhler, Wolfgang: 132, 143–44, 189,
    268, 325, 349, 432, 441
Kounin, Jacob S.: 82, 310
Krechevsky, I.: 358–59
Krieg, Wendell J. S.: 420, 423
Kroeber, A. L.: 107, 153, 189,
    197–98, 402, 404
Kuo, Z. Y.: 310

La Barre, Weston: 119, 176, 189, 291,
    331
Lamarckian principle of heredity:
  116–18
Lamprey, brain of: 248, 410–11
Lancet (Amphioxus): 337
Lange, Carl G.: 315
Langfeld, Herbert S.: 316, 318

Language: 403–404
  and mental processes, 289–90, 292, 324
  significance of, 309
  and social learning, 358
Lankester, Ray: 132
Lapan, Arthur: 73
Larsell, O.: 317, 336
Lashley, K. S.: 292–93, 310, 342, 343, 345, 355, 385, 422–23, 432, 443–44
Lateral line organs: 321, 335
Lawrence, M.: 348
Laws of nature: see Nature
Leadership in social groups: 174–75
Leake, Chauncey D.: 29, 215
Learned quality of perception: 301
Learning: 355–62
  and cortical structure, 385–86
  and intelligence, 354–55
  levels of integration of, 357–58
  mechanisms of, 360–62
  in rats, 422–24
Lemniscus tracts: 420
Lemur, brain of: 326–27, 386
Lessing, G. E.: 55
Levels of organization: 103–11
  analytic and integrative series, 103–10
  of brain structure, 252, 253
  laws of structure and laws of change, 110
Lewin, Kurt: 190
Lief, Alfred: 294
Lifwynn Laboratory: 181–82
Light:
  particle-wave controversy over, 278
  sensitivity to, 334, 336–37
Lillie, Ralph S.: 52–53, 63, 134
Lobachevski, N. I.: 349
Localization of nervous functions: 92, 406–30
Locke, N. M.: 324
Loeb, Jacques: 49–50
Loeb, Leo: 194
Logic, laws of thought in: 45
Logical and mathematical universals: 44–45

Lundberg, George A.: 19, 148, 199–200
Luneberg, Rudolf K.: 349
Lungfishes:
  cortical apparatus of, 376–81
  neuromotor development in, 242

McCulloch, Warren S.: 72, 254, 394, 415, 425, 444–46
Machines: see Mechanisms
Maier, Norman R. F.: 24, 99, 290, 355
Mammals, evolution of: 175
Manners, domain of: 84, 192
Margenau, Henry: 7, 41, 57, 61, 164, 263–64, 266–67, 278, 350, 455
Marrazzi, Amedeo S.: 268
Masserman, Jules H.: 99–100
Materialism: 285–86
Material structure of mechanism: 54–55
Mathematics:
  and biological problems, 29–30
  definitions of, 28
  laws of thought in, 45
  universals in, 44–45
Maxwell, James C.: 264
Mead, G. H.: 29, 133, 207
Mead, Leonard C.: 73
Mead, Margaret: 184
Meanings and values in scientific method: 32–36
Means and ends: 131–35
  inseparability of, 200
Mechanical revolution of present era: 220–22
Mechanics, revolutions in science of: 270–83
Mechanisms: 54–61
  of analysis and integration, 243–44
  computing, 403, 442–48
  human, 66–75
  of living, 46–47
  order in operation of, 61–64
  and organisms, 94
  participation in making of product, 56–61
  of selection and rejection, 129
  and teleology, 131–35
  and vitalistic explanations, 47, 54
  wholes and parts of, 78–80

Medulla oblongata: 245–48

Memory: 302, 435, 443–44
as tuned reasonating circuit, 443–48

Mental disorders: 21, 98–100, 180–81
organic causes of, 408–409
and physical disorders, 282
prevention of, 202
therapy for, 182

Mental therapy: 182, 409

Mental work: 279–82

"Mentation" of Coghill: 275

Metabolism: 90, 292

Metaphysical conception of teleology: 131–35

Metaphysical universals: 44–45

Metaphysics: 44, 96, 461, 468

Methods of study: see Science, methodology of

Mettler, Fred A.: 416

Meyer, Adolf: 293–94, 408

Meyer, Agnes E.: 203

Meynert, Theodor H.: 251

Michelson, A. A.: 138

Midbrain: 376, 378

Military services, aptitude tests used by: 364

Mill, J. S.: 195

Mind:
and animism, 19, 235, 285–86
analytic and synthetic functions of, 301, 350, 431–38, 442
as awareness, 160, 289–92, 456
biological analysis of, 297–305
and body-mind relationship, 42–43, 233–37, 284–98, 368, 411–12, 438, 450–51, 461
consciousness and behavior of, 20–23, 286–88
dimensions of, 277, 453–56
embryology of, 160, 306–19
emergence of consciousness of, 279, 307
evolution of, 320–29
field theories of, 266–68, 438–41, 456
integrative nature of, 87, 97, 103, 322
and intelligence, 359–67
and laws of thought, 45
and learning, 354–59
and mind-stuff, 160, 291, 456
mythical, 284–85
and panpsychism, 160, 291, 306–307, 464
primate, 323–28
quantification of, 272
space and time in mentation, 165, 211–12, 272–79, 340–45
see also Brain: Cortex, cerebral; Experience; Perception; Psychobiology; Psychophysics; Sensation

Minkowski, Hermann: 278

Mollusk, eyes of: 337

Monarchial governments: 174–75, 185

Monkeys: see Primates

Montgomery, Edmund: 25, 53, 94, 133, 346

Moog, Florence: 124

Moral codes:
control of behavior by, 17
and freedom of will, 213–17
and human values, 147–57
need for, 186–87, 191–92, 220–30

Morgan, C. Lloyd: 53, 92–93, 118

Morris, Charles: 152

Motility:
as component of perception, 340
as cradle of behavior and mentation, 240, 312–18

Motivation:
as factor of behavior, 15, 18–21
profit motive in, 152–53
and values, 136–45
see also Satisfaction; Values

Motor activity:
evolutionary changes in, and effect on brain development: 241–43
and localization of cortical functions, 419–24
of lower animals, 239–40, 244–51
and perception, 345–49
and psychogenesis, 312–18

Motor analytic system: 88, 243–48

Moulton, J. F.: 192

Moulyn, Adrian C.: 274–75

Mountford, Charles P.: 184

Mud fishes, transition to amphibians: 242

Mudpuppy: 245, 344, 378

Muller, Herbert J.: 30, 37, 137, 182, 190, 198

Muller, Hermann J.: 54

Murdock, George P.: 358

Murphy, Arthur E.: 41, 149, 156

Muscles:
cerebellar control of, 369
motility of, 240

Mutations: 115
adaptive, 129
and environment, 118
transmission of, 118–19
see also Variations

Mythology: 284–85

Myxomycetes: see Slime molds

Nachmansohn, D.: 259

National Education Association, Educational Policies Commission: 225

National tensions: 181

Natural sciences: 38–45
empirical, 28–30
and experience, 158–60
law of orderly processes of, 42–43
laws and universals of, 44–45
laws of change in, 43–44
method of, 30–32
normative, 28–30
reality in, 40–42
and religion, 461–65
and values, 136–41

Natural selection:
principle of, 105, 112, 114–16, 118–19, 190, 210–11
and adaptation, 129

Nature:
definition of, 39, 462
laws of, 30–31, 42–44
and mechanisms, 61–64
and universals, 44–45

Necturus: 245, 344, 378

Needham, Joseph: 104, 107

Nerve fibers:
conduction of impulses by, 258–63
projection of, 419, 422
extra pyramidal, 378, 419

Nervous system:
analytic apparatus, 243–48
conduction, 258–60

general functions of, 87–90, 257–69, 315
integrative apparatus of, 248–51
mechanisms of learning and intelligence, 360–62
neurosensory and neuromotor relations, 239–43
peripheral and central relations, 261–62
polarized fields, 263–69
reflexology, 253–54
see also Brain, Cortex, cerebral; Nerve fibers

Neural learning: 357–58, 361

Neurograms: 403–04

Neurons: 262–63, 268–69, 391

Neuropil:
of human cortex, 370, 390–93
of primitive vertebrates, 92, 245–51
progressive differentiation of, 410–11

Newtonian mechanics and field theory: 92, 264–67
and means controlled by ends, 131
principles of, 44
revolution in, 270

Nicholson, N. C.: 398

Nissen, Henry W.: 324–25, 327

Nissl method: 391

Normative sciences: 28–29, 44

Northrop, F. S. C.: 105, 133, 264–65, 448

Novikoff, Alex B.: 104–105, 107

Nuclei of brain: 251, 370

O'Brien, Thomas F.: 343

Observations, and facts: 33

Octopus, eyes of: 337

Ogden, Robert M., 93

Økland, F.: 454–55

Olfactory organs:
and cortical evolution 372, 376–77, 379–81, 397
in dogs, 242

Omar Khayyám: 206

Open systems:
and entropy, 50–51
living mechanisms as, 46

Order in nature:
laws of, 42–43
and mechanisms, 61–64

Organic selection: 118–19

Organic theory of nature of White-head, 93–94

Organism:
properties of, 46–47
wholes of and parts of, 78–80

"Organismic" and "nonorganismic" processes of Coghill: 86–87, 273

Orthogenesis: 115–16

Osborn, Henry F.: 115

Osler, Sir William: 409

Ova:
fertilization of, 95
human, 115

Oxford Dictionary: 89

Pain, consciousness of: 415

Pannekoek, A.: 119, 176, 292, 328

Panpsychism: 160, 291, 306–307, 464

Parapsychology: *see* Psi phenomena

Parasites, adaptation of: 122–23

Parietal eye: 337

Parker, G. H.: 239–40, 337

Parmenter, R.: 99

Parsimony, law of: 49
and insect mentality, 322

Partial patterns of behavior: 14, 76–77, 80–85
conflict with total pattern, 98–101

Patrick, G. T. W.: 137

Patterns: 55–56, 60
of behavior, 76–85
as criteria of levels of organization, 104

Pavlov, I. P.: 88, 99, 253, 355–56

Pear, T. H.: 406

Peking man (Sinanthropus), skull capacity of: 386

Penfield, Wilder: 387, 415–16, 428, 443

Perception: 162–63, 339–53
and awareness, 290–91
criteria of, 339–40
as culmination of analytic system, 103
as element of cognition, 300–302
integrative factors in, 349–51
and introspective experience, 292–95
motor factors in, 345–49

"purposive" quality of, 351–52
temporal and spatial factors in, 165, 272–74, 276–77, 341–45
see also Mental processes

Perceptual knowledge: 162, 301

Perry, Ralph Barton: 146

Pfeiffer, John: 416, 425, 445–46, 448

Philanthropy, in United States: 229

Philosophy of animal behavior: 27

Photoreceptors and photosensitive pigment: 336–37

Phrenology: 406–407

Phylogeny: 6, 166

Physalia: 79

Physiological gradients: 90–91

Piel, Gerard: 173

Pineal body: 337

Pithecanthropus erectus: 386

Pitts, W.: 444–45

Planck, Max: 96

Plants, spatial responses of: 336

Plasmagenes: 117–18

Plasmodium: 95

Plato, theory of brain function of: 406

Polarization:
of electromagnetic field, 263–65
of nerve cells, 263, 265–69
of subjective experience against objective experience, 294–95

Political behavior in United States: 224

Polyak, S. L.: 337, 394

Polyps:
budding of, 98
nervous system of, 240–41, 410

Portuguese man-of-war (Physalia): 79

Positivism:
and freedom of choice, 211–13
social, 195–98

Posture, and mentation: 313–17

Predeterminism, and determinism: 211–13

Predicting machines, artificial and natural: 131

Predictive value of perception: 340

Prenatal human development, study of: 81–84, 310

Prenatal life, importance of: 116–17

Price, George R.: 458
Primates:
  localization of cerebral functions in,
    420–21
  mentality of, 290, 309, 323–28
  personal differences in intelligence
    of, 327
  social structure of, 180
  subhuman, brain size of: 386
  symbolism, grasp of, by, 324–25
  transition of, to human, 317, 328,
    386
Probability, laws of, and mechanisms:
  61–64
Problem-solving, and intelligence: 359
Profit motive: 152–53
Progress:
  biological, 123–27
  key to, 226–30
Progressive evolution: see Evolution
Protoplasm: 240, 255, 258–59
Protoplasmic learning: 357, 360–61
Protozoan behavior: 92–93
Psi phenomena: 267, 457–58, 464
Psychoanalysis: 100, 157, 285
Psychobiology: 8, 24, 233–37, 450–59
  expanding horizons of, 257–58
  future paths of study of, 457–58
  pioneers of, 451–52
  scope of, 288, 302–304
  theory of dimensions in, 453–58
  see also Body-mind relationship
Psychogenesis: see Mind, embryology
  of; Panpsychism
Psychology, reorientation in: 271
Psychophysics:
  dimensions of integration, 275–79
  mental work in, 279–82
  principles of, 270–83
  space, time, and space-time in,
    272–75
Psychosurgical operations: 415–16,
  418, 426–27
Public health program in United States:
  202
"Purposive" quality of perception:
  351–52
  see also Directive quality
Pyramidal tract: 420

Quantum mechanics: 92, 264–65, 271
  and causality, 61–72

Racial characteristics: 117
Ramón y Cajal, Santiago: 261
Ramsey, Glenn V.: 351
Random activity and mechanisms:
  61–64
Rank, biological: 14, 119–23
Rapoport, Anatol: 32, 37, 41, 183
Rashevsky, Nicholas: 29, 54, 190
Rasmussen, Theodore: 387, 415–16,
  428
Rats:
  "feelers" of, 335
  mechanisms of learning in, 422–24,
    444
  motor activity and cortical
    localization of, 420
  use of symbols by, 402–403
Reaction as experience: 161
Reality: 40–42
Reason:
  advent of, 167
  sufficient, principle of, 49
Recall, mechanism of: 302
Recapitulation in development: 116,
  311
Redfield, Robert: 107
Reductive explanation of vital
  processes: 48–50, 202
Reflexes: 76
  and behavior, 19–20, 82–85, 253–54
  conditioning of, as learning, 355–58
  see also Nervous System
Regressive trends in evolution: 114,
  122–23
Reiser, Oliver L.: 278, 448
Relationships of facts, in scientific
  method: 30–31
Relativistic concept of determinism:
  211–13
Relativistic space-time: 273–79
Relativity: 266, 277
Religion: 462–65
Repetitive processes, pattern of: 78
Reptiles:
  cortex of, 371–72, 375–76, 378,
    380–81, 419

individualistic traits of, 175
primitive, as ancestors of diverging lines of progressive evolution, 381–82
Reserves of cortical energy: 396, 398
Reticular substance: 419–22
Retina: 337, 394
Ribot, T. A.: 316
Riese, Walther: 95–96
Riesen, Austin H.: 317, 342, 364
Right and wrong: *see* Good and evil
Roberts, Morley: 399
Rockefeller Foundation, reorganization of: 190
Romanell, Patrick: 29, 215–16
Romano, J.: 115
Romer, Alfred S.: 130, 132
Roofe, Paul G.: 81, 124
Rosenblueth, A.: 26
Royce, Josiah: 316
Rubáiyát of Omar Khayyám: 206
Rudebeck, Briger: 380
Russell, Bertrand: 28, 123

Salamander:
brain structure of, 244–52, 344, 371–73, 378–79
Coghill's study of, 81, 316
sensory responses of, 335
Samoan social structure: 184
Santayana, George: 38, 145, 462, 464
Sargent, Stephen S.: 190, 197
Satisfaction:
to animals, 139–40
as criterion of progress, 125–26
as goal of normal behavior, 18–21, 142
see also Values
Scharrer, Ernst: 335
Schepers, G. W. H.: 248, 419
Schneirla, T. C.: 21, 24, 76, 107, 129, 173, 189, 324, 351, 358
Schrödinger, Erwin: 59, 275
Science:
empirical and normative, 28–30
and humanism, 36
and human values, 154–56

methodology of, 26–38
and spiritual faith, 461–66
Scientific dictatorship: 200–201
Scotland, West Highland Survey in: 190
Scott, J. P.: 189–90
Seals, totalitarian social organization among: 174
Seidenberg, Roderick: 53
Selection, mechanisms of: 129
Self: 205–18
biological, 205–208
as free agent, 211–17
social, 190
worth of, 208–11
Sellars, Roy Wood: 72, 134–35, 162, 212, 279, 286, 301–302, 307, 350
Semantic learning: 358, 360–62
Sensation: 242, 300, 330–38
factors of, 331–34
temporal and spatial relations in, 334–37
Weber-Fechner formula, 270
Senses: 330–31
classification of, 432–33
see also Sense organ entries
Sensitivity: 299
as component of perception, 340
Sensorimotor experience: 164–65
Sensorimotor learning: 357–58, 361
Sensory analytic system of Pavlov: 88
Sentiments, nonspatial, nontemporal frame of: 165
Servomechanisms: 447
Shapley, Harlow: 55, 63, 394
Shariff, Ghouse A.: 393
Sheldon, W. H.: 312
Sherrington, Charles S.: 97–98, 164, 246, 252, 313–17, 331–32, 369
Sight: *See* Visual organs
Signals: 401, 441–48
Signs: 326, 401
Simpson, G. G.: 62, 115, 120–21, 125, 129–30, 214–15, 286, 326
Sinanthropus: 386
Sinnott, Edmund W.: 202, 352
Slime molds (Myxomycetes): 79, 95

Smell, sense of: *See* Olfactory organs

Smith, N. M.: 151

Snyder, L. H.: 194

Social control of human behavior: 16–17

Social disorders: 66–67, 180–81, 219–20, 399–400
causes of, 220–23
education as answer to, 223–26
frustration as cause of, 99–100
history of ideological dualism in Europe, 182–83
as racial psychoneurosis, 181–82
therapy for, 100, 182, 193–94

Social frame of human behavior: 16–17

Social heredity: 70, 77, 84, 128–29, 178
education as mechanism of, 196
learning transmitted by, 358
norms imposed by, 181–83

Social organization: 169–88
in democracy, 183–87
innate and acquired factors of, 177–78
sociobiology of, 189–204
totalitarian and individualistic patterns of, 171–76, 191–92
in United States, 203–204

Social sciences, role of, 199–204

Sociobiology: 189

Sonneborn, T. M.: 117–18

Soviet Union, social control in: 183, 204

Space-time:
conception of, in integrative processes, 272–79, 453–54
in relativistic concept of determinism, 211–12

Spatial factors:
in perception, 165, 272–74, 276–77 340–45
in sensation, 334, 336–37
in subhuman vertebrate symbolic response, 324

Spearman, C. E.: 365

Species: 119–21
diversification of, 113–14
elimination of, by nonadaptive behavior, 130

ranking of, 121–22
and social groups, 169

Speech: *see* Language

Spemann, Hans: 266

Spencer, Herbert: 46

Sperry, Roger W.: 69, 237, 260, 262, 268, 315, 340, 346, 437–38, 442

Spiritual faith: 462–65

Spiritual life, natural history of: 233

Spiritual values:
destruction of 66–67
and scientific knowledge, 70

Spitzer, A.: 347

Sponges:
formation of, 94
neuromotor activity in, 239

Spurzheim, Johann Kaspar: 406

Squid and octopus, eyes of: 337

Stephenson, William: 366–67

Stern, Curt: 207

Stevens, Stanley S.: 272

Stevenson, Robert Louis: 150

Strain: *see* Tension

Structure: 54–55
laws of, and laws of change, 110

Subjective experience: *see* Experience

Sumner, W. G.: 195

Supernatural:
definition of, 462
primitive belief in, 234–35
see also Religion

Surgery, brain: 415–16, 418, 426–27

Survival:
and adaptation, 122–23, 129–30
criteria of good and evil in terms of, 3–4
trends away from, 64
of fit, 191–92; *see also* Natural selection
as goal of existence, 123
of human race, 2–3, 399–400
national, individual responsibility for, 192–93

Survival value: 4, 123, 140, 146–47, 192, 214
of communistic ant colony, 173–74

Swan, W. F. G.: 41

Switzerland, democracy in: 185

Symbols: 326, 361, 401–402, 404–405
    animal use of, 289–90, 324–26,
        402–404
    and concepts, 301
    in cortical learning, 358, 441–48
Synapses: 249–50, 262–63, 268–69
Synthesis: 89–91
    and analysis, 86–87, 91–98, 163
    see also Integrative processes

Tapeworms, fission of: 79, 98
Taste, organs of, 245, 331
Tau effect: 344
Taxis: 76, 82
Taxonomy: 119–20
Teleology: 131–35
Temporal factors:
    in perception, 165, 272–74, 276–77,
        340–45
    in relativistic concept of
        determination, 211–13
    in sensation, 334–36
    see also Space-time; Time
Tensions:
    in mechanical operations, 57
    social, 180–81, 193, 219–26
    UNESCO "Tensions Project,"
        202–203
Thalamus: 252, 378, 380, 419
Thales: 72
Thermodynamics, second law of: 51–53
Thompson, D'Arcy W.: 58
Thompson, Laura: 190
Thorndike, E. L.: 146
Thought, laws of: 45
Thrapp, Dan L.: 386
Thurstone, L. L.: 29, 365
Tiger salamander: see Salamander
Time, Grünbaum on meaning of: 53
    see also Space-time
Time: 229
Tinbergen, N.: 189
Titchner, E. B.: 432
Tonicity: 314, 346–47
Tools, invention and use of: 119

Totalitarian social patterns: 171–75,
    191
    communistic insect organization,
        172–74
    tyrannies, animal and human,
        174–75
Total patterns of behavior: 14, 76–77,
    80–85
    conflict of, with partial patterns,
        98–101
    experience as, 159, 166
Touch, organs of: 245, 334–36, 344
Toynbee, Arnold: 193
"Transactions" of Dewey and Bentley:
    15, 162
Tribal organization:
    in Australia, 184
    in Samoa, 184
Troland, Leonard T.: 151
Tropism: 76, 82
Truth, as a value: 154–55
Tryon, Roger C.: 363–64
Tunturi, Archie R.: 343
Turck, Fenton B.: 228
Turtles, cortical structure of: 372,
    383, 419
Tute, Richard: 34
Tyrannical social orders: 174–75, 186

UNESCO "Tensions Project": 202–203
Unitary principle of Lancelot Whyte:
    42, 51–52, 93
Universals: 28, 44–45
Utopian communities: 185

Values:
    cultural, 199–204
    evaluation of, 150–52
    in evolution, 124–27
    as factors in behavior, 17, 23
    of facts, judgment of, in scientific
        method, 32–36
    goodness of, 147–50
    human, 141–45
    natural history of, 136–41
    and profit motive, 152–53
    relational nature of, 145–47
    and social behavior, 181–83
    spiritual, and mechanisms, 66–67, 70

Values (*continued*):
survival, 4, 123, 140, 192, 214
and truth, 154–56

Van der Horst, C. J.: 120

Variations:
search for laws of, 112, 114–15
see also Mutations

Verbalization: 404–405
and mental processes, 289–90

Vertebrates:
amphibian, 244–45
brain development in, 241–43
eyes of, 337
social organization among, 175–76

Vibrations:
sensitivity of animals to, 334–36
sensitivity of human body to, 334–35

Vinacke, W. E.: 304

Visceral functions, levels of: 252

Visual organs, evolution of: 334–37
in fishes, 376
in insects, 336
in lancet, 337
in leech, 336
in mollusks, 337
in octopus, 337
parietal eye, 337
in perception, 339–40
retina, 337, 394
structure of, 341–42, 424–25,
434–35, 444
in worms, 336

Vitalism: 47–48

Vital processes: 46–47
"organismic" and "nonorganismic,"
86–87

Voice of America: 224

Volcano, creative power of: 57

Volition: 299, 313, 318–19, 338
as factor in sensation and perception,
345–46

Von Neumann, John: 26, 57–58, 278

Walls, Gordon L.: 337

Wapner, Seymour: 347

Warden, Carl J.: 24, 189

Warner, Lucien H.: 24

Washburn, Margaret: 24

Water, chemical formula for: 58–59

Watson, D. M. S.: 386

Watson, J. B.: 432

Watts, James W.: 416

Weber-Fechner formula: 270

Weigert method: 391

Weismann's germ plasm: 117

Weiss, A. P.: 48–49

Weiss, Paul: 27, 259, 261–62

Werner, Heinz: 347

Wever, E. G.: 336

Wheeler, William M.: 53, 107, 189,
399

White, Leslie A.: 49, 195–98, 326

Whitehead, Alfred N.: 28, 60, 93–94,
96, 134, 160, 291

Whitman, C. O.: 93, 336

Whittaker, E. T.: 270–71

Wholes and parts: 78–80
disintegration, process of, 98

Whyte, Lancelot L.: 33, 41–42, 51–53,
55, 72, 93, 182, 265, 454

Wiener, Norbert: 29, 270, 344, 445

Williams, Robert R.: 94

Williams, Roger J.: 194–95

Willier, Benjamin H.: 54

Willing: *see* Volition

Wolfe, John B.: 324

Work:
mechanics of, 56–58
mental, 279

Worms, eyes of: 336

Wright, Herbert F.: 82, 310

Wright, Quincy: 181

Wulfeck, Joseph: 73

Yakovlev, Paul I.: 16, 176

Yale Clinic of Child Development,
studies at, 82, 197, 310

Yerkes, Ada W.: 24

Yerkes, Robert M.: 24, 139, 180, 189,
324–25

Yerkes Laboratories of Primate
Biology: 325

Zuckerman, S.: 189, 325